INTRODUCTION
TO
TECHNICAL
MATHEMATICS

ALLYN J. WASHINGTON

Dutchess Community College, Poughkeepsie, New York

CUMMINGS PUBLISHING COMPANY, INC.

Menlo Park, California

To my students, past and present,
whose inquiring minds have kept me on my toes
looking for the right methods

Preface

This text was written for students taking technical programs at two-year colleges and technical institutes. It is intended for those who need to acquire a basic knowledge of mathematics for use in their particular programs. The general topics covered are an arithmetic review, algebra, basic topics from geometry, and a brief introduction to trigonometry. The coverage is appropriate for those whose backgrounds do not include algebra, or are limited such that a review of these basic topics is deemed necessary. Also, since this text discusses many topics normally included in intermediate algebra, it may be used in courses intended as background for further work in mathematics, as well as courses that are terminal in nature. The book has been written primarily for formal courses, but it could easily be used by those students who wish to follow a self-study program.

In the examples and exercises, numerous applications are indicated from the various fields of technology, such as electronics, mechanics, machine design, civil engineering, architecture, physics, chemistry, and data processing. These are included to show the students where and how the given mathematical topic can be applied. No attempt is made to develop the allied technical material.

The material is developed in an informal and intuitive manner. All necessary terms are carefully introduced and basic concepts are developed in order to give the student an understanding of the material and how it relates to other topics. More detail has been included on those topics which experience has shown are more difficult for students. The emphasis throughout the text is to develop the mathematics necessary for technical work, and not to emphasize mathematical exceptions and special cases.

The first chapter, on arithmetic, is intended as a review and as a basis for developing later topics in algebra. A brief section on numbers in base two is included for courses in which such material is deemed appropriate. The second chapter introduces the student to systems of measurement which he will encounter in other courses. Also, by means of unit conversions, he can continue to develop his arithmetic skills.

An introduction to the use of the slide rule is given in Chapter 3. Numerous problems after this chapter are set up for slide-rule solution. Other uses of the slide rule are included in the chapters on logarithms and trigonometry.

Signed numbers and an introduction to algebra are taken up in Chapters 4, 5 and 6. Basic geometric figures are discussed in Chapter 7. By the time the student has completed Chapter 7, he has established a foundation for the more complete development of algebra in Chapters 8 through 15.

Graphical methods are introduced in Chapter 14. Graphical techniques—including the solution of equations and graphical interpretations which are valuable in technical work—are covered.

Chapter 16 includes a brief coverage of geometric concepts, such as the Pythagorean theorem and similar triangles, which are essential to other technical courses. The book concludes with an introduction to trigonometry and some elementary applications of it.

Stated problems appear in most sections of the text. The continual solving of such problems makes the student become more accustomed to them. He encounters the simplest forms of stated problems in the earlier chapters; then, in Chapter 6, a complete section is devoted to analyzing and solving such problems.

Numerous examples and exercises are included. There is a set of exercises with every section (except Section 1–1), and every chapter includes a set of review exercises. The answers to all odd-numbered exercises, including graphical problems, are found in the back of the book.

I wish to acknowledge the help and suggestions given me during the preparation of this text. In particular, I wish to thank Stephen Lange, of the mathematics department of Dutchess Community College, whose valuable comments and suggestions are greatly appreciated. Also the assistance of Harry Boyd and Gail Brittain, of Dutchess Community College, and Samuel Plotkin, formerly of Dutchess Community College, in the preparation of earlier materials used in this text was of great value.

The many comments of users of my earlier texts also were very helpful. The assistance and cooperation of the staff of the Cummings Publishing Company is also deeply appreciated. Finally, I am particularly indebted to my wife, for her assistance in checking answers, and for her encouragement throughout the period of preparing this text.

Poughkeepsie, New York   A.J.W.
January 1969

Contents

Fundamentals from Arithmetic 1

1–1 INTRODUCTION

Scientific and technical knowledge has advanced at an ever-increasing rate during the past few decades. Artificial satellites circle the earth; men have successfully flown to and from the moon; architectural structures (e.g., the Houston Astrodome) once considered almost impossible to build have been constructed; television pictures are transmitted across oceans and across millions of miles of space; atomic power is used to generate electricity in many areas. We could make an almost endless list of such advances which have been made during the last quarter century alone.

One reason for the advances is that science and technology have a strong mathematical foundation. Through mathematics, scientific knowledge can be precisely described and accurate predictions can often be made on the outcome of complicated experiments. Obviously it is not through mathematics alone that these modern accomplishments have been made. Experimentation and research, pure science, and basic technical knowledge have played their indispensable parts also.

If you are to acquire an understanding of your technical field and to advance effectively in it, a knowledge of basic mathematics is essential. Therefore you should study it with a desire to learn the fundamental concepts and how to apply them to scientific and technical problems.

In this text we shall only begin to develop the mathematics which is essential to scientific and technical fields. Much of the mathematics necessary to solve problems that arise today is well beyond the scope of our work here. However, problems that do arise in all fields of technology are solvable by the mathematics presented in this text, and numerous applications are demonstrated. You can readily master all the mathematics presented here if you give the subject sufficient attention. In the case of certain topics which constitute a challenge, give them special attention and you will find that you will be able to grasp them.

1–2 ADDITION AND SUBTRACTION OF NATURAL NUMBERS

Finding the solutions to most applied problems in science and technology involves arithmetical computations. To perform these computations, we use the basic arithmetical operations of addition, subtraction, multiplication, and division. These basic operations are not only essential to performing computations, but they are fundamental to the development of the various branches of mathematics itself. Therefore it is important that these operations be performed accurately and with reasonable speed. Although we assume that you are familiar with these operations, we shall include a brief discussion here for purposes of review and reference.

The most fundamental use of numbers is that of counting. The numbers used for counting, the *natural numbers* (or *positive integers*), are represented by the symbols 1, 2, 3, 4, and so on. In fact, any of the natural numbers can be written with the use of the ten symbols 0, 1, 2, 3, 4, 5, 6, 7, 8, 9 if the actual *position* of a symbol in a given number is properly noted. This very important feature used in writing numbers, that of placing each symbol in a specified position in order to give it a particular meaning, is referred to as *positional notation*.

In the number 3252, read as "three thousand two hundred fifty-two," the left 2 represents the number of hundreds and the right 2 represents the number of ones, because of their respective positions. Even though the symbol is the same, its position gives it a different value. Also, the 3 represents the number of thousands and the 5 represents the number of tens, because of their respective positions.   **Example A**

In the number 325, the 2 represents the number of tens and the 5 represents the number of ones. In the number 352, the 5 represents the number of tens and the 2 represents the number of ones. Even though the same symbols are used, the different relative positions give different numbers.

The process of finding the total number of objects in two different sets of these objects is *addition*. When we are finding the *sum*, the result of addition, we must be careful that we add only like quantities.

If one container has a capacity of 4 quarts and another has a capacity of 2 quarts, we find the combined capacity of the two containers by adding   **Example B**

$$4 \text{ quarts} + 2 \text{ quarts} = 6 \text{ quarts}.$$

If it takes 20 seconds to fill the 4-quart container, there is no meaning to the sum $20 + 4$, since we are adding different quantities.

When we are adding two natural numbers, we must take into account positional notation and add only those numbers with the same positional value. In this way we are adding like quantities.

Example C   When we add 46 and 29, we are saying

$$4 \text{ tens} + 6 \text{ ones}$$
$$2 \text{ tens} + 9 \text{ ones}$$
$$6 \text{ tens} + 15 \text{ ones.}$$

Since 15 ones = 1 ten and 5 ones, we then have

$$6 \text{ tens} + 1 \text{ ten} + 5 \text{ ones} = 7 \text{ tens} + 5 \text{ ones.}$$

Of course, we show this in practice as

$$
\begin{array}{r}
1 \\
46 \\
+29 \\
\hline
75
\end{array}
$$

where the 1 shows the amount "carried" from the ones column to the tens column.

In order to perform addition effectively, it is essential to know the basic sums through $9 + 9 = 18$ without hesitation. If the reader is at all unsure of any of these, he should write them out so that he can review them. Being able to perform addition accurately with reasonable speed comes about as a result of knowing the basic sums well; this takes practice.

It is also well to form the habit of checking one's work. Several methods of checking addition are available. A simple and effective method is to add the various columns in the direction opposite to that used in finding the sum originally.

Example D   If we find the sum of the indicated numbers by adding the columns upward, we can check the results by adding again, this time adding the column downward.

$$
\begin{array}{cc}
\begin{array}{r}
22 \\
327 \uparrow \\
582 \\
695 \\
419 \\
\hline
2023
\end{array}
&
\begin{array}{r}
22 \\
327 \\
582 \\
695 \\
419 \downarrow \\
\hline
2023
\end{array}
\end{array}
$$

The process of "carrying" a number from one column to the next is necessary whenever the sum of the digits in a column exceeds 9. A very similar situation occurs when we add distances which are expressed in more than one measuring unit. Consider the following example.

The *perimeter* of a plane geometric figure is the total distance around it. **Example E** Therefore, to find the perimeter of the figure shown in Fig. 1–1, we must add the indicated lengths. We could leave the result as 17 ft 27 in. However, we can obtain a more useful result by noting that 27 in. = 2 ft 3 in. Therefore we would say that the perimeter of the figure is 19 ft 3 in. Note that we essentially "carried" 2 from the inch column to the foot column.

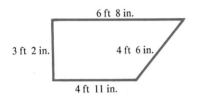

```
                        6 ft  8 in.
                        4 ft  6 in.
                        4 ft 11 in.
                        3 ft  2 in.
                       ─────────────
                       17 ft 27 in.
```

Figure 1–1

Often we have to determine how much greater one number is than another. This leads to the operation of *subtraction*, the inverse of addition. Subtraction consists of reducing the number from which the subtraction is being made (the *minuend*) by the number being subtracted (the *subtrahend*). The result is called the *difference*.

If we wish to subtract 29 from 73, we find that for the number of ones **Example F** involved, we are to reduce 3 by 9. When we consider natural numbers, we cannot perform this. However, if we "borrow" 10 ones from the tens column of 73, the subtraction amounts to subtracting 2 tens + 9 ones from 6 tens and 13 ones. Now, the subtraction follows as

$$
\begin{array}{ll}
73 & \text{minuend} \\
29 & \text{subtrahend} \\
\hline
44 & \text{difference}
\end{array}
$$

Note that "borrowing" in subtraction is essentially the opposite of "carrying" in addition.

The way to check subtraction is to add the difference and the sub-trahend. The sum should be the minuend. This follows directly from the meaning of subtraction. Therefore the check of this subtraction is

$$\begin{array}{r} 44 \\ 29 \\ \hline 73. \end{array}$$

EXERCISES   In Exercises 1 through 12, add the given numbers. Be sure to check your work.

1. 28	2. 83	3. 726	4. 521
37	98	97	879
96	46	813	106

5. 826	6. 278	7. 3973	8. 9806
992	446	5868	3791
809	915	9039	986
67	548	5792	7372

9. 3873	10. 989	11. 30964	12. 87657
9295	3216	9877	93984
4082	4807	92286	57609
399	736	5547	8726
7646	9297	965	92875

In Exercises 13 through 20, perform the indicated subtractions. Check your work.

13. 873	14. 921	15. 8305	16. 2006
292	224	7356	1197

17. 36047	18. 10906	19. 290078	20. 872110
26249	9928	194396	682324

In Exercises 21 through 24, find the perimeters of the given figures.

21.

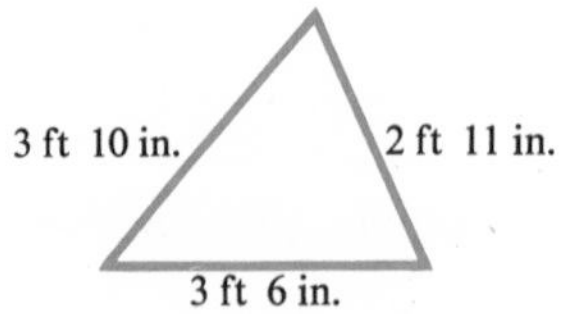

3 ft 10 in.   2 ft 11 in.

3 ft 6 in.

Figure 1–2

22.

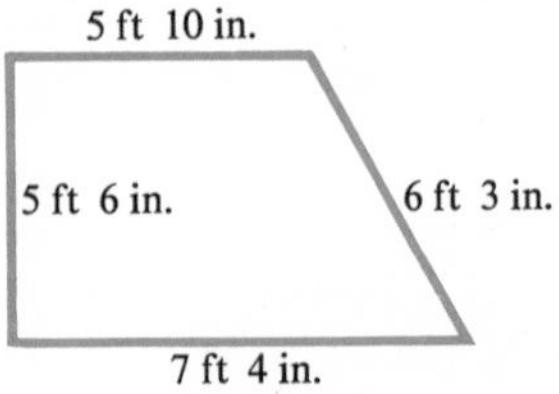

5 ft 10 in.

5 ft 6 in.   6 ft 3 in.

7 ft 4 in.

Figure 1–3

23.

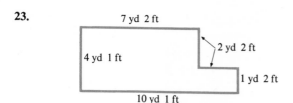

Figure 1-4

24.

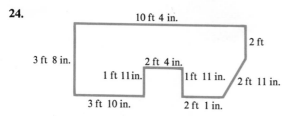

Figure 1-5

In Exercises 25 through 28, find the difference in length of the longest and the shortest side in the indicated figure.

25. Figure 1–2   **26.** Figure 1–3

27. Figure 1–4   **28.** Figure 1–5

In Exercises 29 through 41, solve the given problems and check your work.

29. A man drove 897 mi from New York to Chicago. He then traveled another 1086 mi to Denver. Finally he drove 1318 mi to San Francisco. How far did he travel?

30. In buying furniture for a new home, a housewife spent $785 for living room furnishings, $598 for a dining room set and $388 for a new bedroom set. How much did she spend?

31. Three containers hold 4 gal 2 qt, 3 gal 2 qt, and 2 gal 3 qt, respectively. What is their combined capacity?

32. The times for each of four successive laps for a sports car racing around a certain racetrack were 3 min 42 sec, 3 min 25 sec, 3 min 32 sec, and 3 min 24 sec. What was the total time required for the four laps?

33. The times for each of three successive orbits of a certain satellite circling the earth were 1 hr 36 min 26 sec, 1 hr 34 min 47 sec, and 1 hr 30 min 17 sec. How long did these three orbits take?

34. Four barrels, of differing sizes, hold 3 bu 2 pecks, 4 bu 3 pecks, 2 bu 1 peck, and 3 bu 3 pecks, respectively. What is the combined capacity of these barrels? (4 pecks = 1 bu.)

35. The area of Illinois is 56,400 sq mi and that of New York is 49,576 sq mi. How much larger is Illinois than New York?

36. Due to overheating, the resistance of an electrical resistor changed from 195 ohms to 262 ohms. By how much did the resistance change?

37. A man had $3272 in his bank account before he made a $586 withdrawal. How much did he have in his account after the withdrawal?

38. One container holds 11 gal 1 qt and another holds 6 gal 3 qt. How much more does the larger container hold than the smaller one?

39. How long is it from sunrise to sunset on a day on which the sun rises at 7:38 A.M. and sets at 6:22 P.M.?

40. Two chickens weigh 3 lb 6 oz and 1 lb 15 oz, respectively. What is the difference in their weights?

41. Make a list of all the basic sums from $2 + 2$ to $9 + 9$ (there are 36 of them). Then time yourself to see how long it takes to give the results only. If it takes much more than about 40 seconds, you probably do not know them well enough.

1–3 MULTIPLICATION AND DIVISION OF NATURAL NUMBERS

The basic arithmetic operation in which we find the total number of objects in several sets, each set containing the same number of objects, is called *multiplication*. In this sense, we see that multiplication is a process of adding equal numbers. The number that is multiplied is called the *multiplicand*, the number of times it is taken is the *multiplier*, and the result is the *product*. The basic notations used to denote multiplication are $\times$, $\cdot$, and parentheses.

Example A   By the expression 3×5 we mean

$$3 \times 5 = 5 + 5 + 5 = 15.$$

Here 3 is the multiplier, 5 is the multiplicand, and 15 is the product. The product can also be expressed as

$$3 \cdot 5 = 15 \quad \text{or} \quad (3)(5) = 15.$$

In order to perform multiplication accurately and with reasonable speed, it is necessary, as with addition, to know the basic products through $9 \times 9 = 81$ without hesitation. If you have any doubt about your knowledge of these products, you should review them thoroughly.

The process of multiplication has certain important basic properties. One of these, known as the *commutative law*, is that the order of multiplication does not matter. Another of these, known as the *associative law*, deals with the multiplication of more than two factors. It states that the grouping of the *factors*, the numbers being multiplied, does not matter. Since multiplication is basically a process of addition, these properties also hold for addition.

Since $3 + 5 = 8$ and $5 + 3 = 8$, we see that $3 + 5 = 5 + 3$. This illustrates the commutative law of addition. In the same way,   Example B

$$3 \times 5 = 5 \times 3$$

illustrates the commutative law of multiplication,

$$(3 + 5) + 7 = 3 + (5 + 7)$$

illustrates the associative law of addition, and

$$(3 \times 5) \times 7 = 3 \times (5 \times 7)$$

illustrates the associative law of multiplication. In the product $(3 \times 5) \times 7$ the numbers 3, 5, and 7 are factors of the product.

Another important property of numbers that involves multiplication and addition is known as the *distributive law*. This law states that if the sum of two numbers is multiplied by another given number, each is multiplied by the given number and the products are added to find the final result. Consider the following example.

Applying the distributive law to the product $(4)(3 + 6)$ we have   Example C

$$(4)(3 + 6) = (4)(3) + (4)(6) = 12 + 24 = 36.$$

We see that this gives results consistent with the product $(4)(9) = 36$, since $3 + 6 = 9$.

We can now use the distributive law to show why the usual method of multiplying is employed. Consider the following example.

To find the product of 26 and 124, we would proceed as follows: Example D

$$
\begin{array}{r}
124 \\
26 \\
\hline
744 \\
248 \\
\hline
3224
\end{array}
$$

If we now consider the product as

$$(124)(26) = (124)(20 + 6)$$
$$= (124)(20) + (124)(6) = 2480 + 744 = 3224,$$

we see that the first line (744) obtained in the multiplication process is also one of the products found using the distributive law. We then note that the 248 found in the multiplication process is equivalent to the 2480 product found using the distributive law. The final 0 is not written, but it is accounted for in that the 248 is displaced one position to the left.

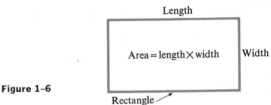

Figure 1-6

Length

Area = length × width   Width

Rectangle

There are innumerable applications of multiplication, some of which are demonstrated in the exercises. One of the most basic applications is in determining the *area* of a *rectangle*, which is defined to be the product of the *length* and the *width* of the rectangle (see Fig. 1-6).

Example E   The area of a rectangle whose length is 26 ft and whose width is 17 ft is:

$$\text{Area} = (26 \text{ ft}) \times (17 \text{ ft}) = 442 \text{ square feet (sq ft)}.$$

Just as subtraction is the inverse process of addition, *division* is the inverse process of multiplication. Therefore we can look upon division as a process of repeated subtraction. For example, if we subtract 2 from 10 five times the result is zero. This means that 10 divided by 2 is 5. Here 10 is the *dividend*, 2 is the *divisor*, and 5 is the *quotient*. A common notation for this is $10 \div 2 = 5$, where $\div$ indicates division.

It can be seen that the product of the quotient and the divisor equals the dividend, if the division "comes out even." This gives us a way to check division, as well as leading us to the basic technique of dividing one number by another. It is assumed that the reader knows the process, although the following example is given for purposes of review and as an explanation of division.

Suppose that we want to divide 3288 by 24. We set up the problem as follows: Example F

$$
\begin{array}{r}
137 \quad \text{(quotient)} \\
\text{(divisor)} \quad 24\overline{)3288} \quad \text{(dividend)} \\
2400 \quad (24 \times 100) \\
\hline
888 \\
720 \quad (24 \times 30) \\
\hline
168 \\
168 \quad (24 \times 7) \\
\hline
\end{array}
$$

We therefore see that

$$3288 = 24 \times 137 = 24 \times 100 + 24 \times 30 + 24 \times 7 = 24(100 + 30 + 7).$$

The meanings of the products 2400, 720, and 168 can be seen in this example. Usually, the extra zeros are not written, and only a sufficient number of digits are "brought down." Normally, the division would appear as

$$
\begin{array}{r}
137 \\
24\overline{)3288} \\
24 \\
\hline
88 \\
72 \\
\hline
168 \\
168 \\
\hline
\end{array}
$$

In many divisions, the divisor will not divide exactly into the dividend. In these cases, there is a *remainder* in the answer. The following example illustrates a division with a remainder.

Let us divide 5286 by 25. Example G

$$
\begin{array}{r}
211 \\
25\overline{)5286} \\
50 \quad (25 \times 200 = 5000) \\
\hline
28 \\
25 \quad (25 \times 10 = 250) \\
\hline
36 \\
25 \quad (25 \times 1 = 25) \\
\hline
11 \quad \text{(remainder)}
\end{array}
$$

Thus $5286 = (25 \times 211) + 11$. Since 11 is smaller than 25, the divisor, the division process is discontinued and 11 becomes the remainder.

There is one number that cannot be used as a divisor. This number is zero. The reason for this will be explained in Chapter 4.

EXERCISES   In Exercises 1 through 8, perform the indicated multiplications.

1. 27×259	**2.** 36×564	**3.** $(329)(7105)$	**4.** $(915)(3794)$
5. 3879	**6.** 9276	**7.** 52438	**8.** 97877
4081	6814	4794	6985

In Exercises 9 through 16, perform the indicated divisions.

9. $3\overline{)729}$ **10.** $81\overline{)2997}$ **11.** $54\overline{)17604}$ **12.** $29\overline{)14674}$

13. $52664 \div 37$ **14.** $59685 \div 28$

15. $607964 \div 387$ **16.** $920337 \div 726$

In Exercises 17 through 18, verify the associative law of multiplication by first multiplying the numbers in parentheses and then completing the multiplication on each side.

17. $(17 \times 38) \times 74 = 17 \times (38 \times 74)$

18. $(326 \times 45) \times 217 = 326 \times (45 \times 217)$

In Exercises 19 through 20, perform the indicated multiplications by use of the distributive law. Check by adding the numbers within the parentheses first and then complete the multiplication.

19. $628(29 + 86)$ **20.** $4159(387 + 832)$

Exercises 21 through 24 give the lengths and widths of certain rectangles. Determine their areas.

21. Length = 17 in., width = 14 in.   **22.** Length = 682 ft, width = 273 ft

23. Length = 3 ft, width = 24 in.   **24.** Length = 274 yd, width = 543 ft

In Exercises 25 through 35, solve the given problems.

25. Suppose that the area of a rectangle is 61,884 sq ft and the length is 573 ft. Find the width.

26. Suppose that the area of a rectangle is 56,056 sq in. and the width is 98 in. What is the length?

27. A jet plane averaged a speed of 595 miles per hour for 17 hours. How far did it travel?

28. How much does it cost to cover the floor of a room 26 ft by 17 ft with tiles which cost $2 per square foot?

29. If a car traveled 342 mi on 18 gal of gasoline, what was its gas consumption in miles per gallon?

30. If $945 is divided evenly among 27 people, how much does each receive?

31. Find the area of the piece of land shown in Fig. 1–7.

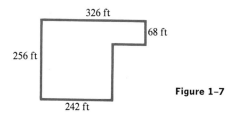

Figure 1–7

32. A flywheel makes 2600 revolutions per minute. How many revolutions does it make in 8 hr?

33. A rocket travels 238,800 mi to the moon. If it takes 15 hr, what is the average speed of the rocket?

34. A special machine part costs $14. If the cost of a shipment of these parts is $514, which includes $10 shipping charges, how many parts were in the shipment?

35. A motor boat can go 10 miles per hour in still water. How far downstream in a river can it go in 3 hr if the river flows at the rate of 2 miles per hour?

1–4 FRACTIONS; LOWEST TERMS

Mathematics can be applied to a great many situations in which only the natural numbers are necessary. However, there are innumerable other cases in which parts of a quantity or less than the total of a group must be considered. For example, if we know the number of boys and the number of girls in a class, we can find the total number of students by addition. However, if we are interested just in the number of boys in the class, we are considering only a part of the entire class.

Considerations such as these lead us to fractions and the basic operations with them. In general, a *fraction* is the indicated division of one number by another. It is also possible to interpret this definition as a certain number of equal parts of a given unit or of a given group. Consider the following example.

Example A

The fraction $\frac{5}{8}$ is the indicated division of 5 by 8. In this fraction, 5 is the *numerator* and 8 is the *denominator*.

It is also possible to interpret the fraction $\frac{5}{8}$ as referring to 5 of 8 equal segments of a line (see Fig. 1–8). Here the line is the given unit, of which 5 parts of eight are being considered. That is, the line segment AB is $\frac{5}{8}$ of the line segment AC.

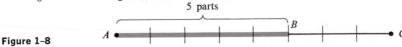

Figure 1–8

If, in a given group of 8 batteries, 5 are 6-volt batteries, we could say that $\frac{5}{8}$ of the group are 6-volt batteries, referring to these five.

If the numerator of a fraction is numerically less than the denominator, the fraction is called a *proper fraction*. If the numerator equals or is numerically greater than the denominator, the fraction is called an *improper fraction*. Since an improper fraction in which the numerator is greater than the denominator represents a number numerically greater than one, it is often convenient to use a *mixed number*, a whole number plus a proper fraction, to represent the same number. Consider the following example.

Example B

The fraction $\frac{4}{9}$ is a proper fraction, whereas $\frac{9}{4}$ is an improper fraction.

It is possible to interpret $\frac{9}{4}$ in terms of a number of equal parts of a given unit. Consider a line which has been divided in $\frac{1}{4}$-in. intervals (see Fig. 1–9). The fraction $\frac{9}{4}$ could then be interpreted as representing 9 of the $\frac{1}{4}$-in. units.

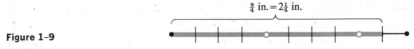

Figure 1–9

The line segment is also seen to be $2\frac{1}{4}$ in. long. Here $2\frac{1}{4}$ is a mixed number meaning $2 + \frac{1}{4}$.

In order to convert an improper fraction to a mixed number, divide the numerator by the denominator. The number of times the denominator will divide evenly is the whole number, and the remainder is the numerator of the proper fraction. In order to convert a mixed number into an improper fraction, multiply the whole number by the denominator of the proper fraction and add this result to the numerator of the proper fraction to obtain the numerator of the improper fraction. The denominator remains the same.

Example C

To convert $\frac{9}{4}$ to a mixed number, we divide 9 by 4. The result is 2 with a remainder of 1. Thus $\frac{9}{4} = 2\frac{1}{4}$.

To convert $2\frac{1}{4}$ to an improper fraction, we multiply 2×4 to get 8, which is then added to 1 to obtain 9. Thus $2\frac{1}{4} = \frac{9}{4}$.

Converting $\frac{73}{14}$ to a mixed number, we divide 73 by 14, obtaining 5 with a remainder of 3. Thus $\frac{73}{14} = 5\frac{3}{14}$.

Converting $6\frac{17}{21}$ to an improper fraction, we multiply $6 \times 21 = 126$. Now 17 is added to 126 to obtain 143. Therefore $6\frac{17}{21} = \frac{143}{21}$.

Two fractions are called *equivalent* if the numerator and denominator of one of the fractions can be multiplied, or divided, by the same number (not zero) in order to obtain the other fraction. A fraction is said to be *reduced* if it is changed to a fraction in which the numerator and denominator are numerically smaller. A fraction is converted to higher terms if the resulting numerator and denominator are numerically larger.

Example D

The fraction $\frac{18}{24}$ can be reduced to $\frac{3}{4}$ by dividing the numerator and the denominator by 6. Therefore $\frac{18}{24} = \frac{3}{4}$.

The fraction $\frac{6}{16}$ can be converted to $\frac{30}{80}$ by multiplying the numerator and denominator by 5. Therefore $\frac{6}{16} = \frac{30}{80}$.

Example E

The following fractions have been changed to equivalent fractions by performing the indicated operations on both numerator and denominator.

$\frac{2}{3} = \frac{4}{6}$ (multiplication by 2) $\qquad$ $\frac{2}{3} = \frac{14}{21}$ (multiplication by 7)

$\frac{5}{8} = \frac{20}{32}$ (multiplication by 4) $\qquad$ $\frac{5}{8} = \frac{45}{72}$ (multiplication by 9)

$\frac{28}{100} = \frac{7}{25}$ (division by 4) $\qquad$ $\frac{12}{54} = \frac{2}{9}$ (division by 6)

$\frac{121}{154} = \frac{11}{14}$ (division by 11) $\qquad$ $\frac{156}{84} = \frac{13}{7}$ (division by 12)

Among the most important operations performed on a fraction is reducing it to *lowest terms* (or *simplest form*). This means that the numerator and denominator are not both divisible by any natural number other than 1. An improper fraction should generally be left as a fraction and not be converted to a mixed number.

Example F   The fraction $\frac{10}{24}$ is not in lowest terms, since both the numerator and denominator are divisible by 2. Thus to reduce $\frac{10}{24}$ to lowest terms we divide the numerator and the denominator by 2 and obtain $\frac{5}{12}$. Since 5 and 12 are not both divisible by any natural number other than 1, the lowest terms of $\frac{10}{24}$ is $\frac{5}{12}$. Therefore $\frac{10}{24} = \frac{5}{12}$.

     The fraction $\frac{24}{9}$ can be reduced to lowest terms by dividing the numerator and the denominator by 3. Thus $\frac{24}{9} = \frac{8}{3}$. The simplest form is $\frac{8}{3}$ and it normally would not be expressed as $2\frac{2}{3}$.

Example G   Other illustrations of the simplest form of fractions are as follows:

$$\frac{10}{18} = \frac{5}{9}, \qquad \frac{18}{21} = \frac{6}{7}, \qquad \frac{45}{50} = \frac{9}{10},$$

$$\frac{7}{42} = \frac{1}{6}, \qquad \frac{152}{96} = \frac{19}{12}, \qquad \frac{33}{187} = \frac{3}{17}.$$

EXERCISES   In Exercises 1 through 4, convert the given improper fractions to mixed numbers.

   1. $\frac{5}{3}$ **2.** $\frac{18}{5}$ **3.** $\frac{273}{62}$ **4.** $\frac{5628}{109}$

In Exercises 5 through 8, convert the given mixed numbers to improper fractions.

   5. $2\frac{3}{5}$ **6.** $6\frac{3}{7}$ **7.** $18\frac{2}{19}$ **8.** $246\frac{19}{25}$

In Exercises 9 through 20, change the given fractions to equivalent fractions by performing the indicated operation on the numerator and the denominator.

   9. $\frac{3}{7}$, multiply by 2   **10.** $\frac{5}{9}$, multiply by 3

  11. $\frac{16}{20}$, divide by 4   **12.** $\frac{15}{125}$, divide by 5

  13. $\frac{4}{13}$, multiply by 6   **14.** $\frac{8}{15}$, multiply by 11

  15. $\frac{60}{156}$, divide by 12   **16.** $\frac{140}{42}$, divide by 7

  17. $\frac{13}{25}$, multiply by 7   **18.** $\frac{17}{15}$, multiply by 12

  19. $\frac{1024}{64}$, divide by 32   **20.** $\frac{289}{340}$, divide by 17

In Exercises 21 through 40, reduce the given fractions to lowest terms.

  21. $\frac{3}{9}$ **22.** $\frac{4}{16}$ **23.** $\frac{12}{26}$ **24.** $\frac{18}{15}$ **25.** $\frac{18}{30}$

  26. $\frac{25}{35}$ **27.** $\frac{54}{63}$ **28.** $\frac{5}{40}$ **29.** $\frac{36}{132}$ **30.** $\frac{42}{120}$

  31. $\frac{104}{72}$ **32.** $\frac{36}{135}$ **33.** $\frac{154}{70}$ **34.** $\frac{240}{135}$ **35.** $\frac{204}{228}$

  36. $\frac{162}{189}$ **37.** $\frac{221}{351}$ **38.** $\frac{132}{385}$ **39.** $\frac{220}{43}$ **40.** $\frac{76}{51}$

In Exercises 41 through 48, solve the given problems. Express all answers in lowest terms.

  41. The area of the 49 United States excepting Alaska is about six times the area of Alaska. What fraction of the total area of the United States is Alaska?

42. A certain factory has a quota of producing 25 units per hour. If they produce 30 units per hour, what fraction of the quota is the actual production?

43. Eight of 28 equal rows in an orchard are apple trees. What fraction of the trees are apple trees?

44. Two cattlemen rent some rangeland. If the first pastures 600 cattle and the second pastures 1400 cattle, what fraction of the cost should the first pay?

45. The time of the fastest mile run by a human is about 3 min 51 sec. Express this in terms of minutes only, as an improper fraction in lowest terms.

46. An object falling under the influence of gravity falls 1296 ft during the first 9 sec and 304 ft during the tenth second. What fraction of the distance fallen during the first 10 sec occurs during the tenth second?

47. The freezing point of water is 32°F (fahrenheit) or 0°C (centigrade or celsius). The boiling point of water is 212°F or 100°C. What is the fraction of °F to °C between the freezing point of water and the boiling point of water?

48. Type *A* punch card sorters can sort 2000 cards each minute. Type *B* can sort 1800 cards each minute. What fraction of the cards sorted by 3 type *A* sorters can be sorted by 6 type *B* sorters?

1–5 ADDITION AND SUBTRACTION OF FRACTIONS

When we discussed the addition of natural numbers in Section 1–2, we noted that we can add directly only like quantities. This is a basic principle of addition that is true regardless of the nature of the numbers.

Considering the meaning of a fraction as a number of equal parts of a given unit or of a given group, we see that each of these parts or units is equal. Therefore, when we add fractions in which the denominators are equal, we are adding like quantities. Consider this example.

When we are adding $\frac{2}{7}$ and $\frac{3}{7}$ we are adding 2 parts, each of which is $\frac{1}{7}$ **Example A**
of a unit, to 3 parts, each of which is also $\frac{1}{7}$ of the unit. Therefore we have a total of 5 of these parts. This means that

$$\frac{2}{7} + \frac{3}{7} = \frac{2+3}{7} = \frac{5}{7}.$$

For the reasons just considered, in order to add fractions in which the denominators are the same, we place the sum of the numerators over the common denominator. In the same way, when we subtract fractions, we place the difference of numerators over the common denominator.

Example B

a) $\dfrac{2}{9} + \dfrac{5}{9} = \dfrac{2+5}{9} = \dfrac{7}{9}$

b) $\dfrac{5}{11} - \dfrac{3}{11} = \dfrac{5-3}{11} = \dfrac{2}{11}$

c) $\dfrac{3}{8} + \dfrac{1}{8} = \dfrac{3+1}{8} = \dfrac{4}{8} = \dfrac{1}{2}$

d) $2\dfrac{1}{7} + \dfrac{3}{7} = \dfrac{15}{7} + \dfrac{3}{7} = \dfrac{15+3}{7} = \dfrac{18}{7}$

e) $\dfrac{7}{12} + \dfrac{1}{12} - \dfrac{5}{12} = \dfrac{7+1-5}{12} = \dfrac{8-5}{12} = \dfrac{3}{12} = \dfrac{1}{4}$

Note that in (c) the result of $\frac{4}{8}$ was put in the simplest form of $\frac{1}{2}$. In (d) the mixed number was first changed to an improper fraction; then the addition was performed. Although this is not the only procedure that can be followed, it is a standard procedure. In (e), where more than two fractions were being combined, the addition was performed first, and then the subtraction. (Until signed numbers are considered in Chapter 4, this procedure should be followed.) Note that the result in (e) was reduced also.

If the fractions being added or subtracted do not have the same denominators, it is necessary to convert them to a form such that all denominators are equal. After this has been completed the fractions can be combined. Although any proper common denominator can be used, any simplification required in the final result will be minimized if this denominator is the least possible value. Consider the following example.

Example C

If we wish to add $\frac{5}{12}$ and $\frac{7}{8}$, we might note that both fractions can be converted to fractions with a common denominator of 96. Therefore, converting these fractions, we have

$$\tfrac{5}{12} = \tfrac{40}{96} \quad \text{and} \quad \tfrac{7}{8} = \tfrac{84}{96}.$$

Adding $\frac{5}{12}$ and $\frac{7}{8}$ is equivalent to adding $\frac{40}{96}$ and $\frac{84}{96}$, or

$$\tfrac{5}{12} + \tfrac{7}{8} = \tfrac{40}{96} + \tfrac{84}{96} = \tfrac{124}{96}.$$

This final fraction, $\frac{124}{96}$, should be reduced to its simplest form. This is done by dividing both numerator and denominator by 4. Therefore

$$\tfrac{5}{12} + \tfrac{7}{8} = \tfrac{40}{96} + \tfrac{84}{96} = \tfrac{124}{96} = \tfrac{31}{24}.$$

If we had seen that a denominator of 24 could have been used, the addition would be

$$\tfrac{5}{12} + \tfrac{7}{8} = \tfrac{10}{24} + \tfrac{21}{24} = \tfrac{31}{24}.$$

In this case, the conversions were simpler, and the final result was in its simplest form.

In Example C we saw that either 96 or 24 could be used as a common denominator. Actually, innumerable other possibilities such as 48, 72, and 120 are also possible. However, 24 is the least of all of the possibilities. It is the *lowest common denominator* for these fractions. In general, the lowest common denominator of a set of fractions is the smallest number which is evenly divisible by all denominators of the set. The advantages to using the lowest common denominator are brought out in Example C. The conversions to higher terms are simpler, as is the simplification of the result. Therefore, when adding or subtracting fractions, we shall always use the lowest common denominator. We shall now proceed to show how the lowest common denominator is determined.

In many simpler cases the lowest common denominator can be determined by inspection. For example, if we are adding the fractions $\tfrac{1}{2}$ and $\tfrac{3}{8}$, we can easily determine that the lowest common denominator is 8. However, if we cannot readily determine the lowest common denominator by observation, we need a definite method that we can follow.

When we discussed multiplication of natural numbers, we said that the numbers multiplied together to form the product were *factors* of the product. A *prime number* is a natural number that is divisible evenly only by itself and 1. By determining the prime numbers which are factors (*prime factors*) of each denominator, we can find the lowest common denominator.

2 is prime, since it is divisible evenly only by 2 and 1.   **Example D**

3 is prime, since it is divisible evenly only by 3 and 1.

4 is not prime, since $4 = 2 \times 2$.

5 is prime, since it is divisible evenly only by 5 and 1.

6 is not prime, since $6 = 2 \times 3$.

Other prime numbers are 7, 11, 13, 17 and 19.

Other numbers which are not prime are 8 $(8 = 2 \times 2 \times 2)$, 9 $(9 = 3 \times 3)$, 10 $(10 = 5 \times 2)$, 12 $(12 = 2 \times 2 \times 3)$, 14 $(14 = 2 \times 7)$, 15 $(15 = 3 \times 5)$, 16 $(16 = 2 \times 2 \times 2 \times 2)$, and 18 $(18 = 2 \times 3 \times 3)$.

In order to find the lowest common denominator of a set of fractions, find all the prime factors in each denominator. The lowest common denominator is the product of all the different prime factors, each taken the greatest number of times it occurs in any one of the denominators.

Example E When we want to find the sum $\frac{5}{12} + \frac{7}{8}$, we must find the prime factors of 12 and 8. Since $12 = 2 \times 2 \times 3$ and $8 = 2 \times 2 \times 2$, we see that the only different prime factors are 2 and 3. Since 2 occurs twice in 12 and three times in 8, it is taken three times in the least common denominator. Since 3 occurs once in 12 and does not occur in 8, it is taken once. Therefore the lowest common denominator is

$$2 \times 2 \times 2 \times 3 = 24.$$

This means that

$$\tfrac{5}{12} + \tfrac{7}{8} = \tfrac{10}{24} + \tfrac{21}{24} = \tfrac{31}{24}.$$

Compare this with Example C.

Example F Combine: $\frac{2}{15} + \frac{11}{27} - \frac{7}{50}$.

First we must determine the prime factors of 15, 27, and 50. Therefore

$$15 = 3 \times 5, \qquad 27 = 3 \times 3 \times 3, \qquad 50 = 2 \times 5 \times 5.$$

We now observe that the necessary prime factors for the lowest common denominator are 2, 3 and 5. The greatest number of times each appears is once for 2 (in 50), three times for 3 (in 27) and twice for 5 (in 50). Therefore the lowest common denominator is

$$2 \times 3 \times 3 \times 3 \times 5 \times 5 = 1350.$$

Therefore we have

$$\begin{aligned}
\frac{2}{15} + \frac{11}{27} - \frac{7}{50} &= \frac{2(90)}{15(90)} + \frac{11(50)}{27(50)} - \frac{7(27)}{50(27)} \\
&= \frac{180}{1350} + \frac{550}{1350} - \frac{189}{1350} = \frac{180 + 550 - 189}{1350} \\
&= \frac{730 - 189}{1350} = \frac{541}{1350}.
\end{aligned}$$

We know that the only *prime* factors of 1350 are 2, 3, and 5. Since none of these divide evenly into 541, the result is in simplest form.

1. Determine which of the following numbers are prime: 21, 23, 27, 29.

2. Determine which of the following numbers are prime: 31, 32, 37, 39.

3. Determine the prime numbers between 40 and 60.

4. Determine the prime numbers between 60 and 80.

In Problems 5 through 12, find the lowest common denominator, assuming that the given numbers are denominators of fractions to be added or subtracted.

5. 2, 4   **6.** 2, 3   **7.** 6, 8   **8.** 6, 9

9. 8, 12, 18   **10.** 6, 10, 14   **11.** 10, 12, 25   **12.** 22, 24, 33

In Problems 13 through 28, perform the indicated additions and subtractions, expressing each result in simplest form.

13. $\frac{1}{5} + \frac{3}{5}$ **14.** $\frac{2}{11} + \frac{5}{11}$ **15.** $\frac{4}{9} + \frac{7}{9} + \frac{1}{9}$

16. $2\frac{1}{16} + \frac{9}{16} - \frac{3}{16}$ **17.** $\frac{1}{2} + 2\frac{1}{4}$ **18.** $\frac{2}{3} - \frac{1}{6}$

19. $\frac{7}{12} - \frac{1}{4}$ **20.** $\frac{13}{18} - \frac{1}{2}$ **21.** $3\frac{5}{6} - \frac{3}{8}$

22. $2\frac{4}{9} + \frac{5}{12}$ **23.** $\frac{11}{20} + \frac{5}{8}$ **24.** $\frac{19}{28} - \frac{5}{24}$

25. $\frac{3}{8} + \frac{7}{12} + \frac{1}{18}$ **26.** $3\frac{2}{9} + \frac{7}{15} - \frac{4}{25}$ **27.** $\frac{1}{3} + 1\frac{9}{14} - \frac{5}{21}$

28. $\frac{26}{27} - \frac{7}{18} + \frac{1}{10}$

In Exercises 29 through 36, solve the given problems.

29. Find the perimeter of a triangle (3 sides) whose sides are $2\frac{1}{2}$ in., $3\frac{1}{4}$ in., and $2\frac{3}{4}$ in.

30. Find the perimeter of a four-sided figure whose sides are $\frac{5}{12}$ ft, $\frac{1}{3}$ ft, $\frac{1}{6}$ ft and $\frac{3}{4}$ ft.

31. A board $6\frac{2}{3}$ ft long has a piece $2\frac{1}{12}$ ft cut from it. What is the length of the remaining piece?

32. In doing a homework assignment a student noted that $2\frac{1}{6}$ hours elapsed from the time he started to the time he finished. If he took a break of $\frac{1}{4}$ hr, how much time did he spend studying?

33. Three electrical resistors are $3\frac{1}{18}$ ohms, $2\frac{5}{24}$ ohms, and $1\frac{7}{15}$ ohms. What is the sum of these resistances?

34. In three successive days of rain, an area had $\frac{3}{4}$ in. the first day, $1\frac{3}{8}$ in. the second day, and $\frac{5}{12}$ in. the third day. What was the total rainfall?

35. A certain alloy is $\frac{2}{5}$ copper, $\frac{1}{3}$ gold, and the rest silver. What fraction is silver?

36. In traveling from city A to city B in two days, a man drove for $6\frac{1}{12}$ hr the first day and $4\frac{3}{8}$ hr the second day. He made the return trip in one day, driving $9\frac{5}{6}$ hr. How much less driving time did the return trip take?

1-6 MULTIPLICATION AND DIVISION OF FRACTIONS

In order to develop the procedure for multiplying one fraction by another, we shall consider the area of a rectangle. Consider, for example, the rectangle in Fig. 1–10. If the rectangle is 7 in. long and 3 in. wide, the area is 21 sq in. Let us now mark both the length and width at one-inch intervals and divide the area into 21 equal areas, as shown. Each of the individual squares has an area of 1 sq in. If we now find the area which is 5 in. long and 2 in. wide, it is 10 sq in. This is equivalent to finding what part of the total area is the rectangle whose length is $\frac{5}{7}$ of the length of the original rectangle and whose width is $\frac{2}{3}$ of the width of the original rectangle. We note that the resulting area is $\frac{10}{21}$ of the area of the original rectangle. Since we find area by multiplying the length by the width, we have

$$\frac{5}{7} \times \frac{2}{3} = \frac{10}{21}.$$

Considerations such as these lead to the following definition: The product of two fractions is the fraction whose numerator is the product of the numerators, and whose denominator is the product of the denominators.

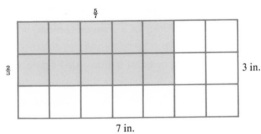

Figure 1–10

$\frac{5}{7}$

$\frac{2}{3}$ 3 in.

7 in.

Example A

$$\frac{5}{7} \times \frac{2}{3} = \frac{5 \times 2}{7 \times 3} = \frac{10}{21} \qquad \frac{9}{4} \times \frac{7}{2} = \frac{9 \times 7}{4 \times 2} = \frac{63}{8}$$

$$\frac{2}{5} \times \frac{8}{9} = \frac{2 \times 8}{5 \times 9} = \frac{16}{45} \qquad \frac{3}{14} \times \frac{15}{4} = \frac{3 \times 15}{14 \times 4} = \frac{45}{56}$$

If the resulting fraction is not in simplest form, it should be reduced to this form. This can be accomplished by multiplying the numerators and denominators and then reducing the resulting fraction. However, this can lead to a great deal more arithmetic than is necessary. Since a fraction is reduced to its lowest terms by dividing both numerator and denominator by the same number, this can be accomplished by dividing any factor of each of the numerator and denominator. Consider the following example.

In finding the product $\frac{24}{7} \times \frac{17}{32}$, we can multiply directly to get   **Example B**

$$\frac{24}{7} \times \frac{17}{32} = \frac{408}{224}.$$

We can now reduce this result by dividing both numerator and denominator by 8, giving

$$\frac{24}{7} \times \frac{17}{32} = \frac{408}{224} = \frac{51}{28}.$$

However, if we only indicate the multiplication as

$$\frac{24}{7} \times \frac{17}{32} = \frac{24 \times 17}{7 \times 32},$$

we note that both 24 and 32 are divisible by 8. If we perform this division before we multiply the factors in the numerator, we have

$$\frac{24}{7} \times \frac{17}{32} = \frac{24 \times 17}{7 \times 32} = \frac{3 \times 17}{7 \times 4} = \frac{51}{28}.$$

We obtain the same result, but the arithmetic operations are simpler and the numbers involved are smaller. Thus we see that we should divide out any factors which are common to both numerator and denominator *before* we actually multiply numerators and denominators.

$$\frac{4}{5} \times \frac{3}{8} = \frac{4 \times 3}{5 \times 8} = \frac{1 \times 3}{5 \times 2} = \frac{3}{10}$$ (divide 4 and 8 by 4)   **Example C**

$$\frac{18}{25} \times \frac{4}{27} = \frac{18 \times 4}{25 \times 27} = \frac{2 \times 4}{25 \times 3} = \frac{8}{75}$$ (divide 18 and 27 by 9)

$$\frac{16}{15} \times \frac{5}{12} = \frac{16 \times 5}{15 \times 12} = \frac{4 \times 1}{3 \times 3} = \frac{4}{9}$$ (divide 16 and 12 by 4 and divide 5 and 15 by 5)

$$\frac{30}{7} \times \frac{28}{33} = \frac{30 \times 28}{7 \times 33} = \frac{10 \times 4}{1 \times 11} = \frac{40}{11}$$ (divide 30 and 33 by 3 and divide 28 and 7 by 7)

In order to multiply a whole number by a fraction, we can write the whole number as a fraction with 1 as the denominator. The result is the same if the whole number is multiplied by the numerator of the fraction. If a mixed number is to be multiplied by another number, the mixed number must first be converted to an improper fraction.

Example D

$$4 \times \frac{3}{7} = \frac{4}{1} \times \frac{3}{7} = \frac{4 \times 3}{1 \times 7} = \frac{12}{7}, \qquad 9 \times \frac{5}{12} = \frac{9 \times 5}{12} = \frac{3 \times 5}{4} = \frac{15}{4},$$

$$2\frac{1}{3} \times \frac{3}{5} = \frac{7}{3} \times \frac{3}{5} = \frac{7 \times 3}{3 \times 5} = \frac{7 \times 1}{1 \times 5} = \frac{7}{5},$$

$$6 \times 3\frac{2}{5} = 6 \times \frac{17}{5} = \frac{6 \times 17}{5} = \frac{102}{5}.$$

If more than two fractions are to be multiplied, the resulting numerator is the product of the numerators and the resulting denominator is the product of the denominators.

Example E

$$\frac{2}{5} \times \frac{3}{7} \times \frac{4}{11} = \frac{2 \times 3 \times 4}{5 \times 7 \times 11} = \frac{24}{385}$$

$$\frac{3}{7} \times \frac{4}{8} \times \frac{5}{13} = \frac{3 \times 4 \times 5}{7 \times 8 \times 13} = \frac{3 \times 1 \times 5}{7 \times 2 \times 13} = \frac{15}{182}$$

$$\frac{25}{12} \times \frac{8}{15} \times \frac{3}{10} = \frac{25 \times 8 \times 3}{12 \times 15 \times 10} = \frac{5 \times 2 \times 3}{3 \times 3 \times 10} = \frac{1 \times 1 \times 1}{3 \times 1 \times 1} = \frac{1}{3}$$

We shall now turn our attention to the division of one fraction by another. In the following example we shall develop the method of division, and see that it follows easily from multiplication.

Example F

When we wish to find the quotient $\frac{2}{3} \div \frac{5}{7}$, we write it as a fraction with $\frac{2}{3}$ as the numerator and $\frac{5}{7}$ as the denominator. We then multiply the numerator and the denominator by $\frac{7}{5}$. This leads to

$$\frac{\frac{2}{3}}{\frac{5}{7}} = \frac{\frac{2}{3} \times \frac{7}{5}}{\frac{5}{7} \times \frac{7}{5}} = \frac{\frac{2 \times 7}{3 \times 5}}{\frac{1 \times 1}{1 \times 1}} = \frac{\frac{14}{15}}{\frac{1}{1}} = \frac{14}{15}.$$

Note that the product of $\frac{5}{7}$ and $\frac{7}{5}$ is 1, which means that the result is obtained by multiplying $\frac{2}{3}$ by $\frac{7}{5}$. The fraction $\frac{7}{5}$ is the fraction $\frac{5}{7}$ inverted; that is, the numerator and denominator are interchanged.

Using the results of Example F, we are led to the following procedure: In order to divide a number by a fraction, invert the divisor and multiply.

Example G

$$\frac{\frac{3}{7}}{\frac{4}{9}} = \frac{3}{7} \times \frac{9}{4} = \frac{3 \times 9}{7 \times 4} = \frac{27}{28}$$

$$\frac{\frac{8}{5}}{\frac{4}{15}} = \frac{8}{5} \times \frac{15}{4} = \frac{8 \times 15}{5 \times 4} = \frac{2 \times 3}{1 \times 1} = 6$$

$$\frac{6}{\frac{2}{7}} = 6 \times \frac{7}{2} = \frac{6 \times 7}{2} = \frac{3 \times 7}{1} = 21$$

$$\frac{\frac{2}{5}}{4} = \frac{\frac{2}{5}}{\frac{4}{1}} = \frac{2}{5} \times \frac{1}{4} = \frac{2 \times 1}{5 \times 4} = \frac{1 \times 1}{5 \times 2} = \frac{1}{10}$$

We have just seen that in division by a fraction it is necessary to invert the divisor. In general, the *reciprocal* of a number is 1 divided by that number. In following this definition we find that the reciprocal of a fraction is the fraction with the numerator and denominator inverted.

Example H

The reciprocal of 8 is $\frac{1}{8}$.

The reciprocal of $\frac{1}{3}$ is

$$\frac{1}{\frac{1}{3}} = 1 \times \frac{3}{1} = 3.$$

The reciprocal of $\frac{7}{12}$ is

$$\frac{1}{\frac{7}{12}} = 1 \times \frac{12}{7} = \frac{12}{7}.$$

Finally let us consider the case of a sum or difference of fractions as being either the numerator or denominator of a fraction. In this case, the addition or subtraction is to be performed first. Consider the following example.

Example I

$$\frac{\frac{1}{5} + \frac{7}{10}}{\frac{2}{6} - \frac{1}{8}} = \frac{\frac{2}{10} + \frac{7}{10}}{\frac{8}{24} - \frac{3}{24}} = \frac{\frac{2+7}{10}}{\frac{8-3}{24}} = \frac{\frac{9}{10}}{\frac{5}{24}} = \frac{9}{10} \times \frac{24}{5} = \frac{9 \times 12}{5 \times 5} = \frac{108}{25}$$

In Exercises 1 through 26, perform the indicated multiplications and divisions.   EXERCISES

1. $\frac{2}{7} \times \frac{3}{11}$ **2.** $\frac{7}{8} \times \frac{3}{5}$ **3.** $3 \times \frac{2}{5}$ **4.** $\frac{2}{7} \times 1\frac{2}{3}$

5. $\frac{7}{8} \div \frac{5}{6}$ **6.** $\frac{7}{4} \div \frac{2}{5}$ **7.** $\frac{5}{9} \div 3$ **8.** $2\frac{1}{2} \div \frac{8}{3}$

9. $\frac{8}{9} \times \frac{5}{16}$ **10.** $\frac{5}{12} \times \frac{3}{7}$ **11.** $2\frac{1}{3} \times \frac{9}{14}$ **12.** $\frac{22}{25} \times \frac{15}{33}$

13. $\frac{8}{15} \div \frac{12}{35}$ **14.** $\frac{21}{44} \div \frac{28}{33}$ **15.** $\frac{8}{17} \div 4$ **16.** $\frac{39}{35} \div \frac{13}{21}$

17. $\frac{3}{5} \times \frac{15}{7} \times \frac{14}{9}$ **18.** $\frac{2}{7} \times \frac{19}{4} \times \frac{21}{38}$ **19.** $(\frac{3}{4} \times \frac{28}{27}) \div \frac{35}{6}$

20. $\frac{18}{25} \div (\frac{17}{5} \div \frac{34}{15})$ **21.** $\frac{9}{16} \times (\frac{1}{2} + \frac{1}{4})$ **22.** $(\frac{9}{16} - \frac{1}{6}) \div 4\frac{3}{4}$

23. $\dfrac{\frac{1}{2} + \frac{1}{3}}{\frac{2}{3}}$ **24.** $\dfrac{\frac{15}{14}}{\frac{7}{8} - \frac{1}{4}}$ **25.** $\dfrac{\frac{2}{6} + \frac{7}{15}}{\frac{7}{10} - \frac{1}{4}}$

26. $\dfrac{\frac{4}{21} + \frac{5}{9}}{\frac{3}{4} + \frac{9}{14}}$

In Exercises 27 through 30, find the reciprocals of the given numbers.

27. 5; 13   **28.** $\frac{1}{6}$; $\frac{1}{8}$ **29.** $\frac{2}{9}$; $\frac{3}{7}$ **30.** $4\frac{1}{3}$; $2\frac{1}{2}$

In Exercises 31 through 40, solve the given problems.

31. What is the sum of the voltages of 50 batteries, each of which is $1\frac{1}{2}$ volts?

32. A certain thin rectangular machine part is $\frac{11}{16}$ in. by $\frac{12}{33}$ in. What is its area?

33. The area of a rectangular metal plate is $2\frac{3}{16}$ sq in. and its length is $1\frac{7}{8}$ in. What is the width?

34. How many blocks $\frac{2}{3}$ ft long must be laid end to end to make a row 40 ft long?

35. A certain machine produced 16 articles in 3 hr. How many will it produce in $2\frac{1}{4}$ hr?

36. Two meshed gears have 20 teeth and 50 teeth, respectively. How many turns will the smaller gear make while the larger gear makes $3\frac{1}{2}$ turns?

37. A farmer plowed $3\frac{1}{4}$ acres in $5\frac{1}{2}$ hours. What was his rate of plowing?

38. A car traveled 87 mi in $2\frac{5}{12}$ hr. What was the average speed?

39. There are approximately $3\frac{7}{25}$ bushels in one barrel. How many bushels are there in $2\frac{3}{16}$ barrels?

40. The acceleration due to gravity on Mars is about $\frac{2}{5}$ of that on the earth. If the acceleration due to gravity on earth is $32\frac{1}{5}$ ft/sec/sec, what is it on Mars?

1–7 DECIMALS

In discussing the basic operations on fractions in the last few sections, we have seen how to express and combine numbers which express parts of quantities. In a great many applied situations fractions are quite useful. However, there are many times in scientific work and in its applications when a different way of expressing parts of quantities proves to be more convenient. Measurements such as meter readings and distances are often expressed in terms of whole numbers and *decimal* parts.

Fractions whose denominators are 10, 100, 1000, etc., are called *decimal fractions*. For example, $\frac{7}{10}$ and $\frac{193}{10000}$ are decimal fractions. Making further use of positional notation, as introduced in Section 1–2, we place a *decimal point* to the right of the units digit and let the first position to the right stand for the number of tenths, the digit in the second position to the right stand for the number of hundredths, and so on. Numbers written in this form are called *decimals*.

thousands	hundreds	tens	units		tenths	hundredths	thousandths	ten-thousandths
6	3	5	2	.	1	8	7	9

Figure 1–11

The meaning of the decimal 6352.1879 is illustrated in Fig. 1–11. We may also show the meaning of this decimal number as

$$6(1000) + 3(100) + 5(10) + 2(1) + \tfrac{1}{10} + \tfrac{8}{100} + \tfrac{7}{1000} + \tfrac{9}{10000}.$$

Example A

In this form we can easily see the relation between decimal and decimal fraction.

Since a fraction is the indicated division of one number by another, we can change a fraction to an equivalent decimal by division. We place a decimal point and additional zeros to the right of the units position of the numerator and then perform the division.

In order to change $\frac{5}{8}$ into an equivalent decimal, we perform the following division.

Example B

$$
\begin{array}{r}
.625 \\
8\overline{)5.000} \\
4\,8 \\
\hline
20 \\
16 \\
\hline
40 \\
40 \\
\hline
\end{array}
$$

Therefore $\frac{5}{8} = 0.625$. (It is a common practice to place a zero to the left of the decimal point in a decimal less than 1. It is used to clarify the fact that the decimal point is properly positioned.)

In many cases when we convert a fraction to a decimal the division does not come out even, regardless of the number of places to the right of the decimal point. In cases like this, the most useful decimal form is one which is *approximated* by *rounding off* the result of the division. (We shall take up the subject of approximate numbers in detail in the next chapter.) When we round off a decimal to a required accuracy, we want the decimal which is the closest approximation to the original, but with the specified number of decimal positions.

Example C   Since $\frac{3}{7} = 0.428\ldots$ (the three dots indicate that the division can be continued), we can round off the result to one decimal place (the nearest tenth) as $\frac{3}{7} = 0.4$, since 0.4 is the decimal closest to $\frac{3}{7}$, with the tenth position as the last position which is written.

Rounded off to two decimal places (the nearest hundredth) $0.428\ldots = 0.43$. Note that, when we rounded off the number to hundredths, we increased the hundredths position by one.

Other examples of rounding off are as follows:

$$0.862 \quad = 0.86 \quad \text{(to two decimal places or hundredths)}$$
$$0.867 \quad = 0.87 \quad \text{(to two decimal places or hundredths)}$$
$$0.09326 = 0.093 \quad \text{(to three decimal places or thousandths)}$$
$$0.09326 = 0.0933 \quad \text{(to four decimal places or ten-thousandths)}$$

In order to change a decimal to a fractional form, we first write it in its decimal fraction form and then simplify it. Consider the illustrations in the following example.

Example D
$$0.5 = \tfrac{5}{10} = \tfrac{1}{2}, \qquad\qquad 0.38 = \tfrac{38}{100} = \tfrac{19}{50},$$
$$0.125 = \tfrac{125}{1000} = \tfrac{1}{8}, \qquad 0.00164 = \tfrac{164}{100000} = \tfrac{41}{25000}.$$

When we consider the addition and subtraction of decimals, we see that the principles are the same as those which were developed for the natural numbers. Since only like quantities can be added or subtracted, we must then add tenths to tenths, hundredths to hundredths, and so on. Therefore, when we add and subtract decimals, we place the decimal points directly below each other and perform the addition or subtraction as we did with the natural numbers.

Example E

$$
\begin{array}{r}
326.49 \\
98.362 \\
\underline{5937.8} \\
6362.652
\end{array}
\qquad
\begin{array}{r}
7862.472 \\
-\ \ 794.56 \\
\hline
7067.912
\end{array}
$$

In order to develop the method for multiplying one decimal by another, we shall express each decimal in its decimal-fraction form and then perform the multiplication. An observation of the results will lead to the appropriate method. Consider the following example.

In order to multiply 0.053 by 3.4, we express the multiplication as

Example F

$$(0.053)(3.4) = \tfrac{53}{1000} \cdot \tfrac{34}{10} = \tfrac{1802}{10000} = 0.1802.$$

We note that there are 3 decimal places (to the right of the decimal point) in the first of the numbers being multiplied, 1 decimal place in the second number and 4 in the final result. Also, the numerator in the product is the product of 53 and 34, and is not affected by the denominators. Therefore the positioning of the decimal point in the numbers being multiplied depends only on the denominators.

Considering the results of Example F, when we multiply one decimal by another, *the number of decimal places (to the right of the decimal point) in the product is the sum of the number of decimal places in the numbers being multiplied.* Also, it is not necessary to line up decimal points as we do in addition and subtraction. The numbers are multiplied as if they were natural numbers, and the decimal point is then properly positioned in the product.

Example G

$$
\begin{array}{r}
5.307 \quad \text{(3 places)} \\
\underline{2.63} \quad \text{(2 places)} \\
15921 \\
31842 \\
\underline{10614} \\
13.95741 \quad \text{(5 places)}
\end{array}
$$

As in the other basic operations, the division of one decimal by another is very similar to the division of natural numbers. Before the division is actually performed, however, the decimal point in the divisor is moved to the right a sufficient number of places to make the divisor a whole number. The decimal point in the dividend is then moved the same number of places. (This is equivalent to multiplying the numerator and denominator of the fraction form of the division by the same number.) The decimal point in the quotient is directly above that of the dividend.

Example H

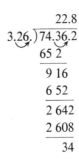

$$
\begin{array}{r}
22.8 \\
3.26.\overline{)74.36.2} \\
65\ 2 \\
\hline
9\ 16 \\
6\ 52 \\
\hline
2\ 642 \\
2\ 608 \\
\hline
34
\end{array}
$$

EXERCISES   In Exercises 1 through 4, write the given decimals as a sum of 1's, 10's, 100's, etc., and decimal fractions, as in Example A.

1. 47.3   **2.** 29.26   **3.** 429.486   **4.** 5230.3727

In Exercises 5 through 12, round off the given decimals to the accuracy indicated.

5. 27.32 (tenths)   **6.** 404.878 (hundredths)

7. 57.544 (two decimal places)   **8.** 6.3833 (three decimal places)

9. 8.0327 (hundredths)   **10.** 0.4063 (hundredths)

11. 17.3846 (tenths)   **12.** 86.30241 (thousandths)

In Exercises 13 through 20, change the given fractions into equivalent decimals. Where necessary round off the result to the accuracy indicated.

13. $\frac{2}{5}$ **14.** $\frac{7}{16}$

15. $\frac{4}{19}$ (hundredths)   **16.** $\frac{11}{23}$ (hundredths)

17. $\frac{47}{27}$ (tenths)   **18.** $\frac{882}{67}$ (tenths)

19. $\frac{362}{725}$ (thousandths)   **20.** $\frac{29}{426}$ (thousandths)

In Exercises 21 through 24, change the given decimals into equivalent fractions in simplest form.

21. 0.45   **22.** 0.002   **23.** 5.34   **24.** 0.0084

In Exercises 25 through 34, perform the indicated operation.

25. 3.26 + 18.941 + 9.094   **26.** 18.87 + 8.9 + 182.825

27. $18.046 + 1924.3 + 874.91$

28. $0.046 + 19.35 + 186.6942$

29. $18.623 - 9.86$

30. $0.8694 - 0.0996$

31. $(2.36)(5.932)$

32. $(37.4)(8.207)$

33. $5.6(3.72 + 18.6)$

34. $0.042(3.072 + 92.23)$

In Exercises 35 through 38, perform the indicated divisions, rounding off to the accuracy indicated.

35. $(32.6) \div (2.6)$ (tenths)

36. $186 \div (0.87)$ (tenths)

37. $\frac{5.923}{17.6}$ (hundredths)

38. $\frac{93.2}{0.471}$ (hundredths)

In Exercises 39 through 47, solve the given problems.

39. Three electrical resistors have resistances of 13.2 ohms, 6.9 ohms, and 8.4 ohms, respectively. What is the sum of these resistances?

40. What is the perimeter of a rectangle if its length is 13.56 in. and its width is 7.84 in.?

41. If a man has \$318.62 in his bank account and then withdraws \$82.74, what is the resulting balance?

42. One end of a machine part is $5\frac{7}{16}$ in. wide and the other end is 4.982 in. wide. How much wider is the first end?

43. A certain metal plate is 5.273 in. long and 3.026 in. wide. What is its area? (Round off the result to hundredths.)

44. An assembly worker earns \$2.84 per hour for the first 40 hr of work in a week. He earns "time and a half" ($1\frac{1}{2}$ times the normal rate) for overtime. If he works $48\frac{1}{4}$ hr in a week, what does he earn for the week?

45. If a car travels 193.6 mi in 4 hr 25 min, what is its average speed? (Round off the result to tenths.)

46. If one meter = 39.37 in., how many meters are there in 8 ft? (Round off the result to hundredths.)

47. The specific gravity of an object can be defined as its weight in air divided by its loss of weight when weighed in water. A certain metallic object weighs 4.15 lb in air and 3.66 lb in water. What is its specific gravity? (Round off the result to tenths.)

1–8   PERCENTAGE

Now that we have considered fractions and decimals, we shall take up the topic of *percentage*. The word "percent" means "per hundred" or "hundredths." The familiar symbol % is used to denote percent.

Example A $3\% $ means $\frac{3}{100}$ or $3(0.01) = 0.03$. Also

$25\% = \frac{25}{100} = 0.25, \qquad 300\% = \frac{300}{100} = 3.00, \qquad 0.4\% = \frac{0.4}{100} = 0.004.$

Percentage is very convenient, since we need consider only hundredths. With fractions we use halves, fifths, tenths, and so on, and comparing fractions is difficult unless the denominators are the same. With decimals we use tenths, hundredths, thousandths, and so on. Comparisons of percentages are easy, since only one denominator is considered.

Example B   Suppose that you were told that $\frac{3}{20}$ of Brand A transistors were defective, and that $\frac{4}{25}$ of Brand B transistors were defective. You would first have to determine that $\frac{3}{20} = \frac{15}{100}$ and that $\frac{4}{25} = \frac{16}{100}$ before you could tell that Brand B has more defective transistors than Brand A. However, if you are told that 15% of Brand A transistors were defective and that 16% of Brand B transistors were defective, the comparison is easy.

Using the meaning of percent allows us to convert percents to decimals, decimals to percents, percents to fractions, and fractions to percent. The following two examples illustrate these conversions.

Example C

$$5\% = \frac{5}{100} = 0.05 \qquad \text{(percent to decimal)}$$
$$132\% = \frac{132}{100} = 1.32 \qquad \text{(percent to decimal)}$$
$$0.2\% = \frac{0.2}{100} = 0.002 \qquad \text{(percent to decimal)}$$
$$0.45 = \frac{45}{100} = 45\% \qquad \text{(decimal to percent)}$$
$$0.3 = \frac{3}{10} = \frac{30}{100} = 30\% \qquad \text{(decimal to percent)}$$
$$0.826 = \frac{826}{1000} = \frac{82.6}{100} = 82.6\% \quad \text{(decimal to percent)}$$

Note that a percent can be changed to a decimal by moving the decimal point two places to the left and omitting the $\%$ sign. Also a decimal can be changed to a percent by moving the decimal point two places to the right and inserting the $\%$ sign.

Example D

$$20\% = \frac{20}{100} = \frac{1}{5} \qquad \text{(percent to fraction)}$$
$$0.6\% = \frac{0.6}{100} = \frac{6}{1000} = \frac{3}{500} \quad \text{(percent to fraction)}$$
$$\tfrac{3}{8} = 0.375 = 37.5\% \qquad \text{(fraction to percent)}$$
$$\tfrac{15}{12} = 1.25 = 125\% \qquad \text{(fraction to percent)}$$

When we change a percent to a fraction, we reduce the resulting fraction to simplest terms. When we change a fraction to percent, we carry out the division (and round off the figure if necessary), and express the resulting decimal as a percent.

In most cases in which percentage is used in calculations, it is converted to its decimal form. The following three examples illustrate some of the numerous applications of percentage.

A state has a sales tax of $3\frac{1}{2}\%$. What is the sales tax on an automobile costing $3000?   **Example E**

Here we wish to find $3\frac{1}{2}\%$ of $3000, or in other words, we want to multiply $3\frac{1}{2}\%$ by $3000:

$$(3\tfrac{1}{2}\%)(\$3000) = (0.035)(\$3000) = \$105.$$

Therefore the sales tax on $3000 is $105.

A man bought a house for $18,000. Later he sold the house for $21,000. What percent of the selling price was profit?   **Example F**

First we determine that his profit was $3,000. Therefore we wish to find out what percent of $21,000 is $3,000. Therefore, we set up the fraction $\frac{3000}{21000}$ and convert to percent:

$$\tfrac{3000}{21000} = \tfrac{3}{21} = \tfrac{1}{7} = 0.14 = 14\% \quad \text{(rounded off)}.$$

Therefore approximately 14% of the selling price was profit.

A certain fuel mixture is 40% of type A fuel and 60% of other types. A particular shipment of the mixture contains 300 gal of type A. How many gallons are in the shipment?   **Example G**

We know that (40%)(total number of gallons) = 300 gal. When we were discussing division we noted that "the product of the quotient and divisor equals the dividend." If we take 40% to be the divisor, and 300 gal to be the dividend, we have

$$\text{Total number of gallons} = \frac{300 \text{ gal}}{40\%}.$$

Therefore, by dividing 300 by 40%, we shall find the total number of gallons in the shipment.

$$\frac{300 \text{ gal}}{40\%} = \frac{300 \text{ gal}}{0.40} = 750 \text{ gal.}$$

Therefore the shipment was 750 gal. From the example we can see that if the percentage and percentage rate are given, we can find the number of which the percentage is being found (the *base*) by dividing the percentage by the rate.

EXERCISES   In Exercises 1 through 6, change the given percentages to equivalent decimals.

1. 8%   **2.** 78%   **3.** 236%

4. 482%   **5.** 0.3%   **6.** 0.082%

In Exercises 7 through 12, change the given decimals to percentages.

7. 0.27   **8.** 0.09   **9.** 3.21

10. 21.6   **11.** 0.0064   **12.** 0.0007

In Exercises 13 through 18, change the given percentages to equivalent fractions.

13. 30%   **14.** 48%   **15.** 2.5%

16. 0.8%   **17.** 120%   **18.** 0.036%

In Exercises 19 through 24, change the given fractions to percentages. Round off to the nearest tenth of a percent where necessary.

19. $\frac{3}{5}$ **20.** $\frac{7}{20}$ **21.** $\frac{4}{7}$

22. $\frac{16}{11}$ **23.** $\frac{8}{35}$ **24.** $\frac{18}{29}$

In Exercises 25 through 46, solve the given problems.

25. Find 20% of 65.

26. Find 2.6% of 230.

27. What is 0.52% of 1020?

28. What is 126% of 300?

29. What percent of 72 is 18?

30. What percent of 250 is 5?

31. 3.6 is what percent of 48?

32. 0.14 is what percent of 3.5?

33. 25 is 50% of what number?

34. 3.6 is 25% of what number?

35. If 1.75% of a number is 7, what is the number?

36. If 226% of a number is 3.7, what is the number (round off to tenths)?

37. The sales tax in a certain state is 4%. What is the tax in this state on an article costing $378?

38. In a particular factory, the workers were given an across-the-board 8% raise in their hourly wage. If a man were earning $3.12 per hour, what would his new rate be?

39. A tire costing $18.00 is to be sold at a 15% discount. What is the new price?

40. A salesman earns $50 per week plus a 12% commission on all sales he makes. What are his earnings for a week in which he sells $1400 worth of merchandise?

41. Of 520 lb of a certain alloy, 182 lb are zinc. What percent of the alloy is zinc?

42. A man put $620 in a bank. At the end of a year he had earned $27.90 in interest. What is the annual rate of interest (in percent) at the bank?

43. A man who earned $9200 in a year paid $1656 in income taxes. What percent of his earnings was paid in income taxes?

44. The efficiency of a motor is defined as power output divided by power input, usually expressed in percent. What is the efficiency of an electric motor whose power input is 850 watts and whose power output is 561 watts?

45. The effective value of an alternating current is 70.7% of its maximum value. What is the maximum value (to the nearest amp) of a current whose effective value is 8 amp?

46. The minimum distance from the earth of an artificial satellite is about 46% of its maximum distance from the earth. If its minimum distance is 1020 mi, what is its maximum distance (to the nearest mile)?

1-9 POWERS AND ROOTS

In a great many situations, we encounter a number which is to be multiplied by itself several times. Rather than writing the number over and over repeatedly, we can use a notation in which we write the number once, and write the number of times it is to be multiplied as an *exponent*. The exponent is a small number to the right and slightly above the number. The expression is usually referred to as a *power* of the number; the number itself is called the *base*.

Instead of writing 3×3, we write 3^2. Here the 2 is the exponent and the 3 is the base. The expression is read as "3 to the second power" or "3 squared."

Example A

Rather than writing $7 \times 7 \times 7$, we write 7^3. Here the 3 is the exponent and the 7 is the base. The expression is read as "7 to the third power" or "7 cubed."

The product $5 \times 5 \times 5 \times 5 \times 5 \times 5$ is written as 5^6. Here 6 is the exponent and 5 is the base. The expression is read as "the sixth power of 5" or "5 to the sixth power."

If a number is raised to the first power, that is, if it appears only once in a product, the exponent 1 is not usually written. Also, if we are given a number written in terms of an exponent, we can write the number in ordinary notation by performing the indicated multiplication. Consider the illustrations in the following example.

Example B $5^1 = 5$ (normally the 1 would not appear)

$$4^5 = 4 \times 4 \times 4 \times 4 \times 4 = 1024$$
$$(2^3)(3^2) = (2 \times 2 \times 2)(3 \times 3) = (8) \times (9) = 72$$

Another problem which often arises is to find the *root* of a number. The root of a number is one of two or more equal factors of the number. If we are looking for one of two equal factors, we are looking for the *square root* of the number. One of three equal factors of a number is its *cube root;* one of four equal factors of a number is its *fourth root;* and so on. The symbol $\sqrt{}$ indicates a square root, $\sqrt[3]{}$ indicates a cube root, $\sqrt[4]{}$ indicates a fourth root, and so on. Until we get to Chapter 11, we shall consider primarily square roots and occasionally cube roots. Other roots will be considered for the moment only as illustrations.

Example C $\sqrt{9} = 3$ (since $3^2 = 9$), $\sqrt{64} = 8$ (since $8^2 = 64$),
$\sqrt[3]{8} = 2$ (since $2^3 = 8$), $\sqrt[3]{64} = 4$ (since $4^3 = 64$),
$\sqrt[4]{16} = 2$ (since $2^4 = 16$), $\sqrt[5]{243} = 3$ (since $3^5 = 243$).

Table 1 in the Appendix gives the squares, square roots, cubes and cube roots of the numbers 1 through 100. All the roots, except those that come out even, are rounded off to the nearest one-thousandth. To this accuracy, the values can be read directly from the table.

Example D $\sqrt{5} = 2.236,$ $\sqrt{71} = 8.426,$
$\sqrt[3]{18} = 2.621,$ $\sqrt[3]{39} = 3.391,$
$19^2 = 361,$ $58^3 = 195{,}112.$

Many square roots cannot be found by inspection or from tables. Therefore we shall illustrate here a method for finding the square root of a number.

The method is outlined in the following three examples.

Determine $\sqrt{1369}$.   **Example E**

First group the digits of the *radicand*, the number whose root is to be found, in pairs, starting at the decimal point. This grouping may be shown as $\sqrt{13\ 69}$.

Next determine the largest integer whose square is no larger than the number pair at the extreme left. In this case the number pair is 13. Since $3^2 = 9$ and $4^2 = 16$, 3 is the largest number whose square is less than 13. We then place the 3 above the 13, and its square, 9, below the 13. This gives the setup shown at the right.

$$\begin{array}{r} 3 \\ \sqrt{13\ 69} \\ 9 \end{array}$$

Now subtract the 9 from the 13, and bring down the next number pair, 69. This gives the next setup.

$$\begin{array}{r} 3 \\ \sqrt{13\ 69} \\ 9 \\ \hline 4\ 69 \end{array}$$

Now double the 3, the first digit of the quotient to be found, giving 6. Multiply this 6 by 10, giving 60. Now determine the number of times 60 will divide into 469, as in long division. This is indicated at the right.

$$\begin{array}{r} 3 \\ \sqrt{13\ 69} \\ 9 \\ 60\,|\ 4\ 69 \end{array}$$

We note that 60 will divide into 469 at least 7 times. We now place 7 in the quotient over the 69 and add 7 to 60. This setup is now shown at the right.

$$\begin{array}{r} 3\ \ 7 \\ \sqrt{13\ 69} \\ 9 \\ 67\,|\ 4\ 69 \end{array}$$

Multiplying 67 by 7, we obtain 469, which we place below the 469 already present. This gives the setup shown.

$$\begin{array}{r} 3\ \ 7 \\ \sqrt{13\ 69} \\ 9 \\ 67\,|\ 4\ 69 \\ \underline{4\ 69} \end{array}$$

Since the remainder is now zero, and no other digits are to be brought down, we have completed the extraction of the square root. Thus $\sqrt{1369} = 37$.

Example F Evaluate $\sqrt{462.25}$.

We first group the digits of the radicand in pairs, starting at the decimal point. Here we note that the left grouping contains only one digit. This is permissible only for this grouping. We note that 4 divides evenly into 4, and we then place the 4 below the 4 of the radicand and its square root, 2, above. We now double the 2 and then multiply by 10, giving 40.

$$
\begin{array}{r}
\phantom{\sqrt{4}}\;2\;\;1.\;5 \\
\sqrt{4\;\;62.\;25} \\
4 \\
\end{array}
$$

$$
\begin{array}{r|l}
41 & 62 \\
 & 41 \\
\hline
425 & 21\;25 \\
 & 21\;25 \\
\end{array}
$$

This divides into the 62, which was brought down, at most once. The 1 is placed above the 62 and also added to 40, giving 41. The product of 41 and 1, which is 41, is placed below the 62 and subtracted, giving 21. The 25 is then brought down. The number now representing the quotient, 21, is doubled and multiplied by 10, giving 420. Now 420 will divide into 21 25, 5 times. The 5 is then placed above the 25 and added to 420, giving 425. Since $425 \times 5 = 2125$, the extraction of the square root is complete. Therefore $\sqrt{462.25} = 21.5$.

Example G Evaluate $\sqrt{0.7013}$ correct to two decimal places.

The complete solution is shown at right. In solving this problem we note that we are to find the result correct to two decimal places. In grouping the digits we can find two decimal places, but if the number in the third decimal position is 5 or greater, we should add 1 to the number in the second position to properly round it off. Thus two zeros are added to the radicand and the number in the third decimal position is determined. Since it is 7, we express our result as $\sqrt{0.7013} = 0.84$.

$$
\begin{array}{r}
0.\;8\;\;3\;\;7 \\
\sqrt{0.\;70\;13\;00} \\
64 \\
\end{array}
$$

$$
\begin{array}{r|l}
163 & 6\;13 \\
 & 4\;89 \\
\hline
1667 & 1\;24\;00 \\
 & 1\;16\;69 \\
\hline
 & 7\;31 \\
\end{array}
$$

EXERCISES In Exercises 1 through 4, write the given expressions, using exponents.

1. $2 \times 2 \times 2 \times 2$ **2.** $8 \times 8 \times 8$

3. $10 \times 10 \times 10 \times 10 \times 10$ **4.** $6 \times 6 \times 6 \times 6 \times 6 \times 6 \times 6 \times 6$

In Exercises 5 through 8, write the given expressions as products.

5. 3^6 **6.** 4^3 **7.** 7^6 **8.** 10^4

In Exercises 9 through 20, evaluate the given expression.

9. $\sqrt{16}$ **10.** $\sqrt{81}$ **11.** $\sqrt[3]{27}$ **12.** $\sqrt[3]{125}$

13. $\sqrt[4]{16}$　　　　　**14.** $\sqrt[5]{32}$　　　　**15.** $(3^3)(2^2)$　　　**16.** $(5^2)(4^3)$

17. $(5^3)(6^2)$　　　**18.** $(7^3)(10^4)$　　　**19.** $(\sqrt{121})(3^4)$　　**20.** $(\sqrt{144})(4^3)$

In Exercises 21 through 26, determine the values of the given expressions by using Table 1 in the Appendix.

21. $\sqrt{47}$　　　　　　　**22.** $\sqrt{92}$　　　　　　**23.** $\sqrt[3]{17}$

24. $\sqrt[3]{79}$　　　　　　**25.** 36^3　　　　　　　**26.** 87^2

In Exercises 27 through 30, determine the square roots by the method of Example E.

27. $\sqrt{729}$　　　**28.** $\sqrt{5476}$　　　**29.** $\sqrt{0.9801}$　　　**30.** $\sqrt{31.9225}$

In Exercises 31 through 34, evaluate the indicated square roots by the method of Example E. Round off the result to the number of decimal places indicated by the number in parentheses.

31. $\sqrt{7.1300}$　(1)　　　　　　　**32.** $\sqrt{0.83555}$　(2)

33. $\sqrt{3.75}$　(2)　　　　　　　　**34.** $\sqrt{0.000143}$　(4)

In Exercises 35 through 41, solve the given problems.

35. The diameter of the earth is about $4 \times (10^7)$ ft. Write this number in ordinary notation.

36. The number of memory units of a certain computer is 2^{15}. Write this number in ordinary notation.

37. The period (in seconds) of a pendulum whose length is 5 ft is found by evaluating $(1.57)(\sqrt{2.5})$. By evaluating the square root (to two decimal places) find the period (round off the result to hundredths).

38. Under certain circumstances, the frequency of vibration (in cycles/sec) in an electric circuit can be found by evaluating

$$\frac{1}{(6.28)(\sqrt{0.000025})}.$$

Find the frequency to the nearest tenth.

39. Find the side (to the nearest tenth of a foot) of a square whose area is 780 sq ft. (The side equals the square root of the area.)

40. The time (in seconds) required for an object to fall 150 ft due to gravity can be found by evaluating

$$\frac{\sqrt{150}}{4}.$$

Find the time required to the nearest tenth of a second.

41. Under certain conditions, the pressure (in atmospheres) of 40 cubic in. of a gas can be calculated to be $(0.003)(\sqrt{40})^3$. Calculate the pressure to the nearest thousandth.

1–10 NUMBERS IN BASE TWO

With high-speed computers in such wide use today, it is of value for us to consider briefly how numbers are written for use on computers. We shall see that, although only two symbols are used to write the numbers, the same idea of positional notation is employed. Also we shall discover that the same methods are employed in the operations of addition and multiplication.

In Section 1–2 we noted that ten symbols (0, 1, 2, 3, 4, 5, 6, 7, 8, 9) are used to write numbers. We also showed the use of positional notation in writing numbers. The following example expands the meaning of positional notation with powers of ten.

Example A   The number 3582 can be written as

$$3582 = 3000 + 500 + 80 + 2$$

or
$$= 3(1000) + 5(100) + 8(10) + 2$$

or
$$= 3(10^3) + 5(10^2) + 8(10) + 2.$$

We note that the right numeral (2) indicates the number of units; the next numeral (8) indicates the number of tens; the next numeral (5) indicates the number of times we count 10^2; the next numeral (3) represents the number of times we count 10^3. Thus the number of times a given power of ten (the *base*) is counted is determined by the value and position of a given numeral.

We have seen that ordinary numbers, written in *base ten*, are written with the use of *ten* symbols and in terms of powers of *ten*. Numbers for a computer are written in base *two*. Only *two* symbols, 0 and 1, are employed, and the various positions denote various powers of *two*.

Example B   The number 1101 in base two can be interpreted as

$$1101 = 1(2^3) + 1(2^2) + 0(2) + 1.$$

By this we see that the numeral on the right indicates the number of 1's, the next numeral indicates the number of 2's, the next numeral the number of 4's ($2^2 = 4$ in the same way that $10^2 = 100$), and the next numeral indicates the number of 8's ($2^3 = 8$). Therefore

$$1101_2 = 13_{10}.$$

Note the manner in which the base is indicated. It should be emphasized that 1101_2 and 13_{10} are both the number thirteen; the way in which thirteen is written is the only difference.

The probable reason for ten being the base of our number system is that we have ten fingers, and many ancient peoples used them for counting purposes. The reason for base two being used in computers is that it simply requires that there is *no* electric current (0) in a given circuit, or that there *is* a current (1).

Example B shows us the basis for changing a number in base two into a number in base ten. That is, we evaluate each position to determine whether that particular power of two is counted. Consider the following example.

Change 1011011_2 into a number in base ten. Example C

Interpreting 1011011_2 in terms of powers of two, we have

$$1011011_2 = 1(2^6) + 0(2^5) + 1(2^4) + 1(2^3) + 0(2^2) + 1(2) + 1$$
$$= 1(64) + 0(32) + 1(16) + 1(8) + 0(4) + 1(2) + 1$$
$$= 64 + 16 + 8 + 2 + 1$$
$$= 91_{10}.$$

When we change a number from base ten to base two we determine the largest power of two that will divide into the number and successive remainders. The following example illustrates the method.

Change 106_{10} into a number in base two. Example D

We look for the largest power of two that will divide into 106. Since $2^7 = 128$, we know that 2^7 is too large. Trying $2^6 = 64$, we see that 64 will divide into 106 once, with a remainder of 42. Therefore we know that the left 1 in the result will represent the 2^6 position. We now try the next smallest power of 2 to determine whether or not it will divide into 42, the remainder. We do this, for we have so far determined that

$$106_{10} = 2^6 + 42.$$

Noting that $2^5 = 32$ will divide into 42 once with a remainder of 10, we now have

$$106_{10} = 2^6 + 2^5 + 10.$$

We now see that $2^4 = 16$ will not divide into 10. Next we try $2^3 = 8$ and see that it divides into 10 with a remainder of 2. This tells us that

$$106_{10} = 2^6 + 2^5 + 2^3 + 2.$$

We therefore have 1's in the 2^6, 2^5, 2^3, and 2 positions, and 0's in the 2^4, 2^2 and 1 positions. Thus $106_{10} = 1101010_2$.

We shall now briefly discuss the addition and multiplication of numbers in base two. For addition, only three basic additions are necessary. They are $0 + 0 = 0$, $1 + 0 = 1$, and $1 + 1 = 10$. This last one undoubtedly looks strange, but all that it says is that "one plus one equals two." We must remember, however, that two is written as 10 (one two and no ones) in base two. Therefore, if we are adding two numbers whose sum is two (10) in any column, it is necessary to carry the 1. Consider the following example.

Example E   Add 1100101_2 and 1001101_2.

Setting up the addition in the ordinary fashion, we have

$$\begin{array}{r} 1100101 \\ 1001101 \end{array}$$

Starting at the right, as usual, we have $1 + 1 = 10$. Thus we place a 0 under the 1's and carry a 1 into the next column. At this point we have

$$\begin{array}{r} {\scriptstyle 1} \\ 1100101 \\ 1001101 \\ \hline 0 \end{array}$$

where the smaller 1 indicates the amount carried. In the 2's column, we then have $1 + 0 + 0 = 1$, which necessitates no carrying. Continuing in the same fashion, we have

$$\begin{array}{r} {\scriptstyle 1 \ \ 11 \ 1} \\ 1100101 \\ 1001101 \\ \hline 10110010. \end{array}$$

If these numbers were converted to base ten, we would see that we just added 101 and 77 to arrive at 178.

In multiplication, the basic process is the same. Three multiplication facts are needed. They are $0 \times 0 = 0$, $0 \times 1 = 0$ and $1 \times 1 = 1$. Consider the following example.

Multiply 1101_2 by 101_2.   Example F

Setting up the multiplication in the ordinary fashion, and following normal multiplication procedures with the above multiplication facts, we have

$$
\begin{array}{r}
1101 \\
101 \\
\hline
1101 \\
0000 \\
1101 \\
\hline
1000001
\end{array}
$$

Note the use of addition in the process. We have just multiplied 13 by 5 to get 65, in base ten.

In Exercises 1 through 8, change the given numbers from base two to base ten.   EXERCISES

  1. 11   **2.** 110   **3.** 1001   **4.** 10110

  5. 1101100   **6.** 1000011   **7.** 100110001   **8.** 111000011

In Exercises 9 through 16, change the given numbers from base ten to base two.

  9. 6   **10.** 10   **11.** 17   **12.** 19

13. 46   **14.** 51   **15.** 79   **16.** 145

In Exercises 17 through 22, perform the indicated additions in base two. Check your results by converting all numbers to base ten.

17. $110 + 1001$ **18.** $1010 + 1110$

19. $10011 + 11010$ **20.** $11110 + 10110$

21. $1100011 + 1110110$ **22.** $1011010 + 1001111$

In Exercises 23 through 28, perform the indicated multiplications in base two. Check your results by converting all numbers to base ten.

23. 11×10 **24.** 110×11 **25.** 1101×1001

26. 1011×1101 **27.** 1100111×10110 **28.** 1001110×11011

In Exercises 29 and 30, subtract the given numbers in base two. Check your results by converting all numbers to base ten. Borrowing is done in just the same manner as with numbers in base ten.

29. $110110 - 11001$ **30.** $1001011 - 101101$

1–11 REVIEW EXERCISES

In Exercises 1 through 42, perform the indicated operations.

1. $3126 + 328 + 9876$ **2.** $98076 + 8992 + 3964$

3. $8764 - 5985$ **4.** $19264 - 9397$

5. $8.12 + 19.092 + 93.9$ **6.** $986.42 + 93.7 + 8.966$

7. $2706.46 - 829.5$ **8.** $2.9064 - 0.918$

9. 476×9172 **10.** 8076×79064

11. $14980 \div 35$ **12.** $511098 \div 129$

13. 3.93×18.4 **14.** 0.0362×19.41

15. $0.04536 \div 3.24$ **16.** $8.0698 \div 0.0257$

17. $3.96(0.042 + 9.33)$ **18.** $92.6(18.4 + 7.82)$

19. $\frac{3}{13} + \frac{2}{13}$ **20.** $\frac{1}{2} + \frac{1}{8}$

21. $2\frac{1}{5} - \frac{3}{10}$ **22.** $\frac{5}{12} - \frac{3}{14}$

23. $\frac{13}{30} + \frac{7}{12} + \frac{1}{6}$ **24.** $\frac{16}{63} + \frac{5}{14} - \frac{1}{21}$

25. $\frac{7}{50} + \frac{6}{35} + \frac{19}{42}$ **26.** $\frac{1}{27} + \frac{11}{45} + \frac{7}{18}$

27. $(\frac{11}{2})(\frac{4}{5})$ **28.** $(\frac{4}{9})(\frac{15}{48})$

29. $(\frac{18}{77} \times \frac{14}{27}) \times \frac{121}{8}$ **30.** $(3\frac{1}{6} \times 1\frac{1}{5}) \times \frac{125}{38}$

31. $\frac{32}{21} \div \frac{8}{7}$ **32.** $\frac{24}{17} \div \frac{12}{7}$

33. $\dfrac{5 \times 19 \times 31}{3 \times 7 \times 11} \div \dfrac{19 \times 31}{7 \times 43}$ **34.** $\dfrac{2 \times 9 \times 20}{3 \times 49 \times 63} \div \dfrac{8 \times 35}{14 \times 27}$

35. $\sqrt{49}$ **36.** $\sqrt{144}$

37. $\sqrt[3]{1000}$ **38.** $\sqrt[6]{64}$

39. $3(4^2)$ **40.** $(2^3)(5^2)$

41. $3^4 - 2^5$ **42.** $3(6^2 + 4^4)$

In Exercises 43 and 44, find the reciprocals of the given numbers.

43. $\frac{2}{9}$; $3\frac{1}{7}$ **44.** $\frac{4}{3}$; $8\frac{2}{5}$

In Exercises 45 through 48, change the given fractions to equivalent decimals, and the given decimals into equivalent fractions.

45. $\frac{9}{32}$ **46.** $\frac{121}{400}$ **47.** 0.56 **48.** 3.155

In Exercises 49 through 52, change the given percentages to equivalent decimals and to equivalent fractions.

49. 82%   **50.** 250%   **51.** 0.55%   **52.** 0.0225%

In Exercises 53 through 56, change the given decimals and fractions to percentages.

53. 0.934   **54.** 87.28   **55.** $\frac{2}{25}$ **56.** $\frac{15}{4}$

In Exercises 57 through 60, determine the value of the given expression from Table 1 in the Appendix.

57. $\sqrt{43}$ **58.** $\sqrt{75}$ **59.** 64^2 **60.** 29^3

In Exercises 61 through 64, determine the square roots by the method of Example E of Section 1–9. In Exercises 63 and 64, round off the result to the number of decimal places indicated by the number in parentheses.

61. $\sqrt{0.538756}$ **62.** $\sqrt{948.64}$ **63.** $\sqrt{9.372}$ (2)   **64.** $\sqrt{8724}$ (1)

In Exercises 65 through 68, change the given numbers from base two to base ten.

✝ 65. 101   **66.** 1010   **67.** 10010   **68.** 11001

In Exercises 69 through 72, change the given numbers from base ten to base two.

69. 14   **70.** 35   **71.** 66   **72.** 150

In Exercises 73 through 95, solve the given problems.

73. Find the perimeter of the triangle (3 sides) whose sides are 3.68 in., 8.21 in., and 6.09 in.

74. Find the perimeter of a rectangle of length 18.2 ft and width 9.3 ft.

75. A barometer reads 30.21 in. before a storm approaches. It then drops 0.67 in. What is the later reading?

76. Find the area of the rectangle of Exercise 74.

77. Given that the area of a rectangle is 70.305 sq ft and its width is 3.27 ft, find its length.

78. A satellite circling the earth travels at 17,300 mi/hr. If one orbit takes 1.55 hr, how far does it travel in one orbit?

79. The total resistance of 18 equal electric resistors is 370.8 ohms. What is the resistance of each?

80. An early (pre-1950) computer could do an addition in 0.0002 sec and later models (about 1969) can do an addition in 0.0000015 sec. How many times faster are the later models?

81. Both sides of a metal plate $\frac{3}{16}$ in. thick are coated with a film $\frac{1}{64}$ in. thick. What is the resulting thickness of the plate?

82. Two-fifths of a piece of wire $11\frac{1}{4}$ ft long is cut off. What is the length of the remaining piece?

83. A bottle contains $3\frac{3}{4}$ pints of acid which is $\frac{6}{25}$ sulfuric acid. If $\frac{2}{3}$ of the acid is poured from the bottle, how much sulfuric acid is left in the bottle?

84. In a house plan, a living room 24 ft 6 in. long, a hall 4 ft 10 in. wide and a bedroom 15 ft 8 in. long are shown across the front of the house. The interior walls are 5 in. thick and the exterior walls are 8 in. thick. What is the width of the front of the house?

85. Suppose that gasoline costs 35.9¢ per gallon. How much does it cost to fill a tank that holds 17.3 gal?

86. The approximate length in feet of a certain pulley belt is found by making the following calculation: $2(4.27) + 3.14(0.83 + 1.42)$. Find the length of the pulley belt to the nearest hundredth of a foot.

87. Approximately 0.71% of uranium is U-235 (the type used for atomic energy). How much U-235 is contained in 50 lb of uranium ore which is 2.13% uranium? (Round off result to nearest one-hundredth of a pound.)

88. A manufacturer makes an article for $18.50. He sells it to a dealer, making a profit of 40% of the cost. The dealer sells it, making a 50% profit of his cost. What is the price charged by the dealer?

89. A man borrows $5000 and then repays the loan by paying $1000 of the principal plus 6% interest each year for 5 years. After the five years, he has paid $900 in interest (see if you can arrive at this figure). What percentage of the total amount he paid was interest? (Round off result to the nearest one-tenth of one percent.)

90. Two months is 6.67% of the guaranteed life of an automobile battery. What is the guaranteed life of the battery to the nearest month?

91. Seventy-five pounds of salt water contain 4% salt. If forty-five pounds of fresh water are added to this solution, what is the percentage of salt in the final solution?

92. Under certain conditions the voltage in a given electric circuit is found by calculating $\sqrt{(16.1)(8.86)}$. Find the voltage to the nearest tenth of a volt.

93. The impedance (effective resistance)(in ohms) of a certain electric circuit is found by calculating $\sqrt{(5.68)^2 + (10.07 - 2.42)^2}$. Calculate the impedance of this circuit to the nearest tenth of an ohm.

94. The fahrenheit degree is $\frac{5}{9}$ of the centigrade degree. If the centigrade temperature rises by $40°$, by how much does the fahrenheit temperature rise?

95. A metal bar is cut into six pieces, each $3\frac{3}{8}$ inches long. Each cut wastes $\frac{1}{16}$ inch. Determine the length of the original bar.

Measurement and Approximate Numbers

2

UNITS OF MEASUREMENT
APPROXIMATE NUMBERS AND SIGNIFICANT DIGITS
ARITHMETIC OPERATIONS WITH APPROXIMATE NUMBERS
REVIEW EXERCISES

2-1 UNITS OF MEASUREMENT

The solution of most technical problems involves the use of the basic arithmetic operations on numbers. However, as we saw in many of the examples and exercises of Chapter 1, many of these numbers represent some sort of measurement or calculation. Therefore, associated with these numbers are *units of measurement*, and in order for the calculation to be meaningful, we must know these units.

Example A   If we measure the length of a piece of metal pipe to be 12, we must also know whether it is being measured in inches, feet, yards, or some other unit of length.

If the time for one rotation of a wheel is measured to be 0.02, we must also know whether the unit of time being used is a second, minute, hour, or some other unit.

Certain universally accepted units are used to measure fundamental quantities. Numerous other quantities are expressed in terms of the units of the fundamental quantities. Quantities which are commonly considered fundamental are (1) length, (2) time, (3) mass, (4) temperature, and (5) electric charge. Other quantities are measurable in terms of these quantities.

Example B   The distance that a plane travels in flying from city *A* to city *B* can be measured in a unit of length, say miles. The time of flight can be measured in a unit of time, say hours. The average velocity of the plane during the flight is then measured in miles per hour. Therefore velocity is measured in terms of the units of length and time.

The unit for electric current, the *ampere*, is defined as one *coulomb* (the unit of electric charge) per second. Therefore we see that electric current is measured in terms of units of electric charge and time.

There are two basic systems of units in common use today: the *British system* and the *metric system*. In each system the fundamental units are specified, and all others are then expressed in terms of these. The British system is used in English-speaking countries for general purposes, including engineering and technical applications. The metric system is used generally in the rest of the world, and for scientific work in all parts of the world. Therefore technicians and engineers need to have some knowledge of both systems.

In the British system, the fundamental unit of length is the *foot* and that of mass (weight and mass are different physical quantities, but for our purposes we shall consider that they are measured with the same units) is the *pound*. In the metric system, the *meter* and the *kilogram* are the fundamental units for length and mass. In both systems the fundamental unit of time is the *second*, and the *coulomb* is the unit of electric charge. As for temperature, degrees *celsius* (centigrade) (°C) are used with the metric system, and degrees *fahrenheit* (°F) are generally used with the British system.

The basic units in either system are not always of a convenient size for certain types of measurements. Therefore other units of more convenient size are used within each system. For example, long distances are not conveniently measured in feet; therefore we generally use miles. For short distances, inches are more convenient and more commonly used. It is the relationship among units within each system which makes the metric system more convenient to use. The metric system is decimalized, whereas the British system has no specific arrangement for relationships among units. This is pointed out, for example, in that 1 mile = 5280 feet and 1 kilometer = 1000 meters.

Table 2–1 lists some of the commonly used units for length, mass, and time for both systems, and gives their abbreviations.

	Length	Table 2-1
British	**Metric**	
1 yard (yd) = 3 ft	1 centimeter (cm) = 0.01 meter (m)	
1 inch (in.) = $\frac{1}{12}$ ft	1 millimeter (mm) = 0.001 m	
1 mile (mi) = 5280 ft	1 kilometer (km) = 1000 m	

	Mass	
British	**Metric**	
1 ounce (oz) = $\frac{1}{16}$ pound (lb)	1 gram (g) = 0.001 kilogram (kg)	
1 short ton (t) = 2000 lb	1 milligram (mg) = 0.001 g	

Time (both systems)	
1 minute (min) = 60 seconds (sec)	1 hour (hr) = 60 min

As we mentioned earlier, the units for other quantities are expressed in terms of the fundamental ones. For example, the units of area, volume, force, speed, energy, pressure, electric current, and voltage are expressed in terms of the units of the fundamental quantities.

Example C   As we have seen, we find the area of a rectangle by multiplying one length by another. Considering the meaning of exponents in Section 1–9, we can think of area as being measured in units of length $\times$ length = (length)^2. Therefore area is measured in square feet (sq ft or ft^2), square miles (sq mi or mi^2), square meters (sq m or m^2), and so on.

To find the *volume* of a rectangular solid, we multiply the length by the width by the the depth. This means that volume is measured in units of length $\times$ length $\times$ length = (length)^3. Thus we measure volume in cubic feet (cu ft or ft^3), cubic centimeters (cc or cm^3), and so on.

Density, which is mass per unit volume, is measured in lb/ft^3 or kg/m^3, for example.

When we are working with numbers that represent units of measurement (referred to as *denominate numbers*), it is sometimes necessary to change from one set of units to another. A change within a given system is called a *reduction*, and a change from one system to another is called a *conversion*.

Example D   To find the cost of floor-covering for a given room, it is necessary to know the area of the room, and this is generally given in square feet. Floor-covering cost is often given in cost per square yard. Therefore it is necessary to reduce square feet to square yards.

Distances in many parts of Europe are given in kilometers. In order to determine equivalent distances in miles, one has to convert kilometers to miles.

For purposes of changing units, Table 2–2 gives some basic reduction and conversion factors. Reduction factors between fundamental units are given in Table 2–1.

In order to change a given number of one set of units into another set of units, we perform multiplications and divisions with the units themselves. These computations are essentially the same as the ones we did when we were working with fractions.

Reduction and Conversion Factors

Table 2-2

Reduction factors

144 sq in = 1 sq ft	2 pints = 1 quart (qt)
9 sq ft = 1 sq yd	4 qt = 1 gallon (gal)
1728 cu in = 1 cu ft	1 milliliter (ml) = 0.001 liter (*l*)
27 cu ft = 1 cu yd	1000 liters = 1 kiloliter

Conversion factors

1 inch = 2.54 cm	1 cu ft = 28.32 liters
1 meter = 39.37 in.	1 pint = 473.2 cc
1 mile = 1.609 km	1 liter = 1.057 qt
1 pound = 453.6 g	
1 kilogram = 2.205 lb	

If we had a number representing feet/second to be multiplied by another number representing seconds/minute, as far as the units are concerned we have

$$\frac{\text{ft}}{\text{sec}} \times \frac{\text{sec}}{\text{min}} = \frac{\text{ft} \times \cancel{\text{sec}}}{\cancel{\text{sec}} \times \text{min}} = \frac{\text{ft}}{\text{min}}.$$

This means that the final result would be in feet/minute.

In actually changing a number of one set of units to another set of units, we use reduction and conversion factors from Tables 2–1 and 2–2, and the principle illustrated in Example E for operating with the units themselves. The convenient way to use the values in the tables is in the form of fractions. Since the given values are equal to each other, their quotient is 1. For example, since 1 in. = 2.54 cm,

$$\frac{1 \text{ in.}}{2.54 \text{ cm}} = 1 \quad \text{or} \quad \frac{2.54 \text{ cm}}{1 \text{ in.}} = 1,$$

since each represents the division of a certain length by itself. Multiplying a given quantity by 1 does not change its value. The following examples illustrate reduction and conversion of units.

Change 30 mi/hr to ft/sec.

$$30\,\frac{\text{mi}}{\text{hr}} = \left(30\,\frac{\cancel{\text{mi}}}{\cancel{\text{hr}}}\right)\left(\frac{5280 \text{ ft}}{1 \cancel{\text{mi}}}\right)\left(\frac{1 \cancel{\text{hr}}}{60 \cancel{\text{min}}}\right)\left(\frac{1 \cancel{\text{min}}}{60 \text{ sec}}\right) = \frac{(30)(5280) \text{ ft}}{(60)(60) \text{ sec}} = 44\,\frac{\text{ft}}{\text{sec}}$$

Note that the only units remaining are those that were required.

Example G   Change $62 \ \text{lb/in}^2$ to kg/m^2.

$$62 \, \frac{\text{lb}}{\text{in}^2} = \left(62 \, \frac{\text{lb}}{\text{in}^2} \right) \left(\frac{1 \text{ kg}}{2.205 \text{ lb}} \right) \left(\frac{1 \text{ in.}}{2.54 \text{ cm}} \right) \left(\frac{1 \text{ in.}}{2.54 \text{ cm}} \right) \left(\frac{100 \text{ cm}}{1 \text{ m}} \right) \left(\frac{100 \text{ cm}}{1 \text{ m}} \right)$$

$$= \frac{(62)(100)(100) \text{ kg}}{(2.205)(2.54)(2.54)\text{m}^2} = 44{,}000 \, \frac{\text{kg}}{\text{m}^2} \, .$$

The result was rounded off to thousands. Note that the in. $\times$ in. of the numerator equals the in.^{2} of the denominator.

EXERCISES   In the following exercises, use only the values given in Tables 2–1 and 2–2. Where applicable, round off to the accuracy noted.

  1. How many yards are there in 1 mile?

  2. How many ounces are there in 1 ton?

  3. How many centimeters are there in 1 kilometer?

  4. How many milligrams are there in 1 kilogram?

  5. Show that 1 sq ft = 144 sq in.

  6. Show that 1 cu yd = 27 cu ft.

  7. Convert 5 in. to centimeters.

  8. Convert 6 kg to pounds.

  9. Reduce 8 gal to pints.

  10. Reduce 20 kiloliters to milliliters.

  11. Convert 10 quarts to liters (round off to hundredths).

  12. Convert 18 cm to inches (round off to hundredths).

  13. Convert 73.8 g to pounds (round off to thousandths).

  14. Convert 0.36 in. to meters (round off to thousandths).

  15. Convert 829 cu in. to liters (round off to hundredths).

  16. Convert 0.068 kiloliters to cubic feet (round off to tenths).

  17. An Atlas rocket weighed 260,000 lb at takeoff. How many tons is this?

  18. An airplane is flying at 37,000 ft. What is its altitude in miles? (Round off to hundredths.)

  19. The speedometer of a European car is calibrated to km/hr. If the speedometer of such a car reads 60, how fast in mi/hr is the car traveling (round off to units)?

  20. The acceleration due to gravity is about $980 \ \text{cm/sec}^2$. Convert this to ft/sec^2 (round off to tenths).

21. The speed of sound is about 1130 ft/sec. Change this speed to mi/hr (round off to units).

22. The density of water is about 62.4 lb/ft³. Convert this to kg/m³ (round off to units).

23. The average density of the earth is about 5.52 gm/cm³. Convert this to lb/ft³ (round off to units).

24. The moon travels about 1,500,000 miles in about 28 days in one rotation about the earth. Express its velocity in ft/sec (round off to tens).

25. At sea level, atmospheric pressure is about 14.7 lb/in². Express this pressure in g/cm² (round off to tens).

26. One horsepower is defined as 550 ft-lb/sec. Express this in kg-cm/sec (round off to units).

27. A unit used to measure the flow of water is the cu ft/min. Convert 1 cu ft/min to liters/sec (round off to hundredths).

28. A unit used in viscosity (fluid friction) is the *poise*, which is 1 g-cm/sec. Convert 60 poise to lb-in/min (round off to tenths).

2–2 APPROXIMATE NUMBERS AND SIGNIFICANT DIGITS

When we perform calculations on numbers, we must consider the accuracy of these numbers, since they affect the accuracy of the results obtained. Most of the numbers involved in technical and scientific work are *approximate*, having been arrived at through some process of measurement. However, certain other numbers are *exact*, having been arrived at through some definition or counting process. We can determine whether or not a number is approximate or exact if we by know how the number was determined.

If we measure the length of a rope to be 15.3 ft, we know that the 15.3 is approximate. A more precise measuring device may cause us to determine the length as 15.28 ft. However, regardless of the method of measurement used, we shall not be able to determine this length exactly.

    If a voltage shown on a voltmeter is read as 116 volts, the 116 is approximate. A more precise voltmeter may show the voltage as 115.7 volts. However, this voltage cannot be determined exactly.

Example A

If a computer counts the cards it has processed and prints this number as 837, this 837 is exact. We know the number of cards was not 836 or 838. Since 837 was determined through a counting process, it is exact.

Example B

When we say that 60 seconds = 1 minute, the 60 is exact, since this is a definition. By this definition there are exactly 60 seconds in one minute.

When we are writing approximate numbers we often have to include some zeros so that the decimal point will be properly located. However, except for these zeros, all other digits are considered to be *significant digits* (or *significant figures*). When we make computations with approximate numbers, we must know the number of significant digits. The following example illustrates how we determine this.

Example C All numbers in this example are assumed to be approximate.

34.7 has three significant digits.

8900 has two significant digits. We assume that the two zeros are place holders (unless we have specific knowledge to the contrary).

0.039 has two significant digits. The zeros are for proper location of the decimal point.

706.1 has four significant digits. The zero is not used for the location of the decimal point. It shows specifically the number of tens in the number.

5.90 has three significant digits. The zero is not necessary as a place holder, and should not be written unless it is significant.

Other approximate numbers with their proper number of significant digits are listed below.

96000	two	0.0709	three	1.070	four
30900	three	6.000	four	700.00	five
4.006	four	0.0005	one	20008	five

Note from the above example that all nonzero digits are significant. Zeros, other than those used as place holders for proper positioning of the decimal point, are also significant.

In computations involving approximate numbers, the position of the decimal point as well as the number of significant digits is important. The *precision* of a number refers directly to the decimal position of the last significant digit, whereas the *accuracy* of a number refers to the number of significant digits in the number. Consider the illustrations in the following example.

Suppose that you are measuring an electric current with two ammeters.   Example D
One ammeter reads 0.031 amp and the second ammeter reads 0.0312 amp.
The second reading is more precise, in that the last significant digit is the
number of ten-thousandths, and the first reading is expressed only to
thousandths. The second reading is also more accurate, since it has
three significant digits rather than two.

A machine part is measured to be 2.5 cm long. It is coated with a film
0.025 cm thick. The thickness of the film has been measured to a greater
precision, although the two measurements have the same accuracy: two
significant digits.

A segment of a newly completed highway is 9270 ft long. The concrete surface is 0.8 ft thick. Of these two numbers, 9270 is more accurate,
since it contains three significant digits, and 0.8 is more precise, since it
is expressed to tenths.

The last significant digit of an approximate number is known not to
be completely accurate. It has usually been determined by estimation or
rounding off. However, we do know that it is at most in error by one-half
of a unit in its place value.

When we measure the length of the rope referred to in Example A to be   Example E
15.3 ft, we are saying that the length is at least 15.25 ft and no longer than
15.35 ft. Any value between these two, rounded off to tenths, would be
expressed as 15.3 ft.

In converting the fraction $\frac{2}{3}$ to the decimal form 0.667, we are saying
that the value is between 0.6665 and 0.6675.

In the last chapter we introduced the process of rounding off a number
in an intuitive informal way. The principle of rounding off is to write
the closest approximation, with the last significant digit in a specified
position, or with a specified number of significant digits. We shall now
formalize the process of rounding off as follows: If we want a certain
number of significant digits, we examine the digit in the next place to
the right. If this digit is less than 5, we accept the digit in the last place.
If the next digit is 5 or greater, we increase the digit in the last place by 1,
and this resulting digit becomes the final significant digit of the approximation. If necessary, we use zeros to replace other digits in order
to properly locate the decimal point. Except when the next digit is a 5,

and no other nonzero digits are discarded, we have the closest possible approximation with the desired number of significant digits.

Example F   70360 rounded off to three significant digits is 70400.
70430 rounded off to three significant digits is 70400.
187.35 rounded off to four significant digits is 187.4.
71500 rounded off to two significant digits is 72000.

With the advent of high-speed electronic computers, another method of reducing numbers to a specified number of significant digits is used. This is the process of *truncation*, in which the digits beyond a certain place are discarded. For example, 3.17482 truncated to thousandths is 3.174. For our purposes in this text, when working with approximate numbers, we shall use only rounding off.

EXERCISES   In Exercises 1 through 8, determine whether the numbers given are exact or approximate.

E **1.** There are 24 hours in one day.

E **2.** The velocity of light is 186,000 mi/sec.

E **3.** The 3-stage rocket took 74.6 hours to reach the moon. A

E **4.** A man bought 5 lb of nails for $1.56.

A **5.** The melting point of gold is 1063°C.

E **6.** The 21 students had an average test grade of 81.6. A

A **7.** A building lot 100 ft by 200 ft cost $3200. E

E **8.** In a certain city 5% of the people have their money in a bank that pays 5% interest. A

In Exercises 9 through 16, determine the number of significant digits in the given approximate numbers.

9. 37.2; 6844   **10.** 3600; 730

11. 107; 3004   **12.** 0.8735; 0.0075

13. 6.80; 6.08   **14.** 90050; 105040

15. 30000; 30000.0   **16.** 1.00; 0.01

In Exercises 17 through 24, determine which of each pair of approximate numbers is (a) more precise and (b) more accurate.

17. 3.764, 2.81   **18.** 0.041, 7.673

19. 30.8, 0.01   **20.** 70,370, 50,400

21. 0.1, 78.0   **22.** 7040, 37.1

23. 7000, 0.004   **24.** 50.060, 8.914

In Exercises 25 through 32, round off each of the given approximate numbers (a) to three significant digits, and (b) to two significant digits.

25. 4.933   **26.** 80.53   **27.** 57893   **28.** 30490

29. 861.29   **30.** 9555   **31.** 0.30505   **32.** 0.7350

In Exercises 33 through 36, answer the given questions.

33. An automobile manufacturer claims that the gasoline tank on a certain car holds approximately 19 gal. What is the very least and the very greatest that the capacity should be?

34. A surveyor measured one side of a building site to be 183.3 ft. According to his measurement, what is the very least and the very greatest possible length of this side of the building site?

35. A machinist measures the thickness of a machine part to be 0.145 in. thick. What is this measurement in mm with the same degree of accuracy?

36. A chemist used 207.0 cc of sulfuric acid. What is this volume in quarts with the same degree of accuracy?

2-3 ARITHMETIC OPERATIONS WITH APPROXIMATE NUMBERS

When performing arithmetic operations on approximate numbers we must be careful not to express the result to a precision or accuracy which is not warranted. The following two examples illustrate how a false indication of the accuracy of a result could be obtained when using approximate numbers.

A pipe is made in two sections. The first is measured to be 16.3 ft long   Example A
and the second is measured to be 0.927 ft long. A plumber wants to know what the total length will be when the two sections are put together.

At first, it appears we might simply add the numbers as follows to obtain the necessary result.

$$\begin{array}{r} 16.3 \ \text{ft} \\ 0.927 \ \text{ft} \\ \hline 17.227 \ \text{ft} \end{array}$$

However, the first length is precise only to tenths, and the digit in this position was obtained by rounding off. It might have been as small as 16.25 ft or as large as 16.35 ft. If we consider only the precision of this first number, the total length might be as small as 17.177 ft or as large as 17.277 ft. These two values agree when rounded off to two significant digits (17). They vary by 0.1 when rounded off to tenths (17.2 and 17.3). When rounded to hundredths, they do not agree at all, since the third significant digit is different (17.18 and 17.28). Therefore there is no agreement at all in the digits after the third when these two numbers are rounded off to a precision beyond tenths. This may also be deemed reasonable, since the first length is not expressed beyond tenths. The second number does not further change the precision of the result, even though it is expressed to thousandths. Therefore we may conclude that the result must be rounded off at least to tenths, the precision of the first number.

Example B   We can find the area of a rectangular piece of land by multiplying the length, 207.54 ft, by the width, 81.4 ft. Performing the multiplication, we find the area to be

$$(207.54 \text{ ft})(81.4 \text{ ft}) = 16893.756 \text{ sq ft.}$$

However, we know that this length and width were found by measurement and that the least each could be is 207.535 ft and 81.35 ft. Multiplying these values, we find the least value for the area to be

$$(207.535 \text{ ft})(81.35 \text{ ft}) = 16882.97225 \text{ sq ft.}$$

The greatest possible value for the area is

$$(207.545 \text{ ft})(81.45 \text{ ft}) = 16904.54025 \text{ sq ft.}$$

We now note that the least possible and greatest possible values of the area agree when rounded off to three significant digits (16900 sq ft) and there is no agreement in digits beyond this if the two values are rounded off to a greater accuracy. Therefore we can conclude that the accuracy of the result is good to three significant digits, or certainly no more than four. We also note that the width was accurate to three significant digits, and the length to five significant digits.

The following rules are based on reasoning similar to that in Examples A and B; we shall use these rules when we perform the basic arithmetic operations on approximate numbers.

1. When approximate numbers are added or subtracted, the result is expressed with the precision of the least precise number.

2. When approximate numbers are multiplied or divided, the result is expressed with the accuracy of the least accurate number.

3. When the root of an approximate number is found, the result is accurate to the accuracy of the number.

4. Before the calculation is performed, all the numbers except the least precise or least accurate should be rounded off to one place beyond that of the least precise or least accurate.

The last of these rules is designed to make the calculation as easy as possible, since carrying the additional figures is meaningless in the intermediate steps. The following examples illustrate the use of these rules.

Add the approximate numbers 73.2, 8.0627, 93.57, 66.296.   *Example C*

The least precise of these numbers is 73.2. Therefore, before performing the addition, we shall round off the other numbers to hundredths. After the addition is performed, we shall round off the result to tenths. This leads to

$$
\begin{array}{r}
73.2 \\
8.06 \\
93.57 \\
66.30 \\
\hline
241.13
\end{array}
$$

Therefore the final result is 241.1.

Divide 292.6 by 3.4.   *Example D*

Since the divisor is accurate only to 2 significant digits, the final result is accurate to 2 significant digits. Therefore we shall round off the dividend to three significant digits, and divide until we have three significant digits in the quotient. The result will then be rounded off to two significant digits.

$$
\begin{array}{r}
86.1 \\
3\,4\,)\overline{2930.0} \\
272 \\
\hline
210 \\
204 \\
\hline
60 \\
34 \\
\hline
\end{array}
$$

Therefore the final result is 86.

Example E   When we subtract 36.1 from 727.842, we have

$$
\begin{array}{r}
727.84 \\
36.1 \\
\hline
691.74
\end{array}
$$

Therefore the result is 691.7.
When we find the product of 2.4832 and 30.5, we have

$$(2.483)(30.5) = 75.7315.$$

Therefore the final result is 75.7.
When we find the square root of 3.7, we have

$$
\begin{array}{r}
1.92 \\
\sqrt{3.7000}
\end{array}
$$

$$
\begin{array}{r r}
 & 1 \\
\hline
29 & \overline{270} \\
 & 261 \\
\hline
382 & 900 \\
 & 764
\end{array}
$$

Therefore the final result is 1.9.

The rules stated in this section are usually sufficiently valid for the computations encountered in technical work. They are intended only as good practical rules for working with approximate numbers. It was recognized in Examples A and B that the last significant digit obtained by these rules is subject to some possible error. Therefore it is possible that the most accurate result is not obtained by their use, although this is not often the case.

If an exact number is included in a calculation, there is no limitation to the number of decimal positions it may take on. The accuracy of the result is limited only by the approximate numbers involved.

EXERCISES   In Exercises 1 through 4, add the given approximate numbers.

1. 3.8	**2.** 26	**3.** 0.36294	**4.** 56.1
0.154	5.806	0.086	3.0645
47.26	147.29	0.5056	127.38
		0.74	0.055

In Exercises 5 through 8, subtract the given approximate numbers.

5. 468.14	**6.** 1.03964	**7.** 57.348	**8.** 8.93
36.7	0.69	26.5	6.8947

In Exercises 9 through 12, multiply the given approximate numbers.

9. (3.64)(17.06)　　　　　　　　**10.** (0.025)(70.1)

11. (704.6)(0.38)　　　　　　　　**12.** (0.003040)(6079.52)

In Exercises 13 through 16, divide the given approximate numbers.

13. 608 ÷ 3.9　　　　　　　　　**14.** 0.4962 ÷ 827

15. $\dfrac{596000}{22}$　　　　　　　　**16.** $\dfrac{53.267}{0.3002}$

In Exercises 17 through 20, find the indicated square roots of the given approximate numbers.

17. $\sqrt{32}$　　　　　　　　　　**18.** $\sqrt{6.5}$

19. $\sqrt{19.3}$　　　　　　　　　**20.** $\sqrt{0.0694}$

In Exercises 21 through 24, evaluate the given expression. All numbers are approximate.

21. 3.862 + 14.7 − 8.3276　　　　**22.** (3.2)(0.386) + 6.842

23. $\dfrac{8.60}{0.46}$ + (0.9623)(3.86)　　　　**24.** 9.6 − 0.1962(7.30)

In Exercises 25 through 28, perform the indicated operations. The first number given is approximate and the second number is exact.

25. 3.62 + 14　　　　　　　　　**26.** 17.382 − 2.5

27. (0.3142)(60)　　　　　　　　**28.** 8.62 ÷ 1728

Some of Exercises 29 through 38 will require the use of the reduction and conversion tables (Tables 2–1 and 2–2). Of those that are listed, the reduction factors are exact and the conversion factors are approximate.

29. Two forces, 18.6 lb and 2.382 lb, are acting on an object. What is the sum of these forces?

30. Three sections of a bridge are measured to be 52.3 ft, 36.38 ft, and 38 ft, respectively. What is the total length of these three sections?

31. Two planes are reported to have flown at speeds of 938 mi/hr and 1400 km/hr, respectively. Which plane is faster, and by how many miles per hour?

32. The density of a certain type of iron is 7.10 g/cm^3. The density of a type of tin is 448 lb/ft^3. Which is greater?

33. If the temperature of water is raised from 4°C to 30°C, its density reduces by 0.420%. If the density of water at 4°C is 62.4 lb/ft^3, what is its density at 30°?

34. The power (in watts) developed in an electric circuit is found by multiplying the current, in amps, by the voltage. In a certain circuit the current is 0.0125 amp and the voltage is 12.68 volts. What is the power that is developed?

35. A certain ore is 5.3% iron. How many tons of ore must be refined to obtain 45,000 lb of iron?

36. An electric data-processing card sorter sorts 32,000 cards, by count, in 10.25 min. At what rate does the sorter operate?

37. In order to find the velocity, in feet/second, of an object which has fallen a certain height, we calculate the square root of the product of 64.4 (an approximate number) and the height in feet. What is the velocity of an object which has fallen 63 meters?

38. A student reports the current in a certain experiment to be 0.02 amp at one time and later notes that it is 0.023 amp. He then states that the change in current is 0.003 amp. What is wrong with his conclusion?

2–4 REVIEW EXERCISES

In Exercises 1 through 4, determine the number of significant digits in the given approximate numbers.

1. 3900; 80.9

2. 0.30; 0.0002

3. 50030; 53000

4. 50.00; 0.010020

In Exercises 5 through 8, determine which of each pair of approximate numbers is (a) more precise and (b) more accurate.

5. 9.82, 98.2

6. 900, 90.0

7. 0.0023, 23.685

8. 506.32, 8.61

In Exercises 9 through 16, round off each of the given approximate numbers (a) to three significant digits, and (b) to two significant digits.

9. 3.827

10. 50.94

11. 367500

12. 73540

13. 57005

14. 896.4

15. 5545

16. 0.3000

In Exercises 17 through 28, perform the indicated operations on the given approximate numbers.

17. 26.3	**18.** 6.8072	**19.** 19.8062	**20.** 806
412.07	14.4	$-$ 8.92	$-$ 4.92
$+$ 0.3492	$+$ 8.626		

21. $(3.96)(0.030)$ **22.** $(9.52)(4000)$

23. $4.924 \div 86$ **24.** $6.80 \div 0.0327$

25. $\sqrt{47}$ **26.** $\sqrt{3.04}$

27. $\sqrt{12} + \dfrac{5.87}{1.42}$ **28.** $(0.3920)(14.65) - 2.96$

In Exercises 29 through 42, the given numbers are approximate.

29. Convert 5.2 in. to centimeters.

30. Convert 36 kg to pounds.

31. Reduce 4.452 gal to pints.

32. Reduce 18.5 km to centimeters.

33. Convert 27 ft^3 to liters.

34. Convert 3.206 km to miles.

35. Reduce 0.43 ft^3 to cubic inches.

36. Reduce 28.3 in^2 to ft^2.

37. Convert 2.45 mi/hr to m/sec.

38. Convert 52 g/cm^3 to lb/in^3.

39. Reduce 14.7 lb/in^2 to $tons/ft^2$.

40. Reduce 36 kg/m^2 to g/cm^2.

41. Convert 18.03 ft^3/sec to cm^3/min.

42. Convert 17.5 ft-lb/sec into kg-m/sec.

Solve the given problems in Exercises 43 through 54.

43. A unit commonly used in measuring the cross-sectional area of wire is the square mil, where 1 mil = 0.001 in. If the cross-sectional area of a wire is 380 mil^2, what is its area in square inches?

44. The density of dried redwood is about 27 lb/ft^3. What is its density in g/cm^3?

45. The density of gasoline is 5.6 lb/gal. What is its density in kilograms/liter?

46. A nautical mile is about 6080 ft, and a knot is one nautical mile per hour. What is a speed of 15.5 knots in centimeters per second?

47. A machinist milled a machine part to a thickness of 0.285 in. thick. Between what two values (the least and greatest possible) should this thickness be?

48. A voltage of 0.35 volts was applied to a transistor. Between what two values (the least and greatest possible) was the voltage?

49. A certain apparatus was weighed in 3 separate parts. The weights reported were 3.652 g, 56.54 g, and 86.3 g. What is the total weight of the apparatus?

50. The pilot of an airplane notes that his airspeed (speed relative to the air) is 592 mi/hr. If the headwind (blowing in the direction opposite to that in which the plane is flying) is blowing at 70 mi/hr, what is the ground speed of the plane?

51. One foot of steel will increase in length by 0.0000067 ft for each 1°F increase in temperature. What is the increase in length, in inches, of a steel girder 120 ft long, if the temperature increases by 45°F?

52. A large piece of sheet metal is cut into 20 pieces. The total thickness of the 20 pieces is 2.85 in. What is the thickness of each sheet?

53. A student wrote in his laboratory report that the time for a full swing of a pendulum was 2 sec, and that the time of the next full swing was 2.2 sec. His conclusion was that the times differed by 0.2 sec. What is probably the error in recording the first time? If his data were correct, is his conclusion correct?

54. In order to find the velocity of an object which has fallen 50 ft, we must evaluate $\sqrt{(64.4 \text{ ft/sec}^2)(50 \text{ ft})}$. Show that the units of the result are those of velocity.

Introduction to the Slide Rule

3

3–1 INTRODUCTION; READING THE SLIDE RULE

The slide rule is an instrument that can be used to perform many numerical operations rapidly. In this chapter we shall see how to perform, by using the simple and convenient slide rule, the operations of multiplication, division, squaring, and finding square roots. We shall discuss additional uses in the appropriate sections in later chapters. The two basic operations of addition and subtraction cannot be done on the slide rule.

The basic limitation of the slide rule is that its result is limited to an accuracy of three significant digits. However, in a great many technical problems, this accuracy is quite sufficient. To solve many problems in this text, in other courses and in laboratory work, you can use the slide rule to find answers rapidly and with sufficient accuracy. Even when greater accuracy is required, the slide rule often provides a way of checking an answer quickly and easily. And even when a computer is readily available, it is a common practice to check a problem on a slide rule to find the approximate value of the result before submitting the problem to the computer for the solution.

The only proper way to learn to operate a slide rule successfully is to *use it*. Ample practice is essential, particularly when a person is first learning the use of the slide rule. Once the first few basic operations are mastered, other operations are easily learned.

There are a great many types of slide rules. However, the discussions in this chapter and in other sections in this text are general enough to apply to most slide rules. Nearly all slide rules come with a manual that you can use to supplement this material, particularly to learn any variations which your rule may have.

In the calculations we shall discuss, the slide rule gives only the significant digits of the answer, and does not indicate where the decimal point should be located. A person can locate the decimal point by approximating the answer. In the approximation, all that we require is a number of the proper general magnitude. The following example shows how approximations can be made, and in later sections when calculations are actually performed, the process will be illustrated further.

Example A   If we were to perform the multiplication 39.1 × 839 on the slide rule, we would find that the first three significant digits of the result were 328. Now by approximating the multiplication as 40 × 800 = 32,000, we know that the result is near 32,000. Therefore we know that the result, to three significant digits, is 32,800.

If we were to calculate the value of

$$\frac{(0.0327)(72.6)}{0.912}$$

on the slide rule, we would find that the first three significant digits of the result were 260. By approximating the value as

$$\frac{(0.03)(70)}{1} = 2.1,$$

we know that the result is 2.60.

The long sliding part in the middle of the rule is called the *slide*. The vertical line on the transparent runner is called the *hairline*. Various *scales*, which are lettered, are found horizontally along the slide rule. Any marking labeled with a 1 is called an *index* of that scale (with the exceptions of the smaller 1's which appear on the C- and D-scales). See Fig. 3–1.

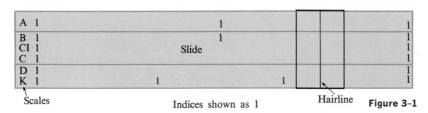

Figure 3–1

In reading a number on a scale of a slide rule, we must keep in mind that only three (possibly four on the C- and D-scales) significant digits of any number can be determined. For example, on any given scale (of those we shall discuss), the numbers 28.5, 0.0285, and 285,000 would be located at the same position. In fact, any number with the three-significant-digit accuracy of 285 would be found at this position.

We shall now describe the way a number is located on the C-scale or D-scale. Since these two scales are identical, the readings are made in the same way on each. Consider the following examples.

Locate 135.6 on the D-scale.   Example B

Since the first significant digit is 1, the position of the number 135.6 will lie between the large (primary) 1 and the primary 2. (See Fig. 3–2.) The second significant digit being 3, the position would then be further located between the small (secondary) 3 and the secondary 4. The

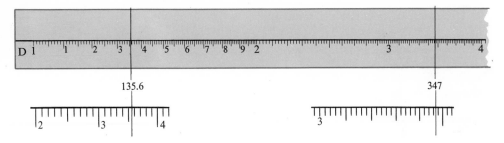

Figure 3–2

divisions between the secondary 3 and 4 are marked but not numbered. Since there are ten divisions, the third of the significant digits, 5, locates the number between the fifth and sixth marks. The final position is found by estimating, as well as possible, six-tenths of the way between these divisions. This position would also be used for 13.56, 0.001356, or for any number with 1356 as the significant digits. It is only for numbers with a first significant digit of 1 that four-place accuracy is possible, and then only on the C- and D-scales.

Example C   Locate 347 on the D-scale.

The first significant digit, 3, locates the position as being between the primary 3 and 4 (see Fig. 3–2). The second significant digit, 4, further locates the position as being between the fourth and fifth secondary division markings. Note that there are only five divisions between these secondary divisions. Thus each of these small divisions represents two units. Therefore the final position lies halfway between the third and fourth of these marks.

Note also that there are only two divisions between the secondary marks for numbers with a first digit of 4 to 9. It is therefore necessary to estimate the third significant digit, remembering that each of the smallest divisions represents 5 units.

Numbers are located on the other scales in a similar manner. The way in which the scale is marked should be carefully noted, so that the estimation of the third digit can be properly determined.

Example D   The locations of 0.244, 45.7, and 6.73 on the A-scale are shown in Fig. 3–3.

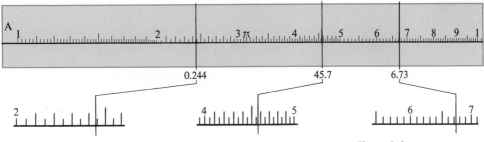

Figure 3-3

In Exercises 1 through 12, read the three (or four) significant digits indicated   EXERCISES
in Fig. 3–4. The number of each arrow is the exercise number.

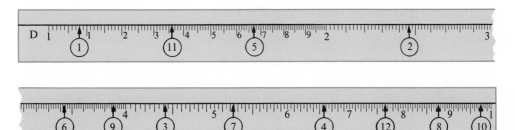

Figure 3-4

In Exercises 13 through 20, locate the three (or four) significant digits on the
D-scale.

13. 470   **14.** 325   **15.** 144   **16.** 250

17. 669   **18.** 946   **19.** 1023   **20.** 404

In Exercises 21 through 28, locate the three significant digits on the A-scale.
Note that the left-hand side and the right-hand side of the A-scale are exactly
the same. Locate the positions on each side.

21. 325   **22.** 892   **23.** 702   **24.** 240

25. 149   **26.** 458   **27.** 809   **28.** 606

In Exercises 29 through 36, find approximations of the results.

29. (829)(0.485)   **30.** (0.0895)(63.7)   **31.** $\dfrac{568,000}{0.0247}$ **32.** $\dfrac{0.0734}{60.8}$

33. $\sqrt{73.9}$ **34.** $\sqrt{846}$ **35.** $\dfrac{(0.934)(726)}{45.2}$ **36.** $\dfrac{\sqrt{1520}}{(9.07)(448)}$

3–2 MULTIPLICATION AND DIVISION

The first of the slide-rule operations that we shall discuss are multiplication and division. We perform each by using two scales together, one on the main portion of the slide rule and the other on the slide. Normally the two scales used are the C- and D-scales. First let us consider how numbers are multiplied on the slide rule.

When one uses the C- and D-scales, the process of multiplication is as follows: (1) Locate the first number on the D-scale. (2) Next, place the index of the C-scale directly over this position. (3) Locate the second number on the C-scale. (4) Place the hairline over this second number. (5) Read the significant digits of the answer on the D-scale, under the hairline. (6) Determine the decimal point by approximating the answer (this also provides a rough check).

Example A   Multiply 12.0 by 41.0. (See Fig. 3–5.)

First we locate 12.0 on the D-scale as directly on the secondary 2, and place the left index of the C-scale directly above this position. Now we locate 41.0 on the C-scale as directly on the first secondary mark past the primary 4. We place the hairline over this position. Under the hairline, on the D-scale, we observe the significant digits 492. A quick calculation tells us that $10 \times 40 = 400$, and therefore the answer is 492.

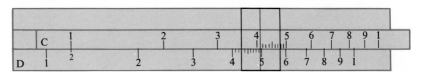

Figure 3–5

About half the time it is necessary to use the right index of the C-scale in the multiplication. In such cases, if the left index is placed over the first number, the second number appears on the C-scale beyond the extent of the D-scale. In order to avoid a trial-and-error process in choosing the index to use, quickly observe the numbers being multiplied. If the product of the first significant digits is less than 10, use the left index; otherwise use the right index. This usually gives the proper index.

Example B   Multiply 0.834 by 28.6.

Since the product of the first significant digits, 8 and 2, is 16, we use the right index. The setup for the multiplication is shown in Fig. 3–6.

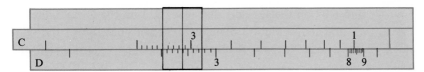

Figure 3–6

The observed significant digits of the result are 239. Since $0.8 \times 30 = 24$, the result is therefore 23.9.

Division is the reverse process of multiplication, a fact which also holds true in the use of the slide rule. When one uses the C- and D-scales for division, here are the steps to follow: (1) Locate the numerator on the D-scale. (2) Locate the denominator on the C-scale, and place it directly over the position of the numerator. (3) Find the significant digits of the answer on the D-scale, directly under the index of the C-scale. (4) Approximate the answer to determine the location of the decimal point. Whichever index of the C-scale is over the D-scale is the proper one, and there is no problem of "which index" in division.

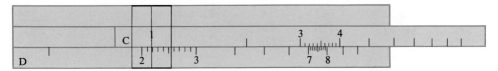

Figure 3–7

Divide 78.3 by 3.57 (see Fig. 3–7).   Example C

First we locate 78.3 on the D-scale. Next we place the position of 3.57 on the C-scale directly above the 78.3. We find the significant digits of the answer, 219, directly under the left index of the C-scale. Approximating the answer as $80 \div 4 = 20$, we find the result to be 21.9.

Divide 6.07 by 926 (see Fig. 3–8).   Example D

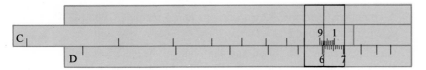

Figure 3–8

First we find 6.07 on the D-scale, and place 926 on the C-scale directly above. We find the significant digits of the result, 656, under the right index of the C-scale. Approximating the answer by $\frac{6}{1000} = 0.006$, the result is 0.00656.

EXERCISES   In Exercises 1 through 32, find the indicated products and quotients on a slide rule.

1. (2.00)(3.00)   2. (4.70)(0.111)

3. (562)(0.320)   4. (99.0)(3.46)

5. (0.0601)(0.1425)   6. (73.4)(0.401)

7. (0.00620)(850)   8. (506)(0.0211)

9. (9.38)(0.000360)   10. (25000)(0.706)

11. (8.37)(88.4)   12. (1060)(732)

13. 14 ÷ 2   14. 85 ÷ 5.0

15. 5.5 ÷ 11   16. 196 ÷ 140

17. 760 ÷ 2.44   18. 0.243 ÷ 0.711

19. 9.34 ÷ 0.0240   20. 65.5 ÷ 8.21

21. 60200 ÷ 0.0411   22. 0.00404 ÷ 1.17

23. 84.4 ÷ 0.0556   24. 2.99 ÷ 860

25. (2.68)(3.10)(502)   26. (0.0360)(20.5)(13.9)

27. (3070)(81.0)(0.913)   28. (0.0990)(1.05)(36.4)

29. $\dfrac{(36.8)(827)}{40.5}$ 30. $\dfrac{(0.0304)(86.1)}{0.944}$

31. $\dfrac{687}{(0.0421)(4070)}$ 32. $\dfrac{70400}{(36.9)(4.19)}$

In Exercises 33 through 44, perform the indicated calculations on a slide rule.

33. Find the area of a rectangle 36.8 in. by 14.9 in.

34. Find the simple interest for a year on $5680 at an annual interest rate of 4.12%.

35. A car travels 387 miles in 7.25 hours. What is the average speed of the car?

36. A computer performs 232 calculations in 7.5 seconds. What is its rate, in calculations/second?

37. Gasoline weighs 5.66 lb/gal and the tank on a certain car holds 17.6 gal. What is the weight of the gas in the tank when the tank is full?

38. A man purchased 23,500 board-ft of lumber at $143 per thousand board-ft. What was the total cost?

39. A piece of wire is 0.0350 in. thick. How many turns of this wire can be wound on a coil 4.25 in. long?

40. A dairy farmer sold 2750 lb of milk to a creamery for $108. How much was he paid per pound?

41. Convert 15.5 in. to centimeters.

42. How many liters are there in 27.5 ft^3?

43. If 3.55 mi of a certain highway cost $8,370,000 to construct, what was the cost per foot?

44. What is the cost of a piece of sheet metal 8.25 ft by 4.88 ft, given that the cost is $4.28 per square foot?

3-3 SQUARES AND SQUARE ROOTS

As is done with multiplication and division, two scales are used together to find the squares and square roots of numbers on a slide rule. However, the scales which are generally used, the A- and D-scales, are both on the main body of the slide rule. Another pair of scales, the B- and C-scales, which are both on the slide, can also be used to find squares and square roots. (Some slide rules use the D-scale in conjunction with the Sq 1 and Sq 2 scales for this purpose. Some added accuracy is obtained in this way.) Since the A- and D-scales are on the main body of the slide rule, the slide does not enter into the process of finding squares and square roots.

The procedure for squaring a number is as follows: (1) Locate the number to be squared on the D-scale. (2) Place the hairline over this position. (3) Read the significant digits of the result on the A-scale under the hairline. (4) Approximate the answer to get the location of the decimal point.

Find the square of 28.4 (see Fig. 3–9).   *Example A*

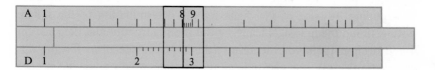

Figure 3-9

First we locate 28.4 on the D-scale, then place the hairline over this position. The significant digits 807 are then found under the hairline on the A-scale. Approximating the answer as $30 \times 30 = 900$, we find the result to be 807.

Example B   Find the square of 0.509 (see Fig. 3–10).

We locate 0.509 on the D-scale, then place the hairline over this position. The significant digits 259 are found under the hairline on the A-scale. When we approximate the answer as $0.5 \times 0.5 = 0.25$, the result is 0.259.

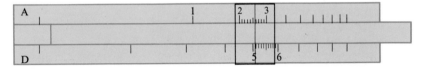

Figure 3–10

Finding square roots is the reverse of finding squares. The number whose square root is to be found is located on the A-scale. By use of the hairline, we can find the significant digits of the result on the D-scale. Finally, an approximation gives us the position of the decimal point.

However, since there are two identical parts of the A-scale, the major problem in finding square roots is in determining which side of the A-scale to use. For example, if we followed the above procedure to find $\sqrt{25}$, we would find the significant digits 158 if 25 is located on the left half of the A-scale, or we would find the significant digits 500 if 25 is located on the right half. Obviously, since $\sqrt{25} = 5$, the significant digits 500 are correct.   (Further observation would tell us, however, that $\sqrt{250} = 15.8$, and therefore the significant digits 158 are not meaningless.)

There are several ways of properly choosing which side of the A-scale to use. We shall adopt a rather simple procedure, based on the method by which square roots were found in Section 1–9, as follows: (1) Indicate the grouping by twos of the digits for the determination of the square root. (2) Find the first significant digit of the square root and the location of the decimal point of the result (this replaces the need for the approximation).   (3) Use the half of the A-scale which gives the proper first significant digit on the D-scale.

To find the square root of	Set up for square root	First significant digit	Use ___ side of A-scale	Approximate result	Example C
31.0	5. $\sqrt{31.00}$	5	Right	5	
310	1　. $\sqrt{3\ 10.00}$	1	Left	10	
5260000	2　　　. $\sqrt{5\ 26\ 00\ 00.}$	2	Left	2000	
526000	7　. $\sqrt{52\ 60\ 00.}$	7	Right	700	
0.000472	.0　2 $\sqrt{0.00\ 04\ 72}$	2	Left	0.02	
0.0000472	.0　0　6 $\sqrt{0.00\ 00\ 47\ 20}$	6	Right	0.006	

Following the procedure outlined for finding square roots, we can find the square root of each of the numbers of Example C by placing the hairline over the position of the given number on the proper side of the A-scale. Therefore we have the following results.   **Example D**

To find the square root of	Significant digits of result	Final result
31.0	557	5.57
310	176	17.6
5260000	229	2290
526000	725	725
0.000472	217	0.0217
0.0000472	687	0.00687

In Exercises 1 through 16, find the squares of the given numbers on the slide rule.   **EXERCISES**

1. 14.0　　　　**2.** 3.10　　　　**3.** 46.0　　　　**4.** 0.360

5. 0.0200　　　**6.** 0.133　　　**7.** 6.71　　　　**8.** 7.85

9. 9.94   **10.** 888   **11.** 66,200   **12.** 0.00315

13. 1550   **14.** 0.0401   **15.** 0.440   **16.** 7090

In Exercises 17 through 32, find the square roots of the given numbers on the slide rule.

17. 41.0   **18.** 410   **19.** 0.0136   **20.** 0.136

21. 572   **22.** 57.2   **23.** 0.572   **24.** 0.0572

25. 47500   **26.** 863   **27.** 0.0652   **28.** 7640

29. 22.4   **30.** 33600   **31.** 9060   **32.** 306

In Exercises 33 through 40, make the indicated calculations on the slide rule.

33. $38.6\sqrt{0.562}$ **34.** $\dfrac{\sqrt{3080}}{69.4}$ **35.** $\dfrac{89400}{(3.92)^2}$ **36.** $(472)^2\sqrt{0.0609}$

37. Find the area of a square 62.9 cm on a side.

38. The electric power, in watts, in a certain electric circuit is found by calculating $(0.327 \text{ amp})^2(10.7 \text{ ohms})$. Perform this calculation.

39. A square piece of land has an area of 23,700 ft^2. What is the length of one side?

40. In order to calculate the speed of a wave moving along a string under certain circumstances, one must make the following calculations:

$$\sqrt{\frac{(20.5 \text{ lb})(32.2 \text{ ft/sec}^2)}{0.00314 \text{ lb/ft}}}.$$

Find the speed of the wave.

3-4 COMBINED OPERATIONS

For problems consisting of several operations, there are numerous methods which might be employed. We cannot cover all possibilities here, but a person who gets experience in using the slide rule normally develops insight as to the best procedures to use.

If a problem consists of several multiplications and divisions, the best procedure is to alternate between division and multiplication, starting with division. This allows one to find the result with the fewest possible settings on the slide rule.

Example A   In order to calculate the value of

$$\frac{(3.10)(0.464)}{(17.5)(0.0105)},$$

the first step is to divide 3.10 by 17.5. The result of this division is under the index of the C-scale, but there is no need to record this result, since we can immediately multiply it by 0.464 by moving the hairline over the 0.464 on the C-scale. By leaving the hairline in place, we can divide this result by 0.0105 by moving the slide so that 0.0105 on the C-scale is under the hairline. The final result, 7.83, is observed under the index of the C-scale. Thus, with only two settings of the slide, it is possible to find the final result. The decimal point is determined by the approximation

$$\frac{(3)(0.5)}{(20)(0.01)} = \frac{1.5}{0.2} = 7.5.$$

For a problem consisting of several indicated multiplications and divisions, quantity to be squared, the best procedure is to find the results of the multiplications and divisions first. This result can then be squared by immediate reference to the A-scale.

When we wish to calculate the value of   *Example B*

$$\left[\frac{(87.5)(0.0236)}{659}\right]^2,$$

the first step is to divide 87.5 by 659. The result of this division is under the index of the C-scale, and it can be multiplied by 0.0236 by placing the hairline over 0.0236 of the C-scale. The result of the division and multiplication is under the hairline on the D-scale. However, it is the square of this result that is required. Therefore, by referring to the square on the A-scale, we obtain the result 0.00000982. We obtain the decimal point by the approximation

$$\left[\frac{(90)(0.02)}{700}\right]^2 = \left[\frac{1.8}{700}\right]^2 = \left[\frac{2}{700}\right]^2 = [0.003]^2 = 0.000009.$$

For a problem such as   *Example C*

$$\frac{(\sqrt{1.37})(4.46)^2}{86.2},$$

it is generally best to first replace the squares and square roots by their equivalent values. This leads to

$$\frac{(1.17)(19.9)}{86.2},$$

which is then solved by dividing 1.17 by 86.2 and then multiplying the result by 19.9. This gives the value of 0.270. The decimal point is found by the approximation

$$\frac{(1)(20)}{80} = 0.25.$$

As we mentioned in Section 3–1, however, only continued practice will enable a person to master the operation of the slide rule. This point cannot be overemphasized, for those who find difficulty in using a slide rule generally have not put in sufficient time practicing.

EXERCISES   In the following exercises, perform all indicated calculations on a slide rule.

1. $\dfrac{(14.0)(2.00)}{4.50}$

2. $\dfrac{(173)(562)}{780}$

3. $\dfrac{19.6}{(0.0159)(372)}$

4. $\dfrac{0.000356}{(456)(0.608)}$

5. $\dfrac{(15.0)(36.0)}{(47.0)(5.56)}$

6. $\dfrac{(4.56)(0.0676)}{(0.798)(50.5)}$

7. $\dfrac{(38.7)(5.62)(1.92)}{307}$

8. $\dfrac{(46.2)(4960)(0.106)}{(0.0309)(727)}$

9. $\left(\dfrac{47.3}{15.1}\right)^2$

10. $\left(\dfrac{0.0306}{4.37}\right)^2$

11. $\left[\dfrac{(12.9)(0.735)}{27.8}\right]^2$

12. $\left[\dfrac{(37.4)(0.436)}{96.2}\right]^2$

13. $\sqrt{\dfrac{86.4}{6.42}}$

14. $\sqrt{\dfrac{9320}{20.7}}$

15. $\sqrt{\dfrac{(67.0)(905)}{14.2}}$

16. $\sqrt{\dfrac{(863)(5.26)}{73.4}}$

17. $\dfrac{\sqrt{15.6}}{46.2}$

18. $\dfrac{\sqrt{829}}{3.63}$

19. $\dfrac{872}{\sqrt{3.72}}$

20. $\dfrac{59.1}{\sqrt{4060}}$

21. $\dfrac{(\sqrt{4.16})(0.814)^2}{36.7}$

22. $\dfrac{\sqrt{(16.4)(72.0)}}{73.5}$

23. $\dfrac{(487)(\sqrt{682})}{(31.4)(655)^2}$

24. $\dfrac{(3.65)^2(0.0526)}{\sqrt{0.00427}}$

25. In order to find the number of revolutions per minute that a certain pulley makes, the calculation

$$\frac{(4.36)(1530)}{9.12}$$

must be performed. The unit of the result is revolutions/minute.

26. In order to calculate the heat loss through a certain window in an hour, the calculation

$$\frac{(5.50)(15.0)(42.0)}{0.188}$$

must be performed. The unit is the BTU (British Thermal Unit), a unit of
heat energy.

27. In order to find the area of a certain circle, the calculation $(3.14)(5.62)^2$
must be performed. The unit of the result is cm^2.

28. In an experiment designed to calculate the acceleration due to gravity, a
student made the calculation

$$\frac{4.12 \text{ ft}}{(0.360 \text{ sec})^2}.$$

What value did he obtain?

29. The velocity of an object which has fallen 820 ft can be found by calculating

$$\sqrt{\left(64.4 \frac{\text{ft}}{\text{sec}^2}\right)(820 \text{ ft})}.$$

Find this velocity.

30. The electric power, in watts, in a certain circuit is found by calculating

$$\frac{(20.6)^2}{75.6}.$$

Find the value.

31. A certain cornfield is 680 ft long and 425 ft wide. If an acre equals 43,500 ft^2,
how many acres are there in the field?

32. A flash of lightning strikes an object 3.25 mi distant from a man. He hears
the thunder 15.5 sec later. What is the speed of sound in ft/sec?

3-5 REVIEW EXERCISES

In the following exercises, perform all indicated calculations on a slide rule.

1. 3.46×4.92 2. 80.5×2.37 3. 362×51.9

4. 0.706×95.1 5. 6480×11.5 6. 0.0460×0.772

7. 89100×27.8 8. 38.9×687 9. $\dfrac{46.7}{1.39}$

10. $\dfrac{509}{26.7}$ 11. $\dfrac{6.32}{0.192}$ 12. $\dfrac{4080}{69200}$

13. $\dfrac{0.754}{0.0888}$ 14. $\dfrac{0.0901}{74.7}$ 15. $\dfrac{3.83}{5.64}$

16. $\dfrac{684}{90.9}$ 17. $(11.8)^2$ 18. $(2.73)^2$

19. $(52.7)^2$ 20. $(818)^2$ 21. $(0.715)^2$

22. $(0.0493)^2$ 23. $(3.79)^2$ 24. $(92.9)^2$

25. $\sqrt{6.85}$ 26. $\sqrt{23.6}$ 27. $\sqrt{4520}$

28. $\sqrt{0.0319}$ **29.** $\sqrt{784}$ **30.** $\sqrt{0.957}$

31. $\sqrt{183000}$ **32.** $\sqrt{54600}$ **33.** $\dfrac{(82.7)(2.40)}{36.5}$

34. $\dfrac{(491)(7.26)}{0.133}$ **35.** $\dfrac{\sqrt{29.7}}{5.68}$ **36.** $\dfrac{\sqrt{683}}{0.712}$

37. $\left[\dfrac{3.55}{0.0443}\right]^2$ **38.** $[(6.88)(12.7)]^2$ **39.** $\sqrt{(86.1)(2.36)}$

40. $\sqrt{\dfrac{7.42}{92.3}}$ **41.** $\dfrac{(8.94)^2}{\sqrt{18.4}}$ **42.** $\dfrac{(2.75)^2\sqrt{7.31}}{52.7}$

43. $\dfrac{(68.5)(14.9)^2}{\sqrt{524}}$ **44.** $\dfrac{(81.5)(3.14)(68.1)}{(799)(0.0574)}$

45. A car burns gasoline at the average rate of 17.3 mi/gal. How far does it travel on 12.4 gal?

46. A rectangular plot of land is 276 ft long and 183 ft wide. What is its area?

47. A contractor is fined $375 for each day late in completing the project. If the job is completed 18 days late, what is his fine?

48. A tank, originally full, took 2.75 hr to empty at the rate of 135 gal/hr. What is the capacity of the tank?

49. Convert 17.3 meters to inches.

50. A board measures 5.25 in. wide after shrinking 12.5% while drying. What was the original width of the board?

51. Convert 328 km to miles.

52. Reduce 14800 ft to miles.

53. Apollo 8 (the first manned spacecraft to the moon, in December, 1968) traveled the 231,000 mi in 2 days and 18 hr. What was its average speed?

54. According to Ohm's law of electricity, the current (in amperes) of a given circuit is found by dividing the voltage by the resistance (in ohms). Find the current in a circuit in which the voltage is 12.7 volts and the resistance is 455 ohms.

55. A piece of sheet metal is a square 17.3 cm on a side. What is its area?

56. Find the side of a square whose area is 57.3 ft^2.

57. A plane travels at 650 mi/hr. What is its speed in miles/second?

Signed 4
Numbers

4–1 SIGNED NUMBERS

In our discussions we have not encountered a situation in which we have attempted to subtract one number from another number which is smaller. In fact, using just the numbers that we have, there would be no answer for such a problem. It is therefore, necessary to introduce a new set of numbers, the *negative numbers*, for this purpose. Negative numbers have applications in numerous practical situations. For example, they can be used to represent temperatures below zero or monetary accounts with deficits. Other situations in which they arise are indicated in the exercises.

A negative number is a number less than zero. The symbols for addition $(+)$ and subtraction $(-)$ are also used to indicate positive and negative numbers, respectively. For example, $+5$ (plus 5) is a positive number, and -5 (minus 5) is a negative number. Since positive numbers correspond directly to the numbers we have already been using (we actually made no attempt to associate a sign with them, only using $+$ and $-$ to designate addition and subtraction), the plus sign may be omitted before a positive number if there is no danger of confusion. However, we shall never omit the negative sign before a negative number.

As indicated in Chapter 1, another name given to the natural numbers is *positive integers*. The negatives of the positive integers are called *negative integers*. The positive integers, *zero* (which is neither positive nor negative), and the negative integers together constitute the set of all *integers*. We shall find it convenient at times to refer to the integers in developing material in later sections.

Example A   The number 7, which equals $+7$, and $+7$ are positive integers. The number -7 is a negative integer. The number 0 is an integer, although it is neither positive nor negative. The number $\frac{2}{3}$ is not an integer, since it is not a natural number or the negative of one.

In this discussion, we see that the plus and the minus signs are used in two senses. One is to indicate addition or subtraction, and the other is to designate a positive or negative number. Consider the following example.

Example B   The expression $3 + 6$ means "add the number 6 to the number 3." Here the plus sign indicates addition, and the numbers are unsigned, although they are positive.

The expression $(+3) + (+6)$ means "add the number $+6$ to the number $+3$." Here the middle plus sign indicates addition, whereas the other plus signs denote signed numbers. Of course, the result here would be the same as $3 + 6$.

The expression $3 - 6$ means "subtract the number 6 from the number 3." Here the minus sign indicates subtraction, and the numbers are unsigned.

The expression $(+3) - (+6)$ means "subtract the number $+6$ from the number $+3$." Note that the plus signs only designate signed numbers.

The expression $(+3) - (-6)$ means "subtract the number -6 from the number $+3$." Here the first minus sign indicates subtraction, whereas the second designates the signed number.

The method of performing these operations will be discussed in the following section.

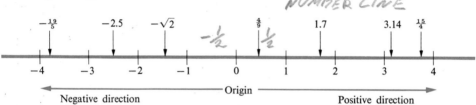

Figure 4–1

Positive and negative numbers can be illustrated on a scale, as shown in Fig. 4–1. On a horizontal line we choose a point which we call the *origin*, and here we locate the integer 0. We then locate positive numbers to the right of 0 and negative numbers to the left of 0. As we see, every positive number has a corresponding opposite negative number.

When numbers are marked plus or minus they are called *signed numbers* (or directed numbers) to indicate their opposite qualities, as shown on the scale. Since positive numbers are directed to the right of the origin, it follows that numbers increase from left to right. Therefore *any number on the scale is smaller than any number on its right.* The symbols $>$ and $<$ mean "greater than" and "less than," respectively. Their use is shown in the following example.

The expression $2 > 1$ means "the number 2 is greater than the number 1." It also means that on the scale in Fig. 4–1 we should find 2 to the right of 1.   **Example C**

The expression $0 < 4$ means "0 is less than 4." This means that 0 is to the left of 4.

The expression $-3 < 0$ means "-3 is less than 0." The number -3 lies to the left of 0 on the scale.

The expression $-3 > -5$ means "-3 is greater than -5." The number -3 is to the right of the number -5 on the scale.

Although the positive direction is conveniently taken to the right of the origin on the number scale, we may select any direction as the positive direction so long as we take the opposite direction to be negative. Consider the illustrations in the following example.

Example D   When we are dealing with the motion of an object moving vertically with respect to the surface of the earth, if the positive direction is up, we then take the negative direction to be down. The zero position can be chosen arbitrarily; often it is ground level.

If a temperature above zero (an arbitrarily chosen reference level) is called positive, a temperature below zero would be called negative.

For an object moving in a circular path, if a counterclockwise movement is called positive, a clockwise movement would be called negative.

The value of a number without its sign is called its *absolute value*. That is, if we disregard the signs of $+5$ and -5, the value would be the same. This is equivalent to saying that the distances from the origin to the points $+5$ and -5 on the number scale are equal. The absolute value of a number is indicated by the symbol $|\ \ |$. The number $+5$ does not equal the number -5, but $|+5| = |-5|$. Absolute values are used in performing arithmetic operations with signed numbers. Consider the following example.

Example E   The absolute value of $+8$ is 8. The absolute value of -2 is 2. The absolute value of $-\frac{3}{2}$ is $\frac{3}{2}$. We may write these equalities as $|+8| = 8$, $|-2| = 2$, and $|-\frac{3}{2}| = \frac{3}{2}$.

EXERCISES   In Exercises 1 through 8, state the meanings of the given expressions, as in Example B.

1. $2 + 7$ **2.** $8 - 5$ **3.** $(+5) + (+9)$

4. $(+6) - (+2)$ **5.** $(-4) + (-3)$ **6.** $(+7) - (-3)$

7. $(-5) - (+2)$ **8.** $(-1) - (-5)$

In Exercises 9 through 16, locate the approximate positions of the given numbers on a number scale such as that in Fig. 4–1.

9. 5   **10.** -0.5 **11.** $+2.3$ **12.** $+\sqrt{3}$

13. -3.14 **14.** $-\frac{17}{6}$ **15.** $+\frac{13}{22}$ **16.** $-\frac{13}{4}$

In Exercises 17 through 20, determine which of the given numbers is the largest.

17. $4, -5, -1$ **18.** $-2, -5, 0$ **19.** $-6, -2, -4$ **20.** $-1, -2, -3$

In Exercises 21 through 28, insert the proper sign, $>$ or $<$ or $=$, between the given numbers.

21. 6   2   **22.** 8 -3 **23.** 0   4   **24.** -1 -5

25. -3 -7 **26.** -3 0   **27.** $|6|$ $|-6|$ **28.** $|-3|$ $-|-3|$

In Exercises 29 through 32, find the absolute value of each of the given numbers.

29. $+6$ **30.** -5 **31.** $-\frac{6}{7}$ **32.** $\frac{8}{5}$

In Exercises 33 through 41, certain applications of signed numbers are indicated.

33. If a deposit of two dollars is represented as $+2$, determine the signed number which represents a bank withdrawal of $100.

34. From the financial section of a newspaper, note the way in which it is shown that a given stock gained or lost value during the day.

35. In an electronic tube, the voltage at a certain point is 200 volts above that of the reference and is designated as $+200$ volts. How is the voltage at a point at which it is 25 volts below the reference designated?

36. If the distance above ground level is represented as a positive number, what signed number represents the level of the bottom of a well 100 ft deep?

37. The Great Pyramid in Egypt was built about 2600 B.C. Assuming that years designated as A.D. are considered positive, state this date as a signed number.

38. The image of an object formed by a lens can be formed either to the right or to the left of the lens, depending on the position of the object. If an image is formed 10 cm to the left, and its distance is designated as -10 cm, what would be the designation of an image formed 4.5 cm to the right?

39. If the number of years to elapse between a future date and now is represented as a positive number, what number would be used to represent the number of years that have elapsed since the United States first put a man in orbit around the earth (1962)?

40. If the amount of money a person owes is represented as a negative number, which person—one whose financial position is -10 or one whose financial position is -20—is in the better financial position?

41. Use the proper sign, $>$ or $<$, to show which temperature, $-30°F$ or $-5°F$, is the higher of the two.

4–2 ADDITION AND SUBTRACTION OF SIGNED NUMBERS

In the previous section we showed the meaning of signed numbers and how they are designated. In this section we shall show how the operations of addition and subtraction are performed with signed numbers. In the next section we shall take up multiplication and division of signed numbers.

Problems in addition are of two types: those in which the signs of the numbers are alike and those in which they are unlike. *To add numbers that are of like signs we add the absolute value of the numbers and give the sum the common sign.*

Example A

$$(+4) + (+5) = +(4 + 5) = +9,$$
$$(-4) + (-5) = -(4 + 5) = -9,$$
$$(+8) + (+5) + (+2) = +(8 + 5 + 2) = +15,$$
$$(-8) + (-5) + (-2) = -(8 + 5 + 2) = -15.$$

To add numbers with unlike signs we add the absolute values of the positive numbers, add the absolute values of the negative numbers, find the difference between the sums, and give the difference the sign of the larger of the two sums.

Example B

$$(+4) + (-5) = -(5 - 4) = -1,$$
$$(-4) + (+5) = +(5 - 4) = +1,$$
$$(+8) + (-5) + (-2) = (+8) + (-7) = +(8 - 7) = +1,$$
$$(-8) + (+5) + (+2) = (-8) + (+7) = -(8 - 7) = -1.$$

The validity of the rules for addition of signed numbers may be verified by referring to the number scale in Fig. 4–2. To find the sum $(+8) + (+5) + (+2)$, we start at $+8$ and move to the right 5 units in order to add on $+5$. We therefore arrive at $+13$ and then move to the right 2 additional units in order to add $+2$. We therefore arrive at $+15$, the sum. Similarly, to find the sum $(+8) + (-5) + (-2)$, we start at

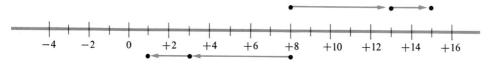

Figure 4–2

$+8$ and move to the left to add -5 (the opposite of $+5$) and thus arrive at $+3$. We then move to the left 2 additional units to add -2, and arrive at $+1$.

In subtracting signed numbers, we use the same principle for subtraction that we used in Chapter 1. That is, we find a number (the difference) which, when added to the number being subtracted (the subtrahend), will give the other number (the minuend). Thus *to subtract one signed number from another, we change the sign of the subtrahend and then add it to the minuend, using the rules for addition of signed numbers.*

$$(+4) - (+6) = (+4) + (-6) = -2, \qquad \text{Example C}$$
$$(+4) - (-6) = (+4) + (+6) = +10,$$
$$(-3) - (-7) = (-3) + (+7) = +4.$$

In the first illustration, the number which must be added to $+6$ to equal $+4$ is -2. In the second illustration, we see that the number which must be added to -6 in order to equal $+4$ is $+10$. In the third illustration, we see that the number which must be added to -7 in order to equal -3 is $+4$.

In each of the second and third illustrations we see that subtracting a negative number is equivalent to adding a positive number of the same absolute value. This might be thought of as removing (subtracting) a debt (a negative number), for when this is done a person's assets are increased (added to).

In general, when we are working with signed numbers, we find it convenient to change the operations so that the result may be obtained by addition and subtraction of positive numbers (written as unsigned numbers). When this is done we must remember that adding a negative number is equivalent to subtracting a positive number, and that subtracting a negative number is equivalent to adding a positive number. Consider the illustrations in the following example.

Example D
$$(+5) - (+2) + (-6) = 5 - 2 - 6 = 5 - 8 = -3,$$
$$(-4) + (-2) - (-7) = -4 - 2 + 7 = -6 + 7 = +1,$$
$$(-5) - (-9) - (+2) = -5 + 9 - 2 = -7 + 9 = +2.$$

EXERCISES   In Exercises 1 through 20, perform the indicated operations.

1. $(+2) + (+8)$ 2. $(+7) + (-3)$

3. $(-6) + (-9)$ 4. $(-8) + (+2)$

5. $(+1) + (-5) + (-2)$ 6. $(+6) + (+5) + (-3)$

7. $(-2) + (-6) + (+4)$ 8. $(-9) + (+1) + (-3)$

9. $(+8) - (+4)$ 10. $(+4) - (+5)$

11. $(-9) - (-7)$ 12. $(+5) - (-10)$

13. $(+2) + (-8) - (+2)$ 14. $(-4) - (+8) + (-9)$

15. $(+5) - (-3) - (+7)$ 16. $(-7) - (-1) - (+6)$

17. $(-9) - (-5) + (-8) - (+5)$ 18. $(-7) - (-5) + (-4) - (+6)$

19. $(-3) - (+5) - (-4) - (+2)$ 20. $(-9) + (-3) - (-4) - (-7)$

In Exercises 21 through 24, indicate the addition and subtraction of the signed numbers on a number line as in Fig. 4–2.

21. $(+7) + (+2)$ 22. $(+5) - (+2)$

23. $(+2) - (+7) + (-3)$ 24. $(-5) - (-8) + (+2)$

In Exercises 25 through 30, set up the given problems in terms of adding and subtracting signed numbers, and then perform the operations.

25. A temperature of $-10°F$ is increased by 25°F. What is the resulting temperature? $+15$

26. Consider an event that took place 25 years ago. How many years is it from that date to 1984?

27. While watching a rocket launching, an observer noted that it was "blast-off minus ten minutes." Assuming no delays, how long has the rocket been in the air 30 min later? $+20$

28. If a velocity is considered negative when an object is moving downward and positive when it is moving upward, what is the change in velocity of a ball moving at 60 ft/sec just before it hits the floor and just after it hits the floor?

29. If a person has $60 and has just paid off a debt of $10, how much money did he have before he paid the debt? 70

30. An object 25 ft above ground level fell to the bottom of a 60-ft well. How far did it fall?

31. What rule of English grammar is equivalent to subtracting a negative number in mathematics?

4–3 MULTIPLICATION AND DIVISION OF SIGNED NUMBERS

In defining the process of multiplication of *signed* numbers, we wish to be able to preserve the meanings that hold for the multiplication of natural numbers. Therefore, as in the case of natural numbers, multiplication is the process of adding a number a specified number of times.

As we pointed out in Chapter 1, the numbers to be multiplied are called factors, and the result is called the product. Also, according to the commutative law, the product of two factors is not changed if the factors are interchanged. With these ideas in mind, consider the illustrations of the following example.

$$3 \times 4 = 4 + 4 + 4 = 12,$$
$$4 \times 3 = 3 + 3 + 3 + 3 = 12,$$
$$3 \times 4 = 4 \times 3,$$
$$(+3) \times (-4) = (-4) + (-4) + (-4) = -12,$$
$$(-4) \times (+3) = (+3) \times (-4) = -12.$$

Example A

We see from the above example that the product of two positive numbers is positive. Also the product of a positive number and a negative number is negative. Hence we may say that *changing the sign of one factor changes the sign of the product.* Applying this principle leads to the fact that the product of two negative numbers is positive.

$$(+3) \times (+4) = +12,$$
$$(+3) \times (-4) = -12,$$
$$(-3) \times (-4) = +12.$$

Example B

This last illustration may also be looked upon as subtracting -4 three times, or $-(-4) - (-4) - (-4) = +12$. Also we see that this is consistent with the fact that the result of subtracting a negative number is equivalent to adding a positive number.

From the above discussion we can state the following results:

A. *If two factors have like signs, their product is positive.*

B. *If two factors have unlike signs, their product is negative.*

If there are three or more factors, we can multiply two at a time in any order and observe the sign of each product, or:

A. Make the product positive if all factors are positive or if there is an even number of negative factors.

B. Make the product negative if there is an odd number of negative factors.

If any factor is zero, it follows that the product is zero, since zero times any number is zero.

Example C

$$(+4) \times (-7) = -28, \quad (-2) \times (+3) \times (-5) = +30,$$
$$(-4) \times (-7) = +28, \quad (-2) \times (+3) \times (+5) = -30,$$
$$(-6) \times (0) \quad = 0, \quad (-2) \times (-3) \times (-5) = -30,$$
$$(-2) \times (-3) \times (-5) \times (+6) \times (-7) = +1260.$$

The next operation we shall consider is division. Again we wish to make our definitions consistent with those of arithmetic, where division is the process of determining how many times one number is contained in another. It is therefore the reverse process of multiplication.

Since division is the inverse of multiplication, it follows that division of numbers with like signs gives a positive quotient and division of numbers with unlike signs gives a negative quotient. In this way we use the same rules for signs that we used in multiplication. The results of division can be verified by multiplication.

Example D

$$(-15) \div (-5) = +3, \text{ since } (-5) \times (+3) = -15,$$
$$(-15) \div (+5) = -3, \text{ since } (+5) \times (-3) = -15,$$
$$(+15) \div (-3) = -5, \text{ since } (-3) \times (-5) = +15,$$
$$\frac{+50}{-2} = -25, \quad \frac{+60}{+15} = +4, \quad \frac{-96}{+16} = -6, \quad \frac{-39}{-13} = +3.$$

There is one number we cannot use as a divisor. That number is zero. Since division is the inverse of multiplication, we can say that $0 \div$ (any nonzero number) = 0, because (any number) $\times$ 0 = 0. This means that 0 divided by any number (not zero) is equal to zero. However, if we perform the division of (any nonzero number) $\div$ 0, we cannot obtain a proper result, since (no number) $\times$ 0 = (the nonzero number). In the case of 0 $\div$ 0, any number can be a solution, since 0 $\times$ (any number) = 0. This is said to be indeterminate. We therefore conclude that

division by zero is excluded at all times,

but that this is the only restriction on the use of zero.

$\frac{0}{4} = 0,$ since $0 \times 4 = 0,$ **Example E**

$\dfrac{-5}{0}$ is excluded since (no number) $\times$ 0 = $-5,$

$\frac{0}{0}$ is excluded since (any number) $\times$ 0 = 0.

The following example gives illustrations combining the basic operations on signed numbers.

Example F

$$(-4) + \frac{-8}{+2} - (-3)(-2) = (-4) + (-4) - (+6)$$
$$= -4 - 4 - 6 = -14.$$
$$\frac{-9}{-3} + (-2)^3 - (-3)^2 - \frac{(-4)(-6)}{-8} = (+3) + (-8) - (+9) - (-3)$$
$$= +3 - 8 - 9 + 3 = -11.$$

Note that the signs for addition and subtraction are left unchanged until the multiplications and divisions have been performed. Also, note that whenever we raise a signed number to a power it is a special case of multiplication.

When we introduced subtraction where the result was not positive, we in turn introduced negative numbers. This was necessary since the results were not expressible in terms of natural numbers. Again, when we divide one integer by another, the results often are not expressible as integers. Therefore the name *rational number* is given to any number which is expressible as the division of one integer by another (not zero). For example, $\frac{2}{3}$, $\frac{8}{4}$, and $\frac{1097}{431}$ are rational numbers. We shall later learn of numbers which cannot be expressed in this way (although we have already met a few: $\sqrt{2}$, for example).

In Exercises 1 through 24, perform the indicated operations.

1. $(-7)(+4)$ **2.** $(-9)(-3)$

3. $(+2)(-8)(-1)$ **4.** $(+4)(+2)(-5)$

5. $(+8)(0)(-4)(-1)$ **6.** $(-1)(-3)(-5)(-2)$

7. $(-4)(-2)(+3)(-7)$ **8.** $(+5)(+2)(-10)(-7)$

9. $(+8) \div (-2)$ **10.** $(-9) \div (-3)$

11. $0 \div (-2)$ **12.** $(+8) \div 0$

13. $(-3)^3$ **14.** $(-1)^8$

15. $\dfrac{(-1)(-6)}{(+3)}$ **16.** $\dfrac{(+2)(-9)}{(-6)}$

17. $\dfrac{(+4)(+9)(-5)}{(-2)(+3)}$ **18.** $\dfrac{(-8)(-12)(+5)}{(-10)(-16)}$

19. $(-8) - (-2)(+2) - (-1)^3$ **20.** $\dfrac{(+1)(+3)}{(-3)} - \dfrac{(-2)^3}{(+2)} - \dfrac{0}{5}$

21. $\dfrac{(-16)}{(-2)(-4)} - \dfrac{(-5)}{(-1)} - \dfrac{(+4)}{(-2)}$ **22.** $\dfrac{(-2)^3}{(-4)} - (-7)(-1)(-2)(-1)^2$

23. $\dfrac{(-4)(+2) - (+6) + (-1)}{(-3)}$ **24.** $\dfrac{(-2)^2 + (-1)(-5) - (-3)(-1)}{(-1)(+6)}$

In Exercises 25 through 30, solve the given problems.

25. Metal expands when heated and contracts when cooled. If a metal rod is 100 cm long and is then cooled by 20°C, find its resulting length if it contracts 0.1 cm for each 1°C it is cooled.

26. For a certain type of lens, if the object is 4 cm to the left of the lens and the image is 12 cm and also to the left, these distances are expressed as $+4$ cm and -12 cm. The magnification in this case is

$$- \left(\frac{-12}{+4} \right).$$

If the magnification is positive, the image is erect with respect to the object. Otherwise it is inverted. Determine the magnification and whether or not the image is erect.

27. A plane is flying at 39,000 ft. It descends 3,000 ft/min for 5 min. The plane then climbs 2,000 ft/min for 8 min. What is the altitude of the plane?

28. An object is thrown vertically upward from the edge of a cliff. The distance (in feet) from the edge of the cliff is a positive number if the object is above it. After 5 sec the distance is found by evaluating $(+70)(5) + (-16)(5)^2$. Determine how far above or below the edge this object is after 5 sec.

29. In order to find the current in a certain electric circuit, it is necessary to evaluate the expression

$$\frac{(+6.00) - (-0.83)(8.00)}{8.00 + 4.00}.$$

Find this current (in amperes).

30. Evaluate $(-1)^2$, $(-1)^3$, $(-1)^4$, $(-1)^5$, $(-1)^6$, $(-1)^7$ and $(-1)^8$. Note the pattern that results.

4–4 REVIEW EXERCISES

In Exercises 1 through 24, perform the indicated operations.

1. $(+4) + (-6)$ **2.** $(-6) + (-2)$

3. $(+2) + (-9) + (-1)$ **4.** $(-8) + (-5) + (-2)$

5. $(-5) - (+8)$ **6.** $(-2) - (-6)$

7. $(-3) - (-9) + (+4)$ **8.** $(+10) - (-4) - (-7)$

9. $(-2)(-6)(+8)$ **10.** $(-1)(+4)(+7)$

11. $(-36) \div (+9)$ **12.** $(-3) \div (-12)$

13. $(+5)(+3)(+2)(-1)$ **14.** $(-10)(+6)(-2)(-3)$

15. $(-2)^2 - (-1)^2$ **16.** $-(-3)^4 + (-8)^2$

17. $\dfrac{(-5)(-6)}{+3}$ **18.** $\dfrac{(+8)(-9)}{(-4)(-3)}$

19. $\dfrac{(-1)(-5)(+45)}{(+9)(+5)(+1)}$ **20.** $\dfrac{(-8)(-16)(+3)}{(-2)(+6)(-4)}$

21. $(-2)(+4) - \dfrac{(-6)}{+2} - (-5)$ **22.** $-(-1)(-5) + \dfrac{(-9)}{(+3)} - \dfrac{(-16)}{(+4)}$

23. $-\dfrac{(-2)(-3)}{(-6)} + (-4)(+2) - \dfrac{(-8)}{(+4)}$

24. $(-5) - (-1)(-5) + \dfrac{(-14)}{(-2)}$

In Exercises 25 through 28, indicate the additions and subtractions on an appropriate number scale.

25. $(+2) + (+4) - (+5) + (-2)$ **26.** $(-4) - (+2) - (-9)$

27. $(-10) - (+2) + (+8) - (-1)$ **28.** $(-6) + (+8) + (-2)$

In Exercises 29 through 32, insert the proper sign, $>$ or $<$ or $=$, between the given numbers.

29. $+4 > -5$ **30.** $|-6| \quad 6$

31. $-8 < -2$ **32.** $-(-4) \quad -|-4|$

In Exercises 33 through 44, solve the given problems.

33. In a chemistry book look up the word "valence." You will see that signed numbers are used to indicate that an atom has extra (in a special sense) electrons or that it lacks electrons. What is the valence of sodium? of chlorine?

34. If 20 min before the hour is denoted by -20, how would you indicate 10 min past the hour?

35. If the loss on a certain sale is proved to be negative, what conclusion can be drawn?

36. If $+50$ mi is used to designate a position 50 mi to the east of a given point, what meaning would be given to -35 mi?

37. Water freezes at 32°F and mercury freezes at 39°F below zero. How many degrees difference are there in the freezing points?

38. Death Valley is 276 ft below sea level and Mt. Whitney is 14,502 ft above sea level. What is the vertical distance from the bottom of Death Valley to the top of Mt. Whitney?

39. A person has $200 in the bank. If he withdraws $20 each week for the next 6 weeks, what will his balance be? (Set up and solve, using a withdrawal as a negative number and future time as positive.)

40. A person has $80 in the bank. If he has withdrawn $20 each week for the past 6 weeks, what was his balance before the first of these withdrawals? (See note after Problem 39.)

41. A rocket was traveling at 10,000 mi/hr. Its speed then increased 1000 mi/hr for each of the following 7 hours. Then its speed decreased 500 mi/hr for each of the next 5 hours. What was its speed after these changes? (Use an increase in velocity as a positive number, and solve, using signed numbers.)

42. The temperature in a certain city is -5°F. For the past 4 hours the temperature decreased 2°F each hour. For the 3 hours before that it rose 3°F each hour. What was the temperature 7 hours earlier? (Use an increase in temperature as positive, and past time as negative. Solve, using signed numbers.)

43. In order to determine the pressure (in lb/in^2) required to compress 400 in^3 of water by 2 in^3 (0.5%), one makes the following calculation:

$$\frac{(-330000)(-2.0)}{400}.$$ Calculate this pressure.

44. Is $|(-4) + (+3)| = |(-4)| + |(+3)|$?
    Is $|(-4) + (-3)| = |(-4)| + |(-3)|$?

Introduction to Algebra 5

5–1 LITERAL NUMBERS AND FORMULAS

Now that we have established the basic operations of arithmetic, we can start the development of algebra. In this chapter we shall show the meaning of algebra and some of the important terminology associated with it. Also we shall introduce the basic operations, although they will be more fully developed in later chapters.

Essentially algebra is a generalization of arithmetic which uses letters to represent numbers. The various other symbols, such as the plus sign and the equals sign, are used to represent the various operations and relations among them. We shall now show why and how letters are used in algebra.

If we wished to find the cost of a piece of sheet metal, we would multiply the area, say in square feet, by the cost of the metal per square foot. If the piece is rectangular, we find the area by multiplying the length by the width. Therefore one can say that the cost equals the length (in feet) times the width (in feet) times the cost of the sheet metal (per square foot).

Rather than writing out such statements as the one just given, we can write

$$C = l \cdot w \cdot c,$$

where it is specified and understood that C is the total cost, l is the length, w is the width, and c is the cost per unit area of the metal.

The above *formula* has been found by writing an algebraic expression for a given statement. In this way we may look upon algebra as a *language*. It is a language in which statements involving numbers can be written simply and in a general way.

If we wish to find the cost of a piece of the sheet metal of particular dimensions, we need only *substitute* the proper numbers into the formula.

Example A   If a given piece of sheet metal is 5 ft long and 4 ft wide, and the cost of a certain type of sheet metal is $3/ft^2, we have

$$l = 5 \text{ ft}, \qquad w = 4 \text{ ft}, \qquad \text{and } c = \$3/\text{ft}^2.$$

Thus $C = l \cdot w \cdot c$ becomes, in this case,

$$C = 5 \cdot 4 \cdot 3 = \$60.$$

It would therefore cost $60 to purchase that particular piece. For another piece of differing dimensions and cost we would still substitute into the same formula, for it is a general representation.

In developing the language of algebra for the operations on *literal symbols* (the letters which represent numbers), we use certain procedures and terms in writing algebraic expressions. These are adopted because they make statements and notation concise and convenient. As various topics are developed, we shall introduce many of these. Since they are used throughout mathematics, it is important that the precise meaning of each be understood as it is introduced.

At this point we shall discuss basic notation and terminology involving numbers being multiplied. If numbers represented by symbols are to be multiplied, the expression is written without the signs of multiplication. The symbols are simply placed adjacent to each other. *One* of these may be an explicitly stated number, in which case it is normally written first, and is called the *numerical coefficient* of the expression.

The expression for the cost of the sheet metal given earlier would be written as   *Example B*

$$C = lwc.$$

If every case of soda in a given shipment contains 12 bottles, then the total number of bottles b is

$$b = 12c,$$

where c is the number of cases. Here 12 is the numerical coefficient of c.

Exponents are used with literal symbols in just the same manner as with numbers. We must be careful to note, however, that the exponent is written only next to the quantity which is being raised to the indicated power.

Instead of writing aa, meaning a times a, we write a^2. We write b^3 rather   *Example C*
than bbb. The product $xxxxx$ is written as x^5.

The expression ab^3 means a times the cube of b. The symbol a is not to be cubed, and the symbol b is to be cubed.

The expression $5x^2y^3$ means 5 times the square of x times the cube of y.

If we wish to group letters, and raise the entire group to a power, we use parentheses: $(axy)^2$ means axy times axy.

In a given product, the numbers being multiplied are called *factors* of the product, just as they were in arithmetic. In general, the numbers multiplying any given factor constitute the *coefficient* of that factor.

Example D
In the expression *lwc*, each of *l*, *w*, and *c* are factors. The coefficient of *c* is *lw* and the coefficient of *lw* is *c*.

In the expression $3ab^2$, the 3, *a*, and b^2 are factors. The coefficient of b^2 is $3a$ and the coefficient of ab^2 is 3.

Wherever mathematics may be used, we may choose symbols to represent the quantities involved. A verbal statement must be translated into an algebraic expression in order that it may be appropriately used in algebra. The following example illustrates several verbal statements and their equivalent algebraic formulas. Note the use of literal symbols and the conciseness of the formulas. Some of these should be familiar to the reader.

Example E

Verbal statement	*Formula*	*Meaning of literal symbols*
1. The area of a rectangle equals the length times the width.	$A = lw$	*A* is the area. *l* is the length. *w* is the width.
2. The volume of a cube equals the cube of the length of one of the edges of the cube.	$V = e^3$	*V* is the volume. *e* is the length of an edge.
3. The pitch of a screw thread times the number of threads per inch equals 1.	$pN = 1$	*p* is the pitch. *N* is the number of threads/in.
4. The distance an object travels equals the average speed times the time traveled.	$d = rt$	*d* is the distance. *r* is the average speed. *t* is the elapsed time.

Verbal statement	*Formula*	*Meaning of literal symbols*
5. The simple interest earned by a principal equals the principal times the rate of interest times the time the money is invested.	$I = Prt$	I is the interest. P is the principal. r is the rate of interest. t is the time.
6. The voltage across a resistor in an electric circuit equals the current in the circuit times the resistance.	$V = IR$	V is the voltage. I is the current. R is the resistance.

These formulas are valid under the conditions specified. As mentioned before, if we wish to determine the result of using any of these formulas for specific values, we substitute these values for the appropriate letters in the formula, and then calculate the result. The following example illustrates this in the case of two of these formulas.

The volume of a cube 3.0 in. on an edge is found by substituting 3.0 for   **Example F** e in the formula $V = e^3$. This gives

$$V = (3.0)^3 = 27 \text{ in}^3.$$

If the cube had been 3.0 cm on an edge, the volume would have been 27 cm^3. We must be careful to attach the proper units to the result.

If the current in a certain electric circuit is 3.0 amperes (amp), the voltage across a 6.0-ohm resistor in the circuit is found by substituting 3.0 for I and 6.0 for R in the formula $V = IR$. This gives

$$V = (3.0)(6.0) = 18 \text{ volts}.$$

Note that the letter V had a different meaning in each of these cases.

In Exercises 1 through 8, identify the factors of the given algebraic expressions.   **EXERCISES**

1. bc **2.** $2ax$ **3.** $9pqr$ **4.** $144x^2$

5. i^2R **6.** $17a^2bc$ **7.** $abcde$ **8.** $3l^2h$

In Exercises 9 through 16, in the given expressions, identify the coefficient of the factor which is listed second.

9. $6x$, x **10.** $2br$, r **11.** $8a^2b$, b

12. me^2Z^4, e^2Z^4 **13.** $4emr$, mr **14.** $qBLD$, D

15. mr^2w^2, r^2 **16.** $36a^2b^3cd$, a^2cd

In Exercises 17 through 24, state the products of the listed factors.

17. a, b **18.** x, y, z **19.** x, x

20. a, a, a, a **21.** $2, w, w$ **22.** $6, a, a, c$

23. a, a, a, b, b **24.** $3, 2, a, a, b, c, c, c$

In Exercises 25 through 30, using the literal symbols listed at the end of each problem, translate the given statements into algebraic formulas.

25. A first number is twice a second number. (x, y)

26. In a given length, the number of inches equals 12 times the number of feet. (i, f)

27. The volume, in gallons, of a rectangular container equals 7.48 times the length times the width times the depth (these dimensions are measured in feet). (V, l, w, d)

28. The heat developed in a resistor in an electric circuit equals the product of the resistance and the square of the current in the circuit. (H, R, i)

29. The distance an object falls due to gravity equals $\frac{1}{2}$ times the acceleration due to gravity times the square of the time of fall. (s, g, t)

30. The rate of emission of energy per unit area of the filament of an electric light bulb equals about 0.00002 times the fourth power of the absolute temperature of the filament. (R, T)

In Exercises 31 through 34, give the required formula.

31. The area A of a square of side s.

32. The number N of square feet in a rectangular area x yd by y yd.

33. The number of bolts N in a shipment if there are n boxes of bolts and each box contains 24 bolts.

34. The cost C of putting an edge strip around a square piece of wood of side s, if the strip cost c cents/ft.

In Exercises 35 through 38, evaluate the required formula for the given values.

35. Find the distance traveled by a rocket if its average speed is 25,000 mi/hr and it travels for 3 days. (See Example E.)

36. Find the simple interest on $500 at an interest rate of 4% for 3 years. (See Example E.)

37. The gasoline tank of a certain truck is 1.0 ft by 2.0 ft by 6.0 ft. Find its capacity in gallons. (See Exercise 27.)

38. Find the heat (in joules) developed in a 12-ohm resistor if the current in the circuit is 2.0 amp. (See Exercise 28.)

In Exercises 39 through 42, evaluate the required formula for the given values by use of a slide rule.

39. In Exercise 31, find A if $s = 31.7$ cm.

40. In Exercise 33, find N if $n = 675$.

41. In Exercise 29, find s if $g = 32.2$ ft/sec^2 and $t = 6.50$ sec.

42. In Exercise 27, find V if $l = 4.56$ m, $w = 2.77$ m, and $d = 2.09$ m.

5–2 BASIC ALGEBRAIC EXPRESSIONS

In the preceding section we introduced the idea of using literal symbols, and we used them in certain simple formulas. However, we mentioned only multiplying literal symbols. Of course, it is often necessary to add, subtract, multiply, divide, and perform other operations on literal symbols and expressions containing them. This section presents an introduction to these operations. Here we shall establish the need for such operations and introduce additional terminology which we shall use in discussions involving algebraic expressions.

The addition or subtraction of quantities gives rise to a great many algebraic expressions. The following example gives some elementary expressions using addition and subtraction.

The perimeter p of a triangle with sides a, b, and c is given by the formula　　*Example A*

$$p = a + b + c.$$

The net profit P from a sale of articles from which the income is I and which originally cost C is

$$P = I - C.$$

The total surface area A of a rectangular box (the total area of all six faces) of dimensions l, w, and h is

$$A = 2lw + 2lh + 2wh.$$

If an algebraic expression consists of several parts connected by plus and minus signs, each part is called a *term* of the expression. If the literal part of one term is the same as the literal part of another term, then the terms are called *like terms* or *similar terms*. The following example illustrates like terms.

Example B The algebraic expression $x + 3xy - 2x$ contains three terms, x, $3xy$, and $-2x$. The terms x and $-2x$ are like terms, since the literal portions are the same. The $3xy$ term is not included since the *factor* y makes the literal portion different.

The expression $3y^2 - 2xy + y^2 + xy$ has four terms, $3y^2$, $-2xy$, y^2, and xy. The terms $3y^2$ and y^2 are like terms, and the terms $-2xy$ and xy are like terms.

Turning our attention to multiplication, we recall that in the preceding section we discussed products such as lwc and $3x^2y$. However, if we want to multiply two algebraic expressions, at least one of which is itself the sum of terms, or the difference of terms, we need to be able to indicate that the sum or difference is to be considered as one of the factors. For this purpose, we use parentheses to group the terms together. The following example illustrates this use of parentheses.

Example C A television dealer charges p dollars for a given set. If he paid c dollars for the set, the profit on the sale of the set is $p - c$ dollars. If he sells n sets, his total profit is
$$P = n(p - c).$$
We do *not* write this as $np - c$, for this arrangement would indicate that n and p are to be multiplied and c is to be subtracted from the product np.

To indicate that the sum of two numbers a and b is to be multiplied by the difference between two other numbers c and d, we write

$$(a + b)(c - d).$$

Both expressions in this example are *one-term* expressions, although some of the *factors* contain two terms.

In algebra, division of one number by another is most commonly designated as a fraction. That is, $a \div b$ would be written as

$$\frac{a}{b},$$

or occasionally as a/b. Here a is the numerator and b the denominator. That division is necessary to the algebraic solution of certain problems is illustrated in the following example.

The frequency f of a radio wave equals its velocity v divided by its wavelength l. This is written as

Example D

$$f = \frac{v}{l}.$$

In a particular type of electric circuitry, the combined resistance C of two resistors r and R is found to be

$$C = \frac{rR}{r + R}.$$

Here we note that the numerator is the product of r and R, and the denominator is the sum of r and R.

Another important type of algebraic expression which we wish to briefly introduce here involves the square root of a number. In Chapter 1 we defined the square root of a number to be one of two equal factors of the number. Algebraically this can be shown as

$$\sqrt{N} = a \quad \text{if} \quad a^2 = N.$$

(At this time we are considering only positive numbers for N and a.) Here again we see the use of a concise algebraic expression.

Numerous important technical applications in algebra involve the use of square roots. The following example illustrates one of them.

One application of square roots is the determination of the time it takes an object to fall. Thus the approximate time (in seconds) that it takes for an object to fall under the influence of gravity equals the square root of the quotient of the distance (in feet) fallen divided by 16. The formula for this is

Example E

$$t = \sqrt{\frac{d}{16}}.$$

As we pointed out in the last section, an algebraic expression can be evaluated for a given set of values by substituting the proper values into the expression. The following example illustrates the evaluation of some of the expressions given in earlier examples.

Example F   In Example A, if $a = 5$ in., $b = 7$ in., and $c = 11$ in., the perimeter

$$p = a + b + c$$

of the triangle becomes

$$p = 5 + 7 + 11 = 23 \text{ in.}$$

In Example C, if $p = \$210$, $c = \$120$, and $n = 6$, the profit on these sales, $P = n(p - c)$ becomes

$$P = 6(210 - 120) = 6(90) = \$540.$$

In Example E, if an object falls 144 ft, the time of fall,

$$t = \sqrt{\frac{d}{16}},$$

becomes

$$t = \sqrt{\frac{144}{16}} = \sqrt{9.0} = 3.0 \text{ sec.}$$

EXERCISES   In Exercises 1 through 4, identify the terms of the given algebraic expressions.

1. $a^2 - 3ab + 7b$ 2. $x^2 + 2xy - \dfrac{y}{x}$

3. $3 - 6ab + 7a - \dfrac{8}{b}$ 4. $3(x + y) - 6a + 3x$

In Exercises 5 through 12, identify the like terms in the given expressions.

5. $2a - x + 3x$ 6. $r + 2rs - 5r$

7. $x - 3y + 2xy + 2x$ 8. $3a - 6b - 5a + 2b + ab$

9. $2m^2 - 2mn + m^2n - mn + \dfrac{m}{n}$ 10. $7x - bx + 3b^2 + 5bx - x$

11. $3x^3 - 5x^3 + 7x^2 - x^3 + \dfrac{1}{x}$ 12. $3(a - b) - 5x - 3y + (a - b)$

In Exercises 13 through 16, indicate the multiplication of the given factors.

13. $6, a, a - x$ 14. $3, x^2, a - x^2$

15. $x^2, a - x, a + x$ 16. $3, a^2, a^2 + x^2, a^2 - x^2$

In Exercises 17 through 20, express the indicated divisions as fractions.

17. $2 \div 5a$ 18. $x^2 \div a$

19. $6 \div (a - b)$ 20. $(3x^2 - 2x + 5) \div (x + 2)$

In Exercises 21 through 30, write the required formula.

21. Express the perimeter p of a rectangle in terms of its length l and width w.

22. The total amount of a bank account receiving simple interest is the sum of the principal and interest. Express the total amount A in terms of the principal p, the rate of interest r, and the time t the account has been in effect.

23. A rectangular box has a square end of side x and a length l. Express the total area A (of the six faces) of the surface in terms of x and l.

24. If a piece x ft long is cut from a board 20 ft long, express the length L of the remaining piece in terms of x.

25. The voltage V across an electric circuit equals the current I times the resistance in the circuit. If the resistance in a certain circuit is the sum of resistances R and r, write the formula for the voltage.

26. The centigrade (or celsius) temperature C equals $\frac{5}{9}$ times the difference of the fahrenheit temperature F and 32 (subtract 32 from degrees F). Find the formula for the centigrade temperature in terms of the fahrenheit temperature.

27. The arithmetic average A of n numbers is the sum of these numbers divided by n. Express a formula for the arithmetic average of the numbers a, b, c, d, and e.

28. The efficiency E of an engine is defined as the difference of the heat input I and heat output P (subtract P from I) divided by the heat input. Express this statement as a formula.

29. The time T for one complete oscillation of a pendulum equals approximately 6.28 times the square root of the quotient of the length l of the pendulum and the acceleration g due to gravity. Find the resulting formula.

30. The length c of the hypotenuse of a right triangle equals the square root of the sum of the squares of the other two sides a and b. This is known as the Pythagorean theorem. Express the formula for the Pythagorean theorem.

In Exercises 31 through 36, evaluate the required formula for the given values. Use a slide rule where applicable.

31. In Exercise 21, find the perimeter if the length is 6.0 in. and the width is 4.0 in.

32. In Exercise 23, find the total area if $x = 3.78$ ft and $l = 6.09$ ft.

33. In Exercise 25, find the voltage if $I = 0.00427$ amp, $R = 82.6$ ohms and $r = 1.08$ ohms.

34. In Exercise 27, find the arithmetic average of the numbers $a = 2$, $b = 5$, $c = 3$, $d = 17$ and $e = 8$.

35. In Exercise 28, find the efficiency if the heat input is 21,500 calories (cal) and the heat output is 7,600 cal.

36. In Exercise 29, find the time T (in sec) if $l = 5.26$ ft and $g = 32.2$ ft/sec^2.

5–3 ALGEBRAIC OPERATIONS

In this section we shall establish certain basic algebraic operations. We shall consider the addition and subtraction of algebraic terms, then demonstrate certain operations involving multiplication and division. We shall find these operations necessary in the development of the sections which follow. However, a more complete and detailed discussion of algebraic operations is needed for the later chapters, so we shall take up this material in Chapter 8.

In the basic operations on algebraic expressions we shall be dealing with various numbers of terms. Specific names have been given to some of these expressions so that one can conveniently refer to them: A *monomial* is an expression with one term. A *binomial* is an expression with two terms. A *trinomial* is an expression with three terms. A *multinomial* is an expression with more than one term. Thus binomials and trinomials are also multinomials.

Example A   The following table gives several illustrations of monomials, binomials, trinomials and multinomials.

	Multinomials		
Monomials	Binomials	Trinomials	Other multinomials
a^2x	$a^2x + y$	$a^2x + y + x$	$a^2x + y + x + 3a$
$3abc$	$3abc + bc$	$3abc + bc + ab$	$3abc + bc - ab + a - 2b$
$\dfrac{a}{b}$	$\dfrac{a}{b} + c$	$\dfrac{a}{b} + c + a^2$	$\dfrac{a}{b} + c + a^2 - 2b + a^3 - c(a + b)$

If a multinomial contains like as well as unlike terms, we may *simplify* it by combining the coefficients of the like terms. The result is expressed as a sum of unlike terms. The following example illustrates the simplification of a multinomial.

In the multinomial
Example B

$$3a^2 - 2ab + a^2 - b + 4ab,$$

the $3a^2$ and a^2 are like terms, and the $-2ab$ and $4ab$ are like terms. Adding $3a^2$ and a^2, we obtain $4a^2$ (the coefficient of a^2 is 1, which is not written). When we subtract $2ab$ from $4ab$, we obtain $2ab$. Thus the given multinomial simplifies to

$$4a^2 + 2ab - b.$$

Since there are no like terms in this result, we cannot simplify the answer further. Thus we have

$$3a^2 - 2ab + a^2 - b + 4ab = 4a^2 + 2ab - b.$$

When we perform addition, we are making use of the basic *axiom* (an accepted but unproved statement) that the order of addition of terms does not matter. This axiom, known as the *commutative law of addition*, was mentioned in Chapter 1 in connection with the addition of numbers. Since algebraic terms represent numbers, it also holds in algebra. In general, it can be stated for numbers a and b as $a + b = b + a$. The following example illustrates the way we actually use this axiom to simplify a multinomial.

The multinomial
Example C

$$x^2 + 5x - 3 + 4x + 5$$

is equivalent to

$$x^2 + 5x + 4x - 3 + 5$$

if we interchange the third and fourth terms according to the commutative law. We then combine like terms, obtaining

$$x^2 + 9x + 2.$$

In general, one does not have to rewrite such expressions in order to add. However, the fact that we can add like terms without concern is due to this axiom. Thus

$$x^2 + 5x - 3 + 4x + 5 = x^2 + 9x + 2.$$

Let us now turn our attention to multiplication, restricting our consideration at this time to the multiplying of certain multinomials by monomials. In order to perform this operation we use the *distributive law*, which was introduced in Chapter 1. In algebraic form, the distributive law for numbers a, b, and c is

$$a(b + c) = ab + ac.$$

Illustrations of the use of the distributive law are shown in the following example.

Example D

$$3(x + y) = 3x + 3y,$$
$$x(3 + 2y) = 3x + 2xy,$$
$$2x(x - y) = 2xx + 2x(-y) = 2x^2 - 2xy,$$
$$3ab(2a - 5bc) = (3ab)(2a) + (3ab)(-5bc)$$
$$= 6aab - 15abbc = 6a^2b - 15ab^2c.$$

Note that if the sign within the parentheses is a minus sign, the multiplication is equivalent to multiplying by a negative number. In fact, if the sign before the expression is negative, we must be careful to observe proper multiplication of signed numbers.

Example E

$$-2(x + a) = (-2)x + (-2)a = -2x - 2a,$$
$$-3a(x - a) = (-3a)x + (-3a)(-a)$$
$$= -3ax + 3aa = -3ax + 3a^2,$$
$$-xy(2x - 3ay) = (-xy)(2x) + (-xy)(-3ay)$$
$$= -2xxy + 3axyy = -2x^2y + 3axy^2.$$

Also, in multiplying these expressions, we have been using the *commutative law of multiplication*, which states that the order of multiplication does not matter. This was introduced in Chapter 1, and can be shown algebraically as $ab = ba$.

Other basic axioms which we have been using in these operations are the *associative laws of addition and multiplication*. These state that the order of grouping terms does not matter. Algebraically these are shown as

$$a + (b + c) = (a + b) + c \qquad \text{and} \qquad a(bc) = (ab)c.$$

In Example C the associative law of addition is used, and in Examples D and E the associative law of multiplication is used.

In the division of algebraic expressions, we shall restrict ourselves at this time to simple cases of division by a monomial. Accepting that any number (not zero) divided by itself is 1, and that division is the reverse of multiplication, we can perform such divisions.

By the statement that division of a number by itself is 1, we mean that $12/12 = 1$, or $59/59 = 1$, or $(-7) \div (-7) = 1$, or in general $a/a = 1$. The statement that division is the reverse process of multiplication can be interpreted to mean that if a product of two factors is divided by one of the factors, the result is the other factor. That is, if

$$a = bc, \qquad \text{then} \qquad \frac{a}{c} = \frac{bc}{c} = b.$$

This leads us to the conclusion that *if a fraction has a factor common to the numerator and the denominator, this factor may be divided out.* This result is consistent with the procedure used to simplify and reduce fractions in Chapter 1.

$$\frac{3xy}{x} = \frac{3y}{1} = 3y.$$

Example F

It is normal practice not to write factors of 1 as coefficients or as denominators. However, if the only factor in the numerator is 1, it must be written.

Other illustrations of division are:

$$\frac{a}{10abc} = \frac{1}{10bc}, \qquad \frac{4x}{6xyz} = \frac{2}{3yz}, \qquad \frac{3x^2y}{x} = \frac{3xxy}{x} = 3xy,$$

$$\frac{6x(a+b)}{3x} = 2(a+b) = 2a + 2b, \qquad \frac{3x(a+b)}{a+b} = 3x.$$

The factors which were divided out in each of these last five illustrations were respectively a, $2x$, x, $3x$, $(a+b)$.

We shall conclude this section with an example which combines the various operations presented in the section.

Given that $a = 5$ and $b = 7$, evaluate

Example G

$$3ab + \frac{a^2(2+b)}{a} - a + \frac{5ab}{b}.$$

It would be possible to substitute immediately in order to evaluate the expression. However, usually it is more convenient to perform the basic algebraic operations first, and then evaluate the simplifed expression. Thus

$$3ab + \frac{a^2(2+b)}{a} - a + \frac{5ab}{b} = 3ab + a(2+b) - a + 5a$$

$$= 3ab + 2a + ab + 4a = 4ab + 6a.$$

Evaluating, we have

$$4ab + 6a = 4(5)(7) + 6(5) = 140 + 30 = 170.$$

EXERCISES   In Exercises 1 through 24, simplify the given expressions; that is, perform any indicated multiplications and divisions and then combine like terms. Express the answers as multinomials with unlike terms.

1. $a - b + 2a$

2. $3xy + 2x - xy$

3. $3a - b^2 + 4a + 5b^2$

4. $2x - y - 5x + x$

5. $5(x + y)$

6. $6(2x - 3y)$

7. $a(x + 2y) + 3ax$

8. $x(y - 2x) - 3x^2$

9. $\dfrac{ax}{a} - y$

10. $a - x^2 - \dfrac{by}{b}$

11. $\dfrac{3ax}{a} - \dfrac{2by}{b}$

12. $\dfrac{7a^2x}{x} - \dfrac{6b^2}{b}$

13. $3(a + 2x) - x(3 - b)$

14. $2a(a - x) + 5x(a + 2)$

15. $7x(x + 2y) - \dfrac{2ax^2}{a}$

16. $3ay(2a - 4y) + \dfrac{a^2y^2}{y}$

17. $\dfrac{axy}{y} + \dfrac{3abc}{b} - \dfrac{2c^2d}{d}$

18. $\dfrac{8abc}{b} - \dfrac{2a(b - c)}{a} + \dfrac{x^2}{x^2}$

19. $\dfrac{6x(a + b)}{2} - 3a(a - x) + xa$

20. $c(x + 2c) + \dfrac{c^3(1 + a)}{c}$

21. $\dfrac{abc^2}{c} + c(ab - c) + b(ac + 1)$

22. $\dfrac{kmx^3}{x} + \dfrac{2km^2x^2}{m} + x^2(3 - km)$

23. $\dfrac{10a^2bc}{5a} + b(3ac + 6) - 5(b + 2)$

24. $\dfrac{24x^2(b + c)}{6x} + \dfrac{2(a + d)}{(a + d)} + \dfrac{50x^3y}{25x^2}$

In Exercises 25 through 30 express the appropriate expression in simplest form.

25. One pole is measured to be $(x - a)$ ft long and another is measured to be $(x + 2a)$ yd long. What is the sum of their lengths in feet?

26. One car goes 30 mi/hr for t hr, and a second car goes 40 mi/hr for $t + 2$ hr. Find the expression for the sum of the distances traveled by the two cars.

27. One rectangular area has dimensions x and y, another $x + 2$ and y, and a third 3 and $y + 5$. What is the expression for the sum of the areas?

28. A carpenter cuts x ft from each of six 20-ft boards, y ft from each of four 15-ft boards, and x ft from a 5y-ft board. Write the expression for the total length of the remaining pieces.

29. A boat travels $9axy$ mi, and its average fuel consumption is $3x$ mi/gal. How many gallons are used?

30. The sum of $3(x + a)$ numbers is $6x(x + a)^2$. What is the arithmetic average of the numbers? (See Exercise 27 of Section 5–2.)

In Exercises 31 through 36, evaluate the required expression for the given values. Perform all algebraic simplifications before evaluating.

31. $a(b + 2) + a(a - 1)$ for $a = 6$ and $b = 3$

32. $6a(x + 2y) + 7x(a + y)$ for $a = 2$, $x = 8$, and $y = -7$

33. $\dfrac{3axy}{ax} - 2(y + 5)$ for $y = 6$

34. $\dfrac{15a^2bc}{3a} + a(bc + a) + \dfrac{2ab^2c}{b}$ for $a = 2$, $b = 3$ and $c = 18$

35. Suppose that $x = 22.0$ in. and $y = 17.0$ in. What is the sum of the areas of the rectangles of Exercise 27?

36. Suppose that $x = 3.18$ ft and $y = 3.98$ ft. How many feet of board did the carpenter of Exercise 28 have remaining?

In Exercises 37 through 38, evaluate the given expressions by (a) substituting directly and (b) substituting in the simplified expression.

37. $\dfrac{3a^2(b + 2)}{a} + 7a(b + 5) - 9ab$ for $a = 18$ and $b = 6$

38. $\dfrac{x^2y(a + y)}{xy} + 7x(y - 2a)$ for $a = 8$, $x = 13$, and $y = 29$

5–4 REVIEW EXERCISES

In Exercises 1 through 24, simplify the given expressions.

1. $x - 3y + 5y + 2x$ 2. $5a^2b + ab - 3ab - a^2b$

3. $2a(3a - x)$ 4. $-5y(6 - 7y)$

5. $3(x + y) - 2y$ 6. $x(2x + 6y) - x^2$

7. $5(a + b) - 3(a + 2b)$

8. $a(a - x) + a(3a + 2x)$

9. $3(a + 2b) + 2b + b(3 - a)$

10. $x(2x - y) + y(2x + 1)$

11. $\dfrac{ax^2}{x} + a(x + 2)$

12. $\dfrac{a^2 c}{c} + \dfrac{a^3 c}{ac} + 2a(a + c)$.

13. $\dfrac{abx}{b} - \dfrac{a^2 x}{a} + a(2 - x)$

14. $\dfrac{by}{b} - y(7 - a)$

15. $ab + 2(a - b) + a(2b - 1)$

16. $x(y + 1) + 6(x - y) - y(x - 2)$

17. $\dfrac{a}{a} + 2(a + 1) + a(3 + x)$

18. $\dfrac{2ax}{a} + \dfrac{x^2}{x} + \dfrac{3b^2 x}{b^2} - 8x$

19. $\dfrac{6x(a + b)}{x} + 3(2a - b) + \dfrac{ab}{b}$

20. $\dfrac{c^2 x^2}{cx} + c(2x - 3) + \dfrac{2cx}{x}$

21. $\dfrac{36a(a + b)}{12a} + \dfrac{2a(x + y)}{x + y} + \dfrac{b^2}{b}$

22. $\dfrac{abc^2}{b} + c(ac - b) + a(3c^2 + b)$

23. $\dfrac{9x(a - y)^2}{3(a - y)} - 2y(x - a) + ax$

24. $m(2a - n) + \dfrac{mn^3}{n^2} - a(2m - a)$

In Exercises 25 through 30, evaluate the required expression for the given values. Perform all algebraic operations before substituting.

25. $3x^2 - 5y + 2x^2 + 8y$ for $x = 4$ and $y = 6$

26. $18xy + 6x^2 + x(2y + x)$ for $x = 5$ and $y = 11$

27. $2(x - 1) + 8x^2 + x(8 - 7x)$ for $x = -4$

28. $15(x + 2a) + 6a(2 + x) + 8ax$ for $a = 7$ and $x = 9$

29. $\dfrac{a^2 bc^3}{a} + c^2(2abc + 5)$ for $a = 6, b = 7$, and $c = 12$

30. $\dfrac{a^2(x - y)^2}{x - y} - x(a^2 + y) + y(a^2 + 5x)$ for $x = 8$ and $y = -6$

In Exercises 31 through 40, determine the appropriate formula in simplest form.

31. The sides of an equilateral triangle are equal. Find the formula for the perimeter p of an equilateral triangle of side s.

32. In the theory of relativity, Einstein found that the equivalent energy E of a mass equaled the product of the mass m and the square of the speed of light c. Write this as a formula.

33. A man invests $100a$ dollars at an interest rate of r and $200a$ dollars at a rate of $(r + \frac{1}{100})$. Find the formula for the total interest I he receives.

34. What is the formula for the sum S of the areas of a square of side x and a rectangle with sides x and y?

35. A person has n nickels, $n + 2$ dimes, and $n + 5$ quarters. Find the formula for the total value V (in cents) of these coins.

−36. When a certain wire is heated from temperature t to temperature T, its length increases by an amount equal to the difference of the temperatures divided by 1000. Write a formula for the increase L in the length.

37. One car travels a mi/hr for t hr. A second car travels $2a$ mi/hr for $t + 1$ hr. A third car travels $3a$ mi/hr for $t + 2$ hr. Find a formula for the total distance d traveled by the three cars.

− 38. One machine produces a articles per hour for t hr. A second machine produces $a + 7$ articles per hour for t hr. A third machine produces a articles per hour for $t − 2$ hr. Find a formula for the total number N of articles produced by the machines.

39. A contractor is charged a dollars per day for each of the first ten days a job is late in being completed. He is charged $2a$ dollars per day for each day after the tenth day. What is the charge C if the job is d days late and $d > 10$?

− 40. The electric current in a circuit equals the voltage divided by the resistance. The voltage in one circuit is expressed as $2x(t − 1)$ and the voltage in a second circuit is $6(8 − 3t)$. What is the sum I of the currents in these circuits, given that the resistances are x and 3, respectively?

In Exercises 41 through 47, evaluate the required expression. Use a slide rule when applicable.

41. In Exercise 31, find p given that $s = 7.0$ in.

−42. In Exercise 33, find the total (annual) interest I, given that $a = 20$ and $r = \frac{4}{100}$.

43. In Exercise 34, find S, given that $x = 45.7$ ft and $y = 76.3$ ft.

− 44. In Exercise 35, find V, given that (a) $n = 8$ and (b) $n = 12$.

45. In Exercise 37, find d, given that (a) $t = 2.00$ hr and $a = 20.0$ mi/hr and (b) $t = 3.25$ hr and $a = 26.3$ mi/hr.

−46. In Exercise 38, find N given that $a = 8$ and $t = 5.00$ hr.

47. In Exercise 39, what is the contractor charged if (a) the job is completed 6 days late, and (b) $d = 16$ days? Let $a = 100$.

6 Simple Equations and Formulas

An *equation* is a mathematical statement that two algebraic expressions are equal. Many algebraic forms are found in equations, but we shall concern ourselves in this chapter with equations that contain one literal symbol, referred to as the *unknown,* for which we are to solve. By *solving* an equation we mean finding a value of the unknown which, when substituted into the equation, makes the two sides of the equation equal.

$3x - 4 = 2x - 1$ is an equation. In this equation it is understood that x is the unknown. If we substitute $x = 3$ into each side of the equation, we obtain $5 = 5$. Thus $x = 3$ is the solution of the equation. This is often stated as "3 *satisfies* the equation." If we try any other value of x, we will find that the two sides of the equation are not equal.

Example A

It is the purpose of this chapter to show methods by which we can solve equations such as the one in Example A. At this time we shall treat only equations with the unknown to the first power, and the methods of solution are based on the basic operations discussed in Chapter 5. Later chapters will show how other types of equations are solved.

A large part of algebra is devoted to the problem of finding solutions to various kinds of equations. Technical and scientific work, in particular, gives rise to equations of all kinds, and their solutions are essential to the attainment or confirmation of scientific information. The following example illustrates some statements about numbers which lead to equations.

In each case we shall let x be the unknown number.

Example B

Statement	Equation
1. A number decreased by 7 equals twelve.	1. $x - 7 = 12$
2. Three added to a number equals nine.	2. $3 + x = 9$
3. A number divided by two equals seven.	3. $\dfrac{x}{2} = 7$
4. Five times a number equals twenty.	4. $5x = 20$
5. Twice a number less three equals one more than the number.	5. $2x - 3 = 1 + x$
6. Sixteen less three times a number equals two added to four times the number.	6. $16 - 3x = 2 + 4x.$

Keeping in mind the meaning of an equation, that the two sides are equal for the appropriate value of x, we see how a solution is obtained. Since the two sides are equal, we can say that:

If the same number is added to each side, the two sides are still equal. Also, if the same number is subtracted from each side, they remain equal to each other. If the two sides are multiplied by the same number, or divided by the same number (provided it is not zero, as we have seen), *they remain equal.*

By performing these operations, we may isolate x on one side of the equation and the other numerical quantities on the other side. The following examples illustrate the method used to solve the equations of Example **B**.

Example C   **1.** Solve $x - 7 = 12$.

We note that when we add 7 to the left side, only x will remain. Thus, by adding 7 to both sides, we obtain

$$x = 19,$$

which is the required solution. We can check the solution (always a good policy) by substituting $x = 19$ in the original equation. This leads to $12 = 12$, which means that the solution is correct.

2. Solve $3 + x = 9$.

When we subtract 3 from each side, only x will remain on the left side. Performing this operation, we have

$$x = 6.$$

Substitution into the original equation gives $9 = 9$. Therefore the solution checks.

Example D   **1.** Solve $\dfrac{x}{2} = 7$.

If we multiply the left side by 2, it becomes $2x/2$, or x. Thus, by multiplying both sides by 2, we obtain the solution

$$x = 14.$$

Substitution into the original equation gives $7 = 7$, which means that the solution checks.

2. Solve $5x = 20$.

If we divide both sides by 5, the left side then becomes x, and the solution is

$$x = 4.$$

Substitution in the equation gives $20 = 20$.

Each of the equations in the above examples was solved by one of the basic operations. However, for most equations we must perform several operations to obtain the solution. The following examples illustrate the solution of such equations (see Example B).

Solve $2x - 3 = 1 + x$.   **Example E**

By combining terms containing x on one side and the other terms on the other side, we may isolate x, and thereby find the solution. The solution proceeds as follows.

$$
\begin{aligned}
2x - 3 &= 1 + x && \text{(original equation),} \\
2x &= x + 4 && \text{(add 3 to each side),} \\
x &= 4 && \text{(subtract } x \text{ from each side).}
\end{aligned}
$$

Since the last equation gives the desired value of x directly, the solution is complete.

Check: Substituting in the original equation, we obtain $5 = 5$.

Solve $16 - 3x = 2 + 4x$.   **Example F**

The solution proceeds as follows.

$$
\begin{aligned}
16 - 3x &= 2 + 4x && \text{(original equation),} \\
14 - 3x &= 4x && \text{(subtract 2 from each side),} \\
14 &= 7x && \text{(add } 3x \text{ to each side),} \\
2 &= x \quad \text{or} \quad x = 2 && \text{(divide each side by 7).}
\end{aligned}
$$

Check: Substituting in the original equation, we obtain $10 = 10$.

The question often arises as to how one knows the order of proceeding in the solution of an equation. No specific order is required; for most equations one can follow any of several variations in procedure. However, the form of the equation suggests the procedure, and with sufficient practice, solving an equation should become essentially automatic.

Example G   Solve $3(2x + 1) = 2x - 9$.

We may proceed as follows:

$$3(2x + 1) = 2x - 9 \qquad \text{(original equation)}$$
$$6x + 3 = 2x - 9 \qquad \text{(perform multiplication)}$$
$$6x = 2x - 12 \qquad \text{(subtract 3 from each side)}$$
$$4x = -12 \qquad \text{(subtract } 2x \text{ from each side)}$$
$$x = -3 \qquad \text{(divide each side by 4)}$$

Check: Substituting in the original equation, we obtain

$$3(2(-3) + 1) = 2(-3) - 9,$$
$$3(-6 + 1) = -6 - 9,$$
$$3(-5) = -15,$$
$$-15 = -15.$$

Instead of the procedure followed above, we show here a variation which, as you will see, leads to the same solution.

$$3(2x + 1) = 2x - 9 \qquad \text{(original equation)}$$
$$6x + 3 = 2x - 9 \qquad \text{(perform multiplication)}$$
$$6x + 12 = 2x \qquad \text{(add 9 to each side)}$$
$$12 = -4x \qquad \text{(subtract } 6x \text{ from each side)}$$
$$-3 = x \quad \text{or} \quad x = -3 \qquad \text{(divide each side by } -4)$$

Now we come to two final points about equations: First, some equations are valid for all values of x. Such equations are referred to as *identities*. The equations which we have been solving, those which are true only for specific values of the unknown, are often called *conditional equations*. Second, some equations are not valid for any values of x, since no values of the unknown will satisfy them. The following example illustrates an identity and an equation which has no solution.

Example H   **1.** $2x + 2 = 2(x + 1)$ is true for all values of x, and is therefore an identity. Proceeding with the solution, we would arrive at $0 = 0$, which is true regardless of the value of x.

2. $x + 1 = x + 2$ is an equation, although in solving it we obtain $1 = 2$, which is not true for any value of x.

In Exercises 1 through 24, solve the given equations for x. Check each equation by substituting the value found in the equation.

1. $x - 2 = 3$ **2.** $x - 4 = 18$ **3.** $x + 4 = 7$

4. $x + 5 = 3$ **5.** $2x = 16$ **6.** $3x = 21$

7. $\dfrac{x}{7} = 5$ **8.** $\dfrac{x}{3} = 8$ **9.** $5 - 2x = 13$

10. $3x - 2 = 16$ **11.** $3 + 6x = 24 - x$ **12.** $5 - x = 8x - 13$

13. $\dfrac{x}{2} = x - 4$ **14.** $\dfrac{x}{3} = 12 - x$ **15.** $6 + 3x = x - 18$

16. $14 + 2x = 5x + 2$ **17.** $2(x - 5) = x - 3$

18. $6(2x + 1) = 3(x + 8)$ **19.** $3(x - 1) + x = 2(x - 1)$

20. $2(1 - 2x) = x - 1$ **21.** $2(2x + 8) = 7(x + 2)$

22. $6x + 1 = 3(x - 2) + 6$ **23.** $x + \dfrac{1}{3} = \dfrac{x}{3} - 3$

24. $x - \frac{1}{2} = 2x - 1$

In Exercises 25 through 34, set up the equation from the given statement and then solve.

25. A number less six equals seven.

26. Five more than a number is eight.

27. Three times a number is thirty-three.

28. A number divided by four is seventeen.

29. Twice a number plus six equals four times the number.

30. Three less than five times a number is eleven less than the number.

31. Half a number equals twice the number minus twelve.

32. Five less four times a number equals one-fifth of the number.

33. Seven less six times a number equals the number less fourteen.

34. Sixteen times a number less four equals seven less six times the number.

35. Distinguish between $x + 1 = x - 5$ and $x + 1 = 5 - x$.

36. Which of the following are identities?
     a) $2(x + 1) + 1 = 3 + 2x$,   b) $3(x + 1) = 1 + 3x$,
     c) $5x = 4(x + 1) - x$.

6–2 SIMPLE FORMULAS AND LITERAL EQUATIONS

In introducing the solution of equations, we considered only equations containing the unknown x and other specific numbers. All the formulas illustrated in Chapter 5 are actually equations, since they express equality of algebraic expressions. Most of these formulas contained more than one literal symbol. In this section we shall show how the methods of solving equations are applied to formulas and other equations containing more than one literal symbol. Consider the following example.

Example A   The formula for the average A of two numbers a and b is

$$A = \frac{a + b}{2}.$$

There may be times when it is advantageous, or even necessary, to have an expression for one of the numbers, say b, rather than for the average. Such an expression can be found by solving the equation for b. Of course, our answer, the resulting formula for b, will be in terms of A and a, rather than some explicit number, as in the preceding section.

The solution proceeds as follows.

$$A = \frac{a + b}{2} \quad \text{(original formula)},$$

$$2A = a + b \quad \text{(multiply each side by 2)},$$

$$2A - a = b \quad \text{(subtract } a \text{ from each side)}.$$

Therefore our solution is $b = 2A - a$.

Actually any equation containing literal symbols other than the unknown, or required symbol, is solved in the same general manner. In each case the result will be in terms of literal symbols and not an explicit number. Also, many of the operations will be in terms of literal symbols. Consider the following examples.

Example B   In the equation $ay + b = 2c$, solve for b.

Since the object is to isolate b, we subtract ay from each side of the equation. This gives

$$b = 2c - ay,$$

which is the required solution.

In the equation $y/a + b = 2c$, solve for y.   Example C

The solution proceeds as follows.

$$\frac{y}{a} + b = 2c \qquad \text{(original equation),}$$

$$\frac{y}{a} = 2c - b \qquad \text{(subtract } b \text{ from each side),}$$

$$\frac{ay}{a} = a(2c - b) \qquad \text{(multiply each side by } a \text{),}$$

$$y = 2ac - ab \qquad \text{(simplify).}$$

The final equation is the required solution for y.

In the equation $2a(f + x) - 3b = 4(b + x)$, solve for f.

The solution proceeds as follows.

$$2a(f + x) - 3b = 4(b + x) \qquad \text{(original equation),}$$

$$2af + 2ax - 3b = 4b + 4x \qquad \text{(remove parentheses),}$$

$$2af + 2ax = 7b + 4x \qquad \text{(add } 3b \text{ to each side),}$$

$$2af = 7b + 4x - 2ax \qquad \text{(subtract } 2ax \text{ from each side),}$$

$$f = \frac{7b + 4x - 2ax}{2a} \qquad \text{(divide each side by } 2a \text{).}$$

In many problems it is necessary to refer to two or more values of a given quantity. For example, we may wish to denote the prices of several different items, representing the price by the letter p. Instead of choosing a different letter for each of the prices, we may use *subscripts* on the letter p for this purpose. Thus p_1 could be the price of the first item, p_2 the price of the second item, etc. Remember that p_1 and p_2 are different literal symbols. Next let us solve a literal equation involving subscripts.

Solve the equation $as_1 + bs_2 = 3a(s_1 + a)$ for s_1.

The solution proceeds as follows.

$$as_1 + bs_2 = 3a(s_1 + a) \qquad \text{(original equation),}$$

$$as_1 + bs_2 = 3as_1 + 3a^2 \qquad \text{(remove parentheses),}$$

$$bs_2 = 2as_1 + 3a^2 \qquad \text{(subtract } as_1 \text{ from each side),}$$

$$bs_2 - 3a^2 = 2as_1 \qquad \text{(subtract } 3a^2 \text{ from each side),}$$

$$\frac{bs_2 - 3a^2}{2a} = s_1 \qquad \text{(divide each side by } 2a \text{).}$$

Thus

$$s_1 = \frac{bs_2 - 3a^2}{2a}$$

is the required solution.

   A statement which leads to a formula, which in turn must be solved for one of its symbols, is demonstrated in the following example.

Example F   If one car goes v_1 mi/hr for 3 hr and another car goes v_2 mi/hr for $3 + t$ hr, the total distance they travel is d. Solve the resulting formula for t.

Since the distance the first car goes is $3v_1$ and the distance the second car goes is $v_2(3 + t)$, we have the total distance d as

$$d = 3v_1 + v_2(3 + t).$$

Solving this formula for t, we have the following.

$$d = 3v_1 + 3v_2 + v_2t \quad \text{(remove parentheses),}$$
$$d - 3v_1 - 3v_2 = v_2t \quad \text{(subtract } 3v_1 \text{ and } 3v_2 \text{ from each side),}$$
$$t = \frac{d - 3v_1 - 3v_2}{v_2} \quad \begin{array}{l}\text{(divide each side by } v_2 \text{, and} \\ \text{then switch sides).}\end{array}$$

The last formula is the desired result.

EXERCISES   Each of the formulas in Exercises 1 through 16 arises in the technical area listed at the right. Solve for the indicated letter.

1. $I = \dfrac{5300\ CE}{d^2}$, for C (atomic physics)

2. $E = IR$, for I (electricity)

3. $v_2 = v_1 + at$, for v_1 (physics: motion)

4. $P = \dfrac{N + 2}{D_0}$, for N (mechanics: gears)

5. $PV = RT$, for T (chemistry: gas law)

6. $E = \dfrac{mv^2}{2}$, for m (physics: energy)

7. $l = \dfrac{yd}{mR}$, for R (optics)

8. $F = \frac{9}{5}C + 32$, for C (temperature conversion)

9. $L = 3.14(r_1 + r_2) + 2d$, for r_1 (mechanics: pulleys)

10. $Q_1 = P(Q_2 - Q_1)$, for Q_2 (refrigeration)

11. $L = L_0(1 + at)$, for a (temperature expansion)

12. $F = A_2 - A_1 + P(V_2 - V_1)$, for V_2 (chemistry: energy)

13. $p - p_a = dg(y_2 - y_1)$, for y_2 (pressure gauges)

14. $Q = \dfrac{kAT(t_2 - t_1)}{d}$, for t_2 (heat conduction)

15. $f = \dfrac{f_s u}{u + v_s}$, for v_s (sound)

16. $P = \dfrac{V_1(V_2 - V_1)}{gJ}$, for J (jet engine power)

In Exercises 17 through 30, solve the given equations for the indicated letter.

17. $a = bc + d$, for d 18. $2x + 2y = 3t$, for x

19. $ax + 3y = f$, for x 20. $3ay + b = 7q$, for y

21. $2a(x + y) = 3y$, for x 22. $3x(a - b) = 2x$, for a

23. $\dfrac{a}{2} = b + 2$, for a 24. $\dfrac{y}{x} = 2 - a$, for y

25. $x_1 = x_2 + a(3 + b)$, for b 26. $R_3 = \dfrac{R_1 + R_2}{2}$, for R_2

27. $7a(y + z) = 3(y + 2)$, for z 28. $3x(x + y) = 2(3 - x)$, for y

29. $3(x + a) + a(x + y) = 4x$, for y

30. $2a(a - x) = 3a(a + b) + 2ax$, for b

In Exercises 31 through 35, set up the required formula and solve for the indicated letter.

31. The average A of three numbers a, b, and c equals their sum divided by 3. Solve for c.

32. A carpenter cuts x ft from each of three 20-ft boards, leaving y ft. Solve for x.

33. A man has x dimes, $x + 2$ quarters, and $x + 3$ half-dollars. These coins have a total value of y cents. Solve for x.

34. The current I in a circuit with a resistor R and a battery with voltage E and internal resistance r equals E divided by the sum of r and R. Solve for R.

35. A machine produces a articles per hour for t hr. A second machine produces $a + 5$ articles per hour for t hr. Together they produce b articles. Solve for a.

6–3 FROM STATEMENT TO EQUATION

Mathematics is of particular use in many technical areas because through its use we can solve many applied problems. Some of these problems are in direct formula form and therefore lend themselves to direct solution. However, we often encounter problems which must first be set up mathematically before direct methods of solution may be used. Such problems are therefore first formulated as verbal problems, and it is necessary to translate them into mathematical terms for solution. Already, in a number of situations, we have put verbal statements into mathematical symbols and then proceeded to the required solution. However, these have been very explicit statements. A number of problems which can be solved quite directly by elementary algebraic methods are not as explicitly stated as those we have met so far.

It is the purpose of this section to indicate how to solve such problems. In so doing we shall concentrate primarily on the interpretation of verbal statements. It is not possible to state specific rules which tell you how to interpret verbal statements for mathematical formulation. Certain conditions are *implied*, and these are the ones we must be careful to properly recognize. A very important step to the solution is a careful reading of the statement to make sure that all terms and phrases used are understood.

Following now are several examples. Through these examples we shall develop a general procedure which should be followed in solving such stated problems. After the first three examples have been presented, this procedure will be stated in outline form. Keep in mind that the primary goal is to obtain an equation from the statement through a proper interpretation of the statement. Once this is accomplished, the solving of the equation is relatively simple and straightforward. (In problems which lead to equations, which in turn must be solved, significant-digit considerations may not be strictly followed.)

Example A   A rectangle whose length is 2 in. more than its width has a perimeter of 36 in. Find the dimensions.

In proceeding with the interpretation of this statement, we must understand the meaning of all terms used. For example, here we must know what is meant by rectangle, perimeter, and dimensions. Once we are sure of the terms, we must recognize what is required. Here we are told to find the dimensions. This should mean to us "find the length and the width of the rectangle." Once this is established, we let x (or any appropriate symbol) represent one of these quantities. Thus we write:

Let x = the width, in inches, of the rectangle.

Next we look to the statement for other pertinent information. The order in which we find it useful may not be the order in which it is presented. For example, here we are told that the rectangle's length is 2 in. more than its width. Since we let x be the width, then

$x + 2$ = the length, in inches, of the rectangle.

We now have a representation of both required quantities.

Now that we have identified the unknown quantities, we must look for information by which we can establish an equation. We look to the portion of the statement which is as yet unused. That is, "A rectangle . . . has a perimeter of 36 in." Recalling that the perimeter of a rectangle equals twice the length plus twice the width, we can now multiply the width x by 2, add this to twice the length, $x + 2$, and then equate this sum to 36, the known value of the perimeter. This leads to the equation

$$2x + 2(x + 2) = 36,$$

which we can now solve as follows:

$$2x + 2x + 4 = 36,$$
$$4x + 4 = 36,$$
$$4x = 32,$$
$$x = 8.$$

Therefore the width is 8 in. and the length is 10 in. Checking this result with the *statement of the problem*, not the derived equation, we note that a rectangle with these dimensions has a perimeter of 36 in., which means that the solution checks.

Our analysis was complete once we established the equation. Probably a great deal of what was just stated seemed quite obvious. However, even more involved problems require a similar technique of reading and interpreting, which is the key to the solution.

Example B   A person has $1.40 in nickels and dimes. How many of each has he if there are 17 coins in all?

The phrase, "how many of each" tells us that the number of nickels and the number of dimes are to be determined. Thus choosing one quantity as x, we write:

$$\text{Let } x = \text{ the number of nickels.}$$

Then the phrase "17 coins in all" means that

$$17 - x = \text{ the number of dimes.}$$

Since the total value of the coins is $1.40, by multiplying the number of nickels, x, by 5 and the number of dimes, $17 - x$, by 10, and equating this sum to 140 (the number of cents), we find the equation, which is

$$5x + 10(17 - x) = 140.$$

Solving this equation, we have

$$5x + 170 - 10x = 140,$$
$$-5x = -30,$$
$$x = 6.$$

Therefore there are 6 nickels and 11 dimes. Checking this, we see that these coins have a total value of $1.40, which means that our solution checks.

Example C   A machinist made 132 machine parts of two different types. He made 12 more Type 1 than of Type 2 parts. How many of each did he make?

From the statement of the problem, we see that we are to determine the number of each type. Therefore we write:

$$\text{Let } x = \text{ number of Type 1 parts}$$

and

$$132 - x = \text{ number of Type 2 parts.}$$

From the statement, "he made 12 more Type 1 than of Type 2 parts," we write

$$x = (132 - x) + 12,$$

which is the required equation. Solving this equation, we have

$$x = 132 - x + 12,$$
$$2x = 144,$$
$$x = 72.$$

Therefore he made 72 Type 1 parts and 60 Type 2 parts. Note that this checks with the statement of the problem.

Having analyzed the statements of the first three examples, and having solved the resulting equations, we shall now state the basic steps that have been followed, and that should be followed in all such problems. This general procedure is as follows:

1. *Read the statement of the problem carefully.*

2. *Clearly identify the unknown quantities, and then assign an appropriate letter to represent one of them, stating this choice clearly.*

3. *Specify each of the other unknown quantities in terms of the one specified in step 2.*

4. *Analyze the statement of the problem in order to establish the necessary equation.*

5. *Solve the equation, clearly stating the solution.*

6. *Check the solution obtained* **with the original statement** *of the problem.*

We shall now present two more examples of stated problems. Note the manner in which the above steps are followed.

A car travels 40 mi/hr for 2 hr along a certain route. Then a second car   **Example D**
starts along the same route, traveling 60 mi/hr. When will the second car overtake the first?

The one word "when" means "at what time" or "for what value of t." We may let t represent the time either car has been traveling; so, choosing one quantity, we write:

Let $t =$ the time, in hours, the first car has traveled.

The fact that the first car has been traveling for 2 hr when the second car starts means that

$t - 2 =$ the time, in hours, the second car has traveled.

The key to setting up the equation is the word "overtake," which implies, although it does not state explicitly, that *the cars will have gone the same distance.* Since, in general, distance equals rate times time, we establish the equation by equating the distance the first car travels, $40t$, to the distance the second car travels, $60(t - 2)$. Therefore the equation is

$$40t = 60(t - 2).$$

Solving this equation, we have

$$40t = 60t - 120,$$
$$-20t = -120,$$
$$t = 6.$$

Therefore the first car travels 6 hr, and the second car 4 hr. Note that a car traveling 40 mi/hr for 6 hr goes 240 mi, as does a car traveling 60 mi/hr for 4 hr. Therefore the solution checks.

Example E   One hundred pounds of a cement–sand mixture is 40% sand. How many pounds of sand must be added so that the resulting mixture will be 60% sand? (Let $n =$ the number of pounds of sand to be added.)

We establish the equation by expressing the number of pounds of sand in the final mixture as a sum of the sand originally present, 40 lb, and that which is added, n lb, and equating this to the amount in the final mixture, which is $0.60(100 + n)$. (The final mixture is 60% sand, and there is a total of $100 + n$ lb.) Thus

$$40 + n = 0.60(100 + n),$$
$$40 + n = 60 + 0.60n,$$
$$0.40n = 20,$$
$$n = 50 \text{ lb}.$$

Checking this with the original statement, we find that the final mixture will be 150 lb, of which 90 lb will be sand. Since

$$90/150 = 0.60,$$

the solution checks.

Solve each of the following problems. Be certain to follow the steps outlined
after Example C.

1. The length of a rectangle is 1 in. less than twice the width. Given that the perimeter is 40 in., find the dimensions,

2. If each side of a certain square were reduced by 2 in., the perimeter would be 24 in. What is the side of the square?

3. The side of one square metal part is 3 mm more than the side of another square part. The perimeter of the larger part is 36 mm. What is the perimeter of the smaller part?

4. A rectangular field is bounded on one side by a river. The other side and the two ends are to be fenced. The side along the river is 50 ft longer than either of the ends, and 950 ft of fencing are used. What are the dimensions of the field?

5. An 8-ft board is cut into two pieces, one of which is 10 in. longer than the other. What are the lengths of the pieces?

6. One engine has 2 hp more than a second engine and 3 hp less than a third engine. All three together have 16 hp. What is the power of each?

7. One electronic data card-sorter operates 2.5 times as fast as another. Together they can sort 1050 cards per minute. What is the sorting rate of each sorter?

8. Oil tank *B* has a capacity of 100 gal more than tank *A*. Tank *C* has a capacity twice that of tank *A*. The three tanks together have a capacity of 3100 gal. What is the capacity of each tank?

9. Twenty-one nickels and quarters have a total value of $2.65. How many of each are there?

10. Eighteen coins—dimes and quarters—have a total value of $4.05. How many dimes are there?

11. A pile of coins, consisting of some dimes and the same number of nickels as quarters, has a total value of $4.10. There are thirty coins in all. How many dimes are there?

12. A man has 500 shares of two kinds of stocks which have a total value of $20,000. One of the stocks is worth $55 per share and the other is worth $30 per share. How many of each has he?

13. Two cars, 598 mi apart, start toward each other. One travels at the rate of 50 mi/hr and the other at 42 mi/hr. When will they meet?

14. Two cars, originally 800 mi apart, start at the same time and travel toward each other. One travels 10 mi/hr faster than the other, and they meet in 8 hr. What is the speed of each?

15. A man travels to and from a city along the same route in 12 hr. His average speed on his trip to the city was 45 mi/hr, and on the return trip it was 55 mi/hr. How long did each part of the trip take?

16. Two trains start from a city traveling in opposite directions. After 4 hr they are 320 mi apart, with one averaging 8 mi/hr more than the other. What is the average speed of each?

17. How many quarts of pure alcohol must be added to 10 qt of a solution which is 50% alcohol in order to make a solution which is 70% alcohol?

18. How many cm^3 of water must be added to 100 cm^3 of a 50% solution of sulfuric acid to make a 10% solution?

19. Eighty grams of solder which is 50% tin is to be melted with solder which is 10% tin. How many grams of the second type of solder must be used if the resulting solder is to be 20% tin?

20. How many pounds of an alloy containing 60% nickel must be melted with an alloy containing 20% nickel to get 100 lb of an alloy containing 50% nickel?

21. The sum of the perimeters of two squares is 52 in. The side of one of the squares is 3 in. longer than that of the other square. What is the side of each square?

22. The sum of three electric currents which come together at a point in the circuit is zero. If the second current is double the first, and if the third is five more than the first, what are the currents (in amps)?

23. A man purchased 140 acres of land for $37,000. If part of the land cost $200 per acre and the remainder cost $300 per acre, how much did he buy at each price?

24. A company has $21,000 to distribute among its employees for bonuses. It is decided to give a basic amount for each ten years of employment. There are 200 employees with 10 years of employment, 60 with 20 years of employment, 20 with 30 years of employment and 10 with 40 years of employment. How much does each person in each category receive?

25. A traveler drove 9 hr to go from city A to city B. In returning along the same route, he drove 7 hr while going 10 mi/hr faster. What was the distance from city A to city B?

26. A plane travels with a speed relative to the air of 560 mi/hr. The trip between two given cities takes one-half hour longer when the plane is flying against a 40 mi/hr wind than when it is flying with it. How far apart are the cities?

27. An automobile has a 12-qt cooling system. It is filled with a 25% alcohol solution. How many quarts must be drained off and replaced by pure alcohol to make the solution 60% alcohol?

One might wonder how the formulas that are used in the various fields of technology are formulated. Part of the answer will be seen in the next chapter, when we start the study of geometry, where certain concepts are *defined*, and a number of formulas for measuring quantities result. Many other formulas are derived through observation and experimental evidence. Since this method is of particular importance in technology, in this section we shall show how a number of formulas are established in this way.

In many applied situations the *ratio* of one quantity to another remains the same. By ratio is meant the quotient of the first quantity divided by the second. This fact is the basis for determining many important formulas. Consider the illustrations in the following example.

1. In a given length, the ratio of the length in inches to the length in feet is 12. This may be written as

$$\frac{i}{f} = 12.$$

Example A

2. Experimentation shows that the ratio of the electric resistance of a given wire to the length of the wire is always the same. This may be written as

$$\frac{R}{l} = k.$$

3. It can be shown that for a given mass of gas, if the pressure remains constant, the ratio of the volume of the gas to the absolute temperature remains constant. This may be written as

$$\frac{V}{T} = k.$$

This leads us to the concept of a *variable*. This is a quantity that may take on different values in a given discussion. On the other hand, a *constant* takes on only one value during a given discussion. We may express the fact that a ratio of two variables remains constant by the equation

$$\frac{y}{x} = k,$$

where x and y are the variables and k is the constant.

Example B

1. In the first illustration of Example A, the number of inches i and the number of feet f are variables, in that each may take on essentially any value so long as their ratio remains 12. This means that when we consider many different distances, and therefore many different values of i and f, the ratio is always 12.

2. In the second illustration of Example A, the resistance R and length l are the variables and k is the constant. The value of k may differ for different wires, but *for a given wire* k takes on a specific value, regardless of the length of the wire.

3. In the third illustration of Example A, the volume V and temperature T are the variables and k is the constant. Again k may differ from one body of gas to another, but for a given body of gas k takes on a specific value, whereas the volume and temperature of that body of gas may change.

By convention, letters near the end of the alphabet, such as x, y, and z, are used to denote variables. Letters near the beginning of the alphabet, such as a, b, and c, are used as constants. The meaning of other letters, such as k in this case, are specified in a given problem.

If we solve the equation $y/x = k$ for y, we have

$$y = kx.$$

This equation is read as "y is *proportional to* x" or "y *varies directly* as x." This type of relationship is known as *direct variation*.

Given a set of values for x and y, we can determine the values of the *constant of proportionality* k. Then we can substitute this value for k to obtain the relationship between x and y. Then we can find y for any other value of, say x, and conversely. Consider the following example.

Example C

If y varies directly as x, and $x = 6$ when $y = 18$, find the value of y when $x = 5$.

First we write $y = kx$

to denote that y varies directly as x. Next we substitute $x = 6$ and $y = 18$ into the equation. This leads to

$$18 = 6k,$$

or $k = 3$. Thus for the present discussion the constant of proportionality is 3, and this may be substituted into $y = kx$, giving

$$y = 3x$$

as the equation between y and x. Now, for any given value of x, we may find the value of y by substitution. For $x = 5$, we have

$$y = 3(5) = 15.$$

In many problems one variable will vary directly as some power other than the first of another variable. The following example illustrates this in the case of an applied problem.

The distance d that an object falls under the influence of gravity is proportional to the square of the time t of fall. If an object falls 64 ft in 2 sec, how far does it fall in 6 sec?

Example D

To express the fact that d varies directly as the square of t, we write

$$d = kt^2.$$

Then, using the fact that $d = 64$ ft when $t = 2$ sec, we have

$$64 = k(2^2)$$

which gives us $k = 16$ ft/sec^2. Thus, in general,

$$d = 16t^2.$$

We now substitute $t = 6$ sec, which gives

$$d = 16(6^2) = 16(36) = 576 \text{ ft.}$$

This means that an object falling under the influence of gravity will fall 576 ft in 6 sec.

Note that the constant of proportionality in Example D has a set of units associated with it. This will be the case unless the quantities related by k have precisely the same units. We can determine the units for k by solving the equation for k, and noting the units on the other side of the equation.

Example E   In Example D, when we solve for k, we can find its units as well as its value, if we include the units in the calculation. In this case we have

$$d = kt^2,$$
$$64 \text{ ft} = k(2 \text{ sec})^2,$$
$$k = \frac{64 \text{ ft}}{4 \text{ sec}^2} = 16 \text{ ft/sec}^2.$$

In the first illustration of Example A, the 12 has units of in/ft. In the second illustration, if R is measured in ohms and l in feet, the units for k are ohms/ft. In the third illustration, if V is measured in liters and T in °K (degrees Kelvin equal degrees centigrade plus 273), the units for k are liters/°K. The units actually used in a given problem will determine the units in which k will be measured in that problem.

Another important type of variation is *inverse variation*, which is expressed by the equation

$$y = \frac{k}{x}.$$

Here y *varies inversely* as x, and k is the constant of proportionality.

Example F   If s varies inversely as t, we write

$$s = \frac{k}{t}.$$

Now if $s = 6$ when $t = 7$, we have

$$6 = \frac{k}{7},$$

or $k = 42$. This means that for this case the equation relating s and t is

$$s = \frac{42}{t}.$$

For any value of t we may now find the corresponding value of s. For example, if $t = 14$,

$$s = \tfrac{42}{14} = 3.$$

Finally, it is possible to relate one variable to more than one other variable by means of *combined variation*. Let us consider the following example.

1. The equation expressing the fact that the force F between two electrically charged particles, with charges q_1 and q_2, varies directly as the product q_1 and q_2 is
Example G

$$F = kq_1q_2.$$

2. The equation expressing the fact that y varies directly as x and inversely as z is

$$y = \frac{kx}{z}.$$

Note that the word "and" appears in the statement, but that the formula contains only products and quotients. The word "and" is used only to note that y varies in more than one way, and does not infer addition.

3. The equation expressing the fact that s varies directly as the square of t and inversely as the cube of v is

$$s = \frac{kt^2}{v^3}.$$

Note again that only a product and quotient appear in the formula.

As before, in each case we can determine k by knowing one set of values of the variables. Then we can evaluate one of the variables for a given set of values of the others.

In Exercises 1 through 12, express the given statements as equations.
EXERCISES

1. y varies directly as t.

2. x varies directly as s.

3. y varies directly as the square of s.

4. s varies directly as the cube of t.

5. t varies inversely as y.

6. y varies inversely as the square of x.

7. y varies directly as the product st.

8. s varies directly as the product xyz.

9. y varies directly as s and inversely as t.

10. y varies directly as s and inversely as the square of t.

11. x varies directly as the product yz and inversely as the square of t.

12. v varies directly as the cube of s and inversely as t.

In Exercises 13 through 18, give the equation relating the variables after evaluating the constant of proportionality for the given set of values.

13. y varies directly as s, and $y = 25$ when $s = 5$.

14. y varies inversely as t, and $y = 2$ when $t = 7$.

15. s is proportional to the cube of t, and $s = 16$ when $t = 2$.

16. v is proportional to the product st, and $v = 18$ when $s = 2$ and $t = 3$.

17. u is inversely proportional to the square of d and $u = 17$ when $d = 4$.

18. t is directly proportional to n and inversely proportional to p, and $t = 21$ when $n = 3$ and $p = 5$.

In Exercises 19 through 24, find the required value by setting up the general equation and then evaluating.

19. Find s when $t = 4$ if s varies directly as t and $s = 20$ when $t = 5$.

20. Find y when $x = 5$ if y varies directly as the square of x and $y = 36$ when $x = 2$.

21. Find q when $p = 5$ if q varies inversely as p and $q = 8$ when $p = 4$.

22. Find v when $t = 7$ if v varies inversely as the square of t and $v = 1$ when $t = 6$.

23. Find y when $x = 4$ and $z = 6$ if y varies directly as the product xz and $y = 9$ when $x = 3$ and $z = 5$.

24. Find s when $p = 75$ and $q = 5$ if s varies directly as p and inversely as the square of q and $s = 100$ when $p = 4$ and $q = 6$.

In Exercises 25 through 34, solve the given applied problems.

25. The velocity v of an object falling under the influence of gravity is proportional to the time t of fall. Find the equation relating v and t if $v = 64$ ft/sec when $t = 2.0$ sec.

26. The voltage V across part of an electric circuit varies directly as the current I. Given that $V = 12$ volts when $I = 3.0$ amp, find the equation relating V and I.

27. The kinetic energy E (energy due to motion) of an object varies directly as the square of its velocity v. Given that $E = 6000$ g-cm^2/sec^2 and $v = 20$ cm/sec, find the equation relating E and v. What are the units of k?

28. The increase in the length of a steel bar due to a temperature increase varies directly as the product of its original length L_0 and the change in temperature $T_2 - T_1$. A steel girder 200 ft long increases in length by 0.12 ft when the temperature changes from 0°C to 50°C. Find the constant of proportionality.

29. The horsepower required to propel a motorboat is proportional to the cube of the speed of the boat. Suppose that 4.00 hp drives a given boat at 8.00 mi/hr. What power is required to drive it at 12.0 mi/hr?

30. The intensity of illumination I of a light source varies inversely as the square of the distance d from the source. Express the equation between I and d if $I = 25$ units when $d = 4.0$ ft.

31. In chemistry, the general gas law states that the pressure P of a gas varies directly as the absolute temperature T and inversely as the volume V. Express this statement as a formula. The constant of proportionality is called R.

32. The time t necessary for an elevator to rise varies directly as the product of the weight w being lifted and the distance s. If 10 sec are required to lift 400 lb through 60 ft, how long will it take the elevator to lift 500 lb through 80 ft?

33. The electric resistance R of a wire varies directly as the length l and inversely as the square of the diameter d of the wire. Express this as an equation and then solve for l.

34. For two meshing gears, the number of teeth N on one gear varies directly as the number of revolutions per minute of the other gear, r_2, and inversely as the number of revolutions per minute it makes, r_1. A given gear makes 120 rev/min and is meshed with another gear that makes 160 rev/min. How many rev/min will it make if the other gear makes 128 rev/min?

6–5 REVIEW EXERCISES

In Exercises 1 through 28, solve the given equations. In equations in which more than one letter is present, solve for the indicated letter.

1. $x - 3 = 5$ **2.** $x + 14 = 23$

3. $3y = 27$ **4.** $26q = 13$

5. $3x + 8 = 2$ **6.** $9 - 2x = 5$

7. $R = R_1 + R_2 + R_3$, for R_3 (from electricity)

8. $F = \dfrac{wa}{g}$, for g (from physics: force)

9. $r = \dfrac{ms_1}{s_2}$, for s_2 (from statistics)

10. $P = I^2R$, for R (from electricity)

11. $3(x + 1) = x + 11$ **12.** $2(y - 1) = 5(y - 10)$

13. $7(1 - s) + 2(s + 2) = 3s + 27$ **14.** $8(t + 2) = 3(2t + 13)$

15. $2(x - 4) - 5(x + 1) = 7 - 5x$
16. $3(5 - 2x) = -7 - 8x$
17. $d_m = (n - 1)A$, for n　　(from optics)
18. $T_2w = q(T_2 - T_1)$, for T_1　　(from chemistry: energy)
19. $W = T(S_1 - S_2) - H_1 + H_2$, for T　　(from refrigeration)
20. $2p + dv^2 = 2d(C - W)$, for C　　(from mechanics: fluid flow)
21. $a(2 + 3x) = 3y + 2ax$, for y
22. $c(ax + c) = b(x + c)$, for a
23. $a(x + b) = b(x + c)$, for c
24. $2(y + a) - 3 = y(2 + a)$, for y
25. $3(2 - x) = a(a + b) - 2x$, for b
26. $r_1(r_1 - r_2) - 3r_3 = r_1r_2 + r_1^2$, for r_3
27. $3a(a + 2x) + a^2 = a(2 + a)$, for x
28. $\dfrac{x(a + 4)}{2} = 3(x + 5)$, for a

In Exercises 29 through 34, set up the required equation and solve for the number.

29. Five more than twice a number equals eleven.
30. Six less than one-third a number equals four.
31. Half a number equals three less than twice the number.
32. Two more than a number equals three times the number.
33. Five less three times a number equals twice the sum of the number and ten.
34. Eight times a number plus three equals nine less than twice the number.

In Exercises 35 through 40, express the given statements as formulas.

35. y varies directly as the square of x.
36. y varies inversely as the cube of q.
37. v varies directly as the product st^2.
38. t is directly proportional to s and inversely proportional to the fourth power of x.
39. f is directly proportional to the square root of t.
40. s is directly proportional to the square root of a and inversely proportional to p.

In Exercises 41 through 52 solve each of the given problems. Be certain to follow the steps outlined after Example C in Section 6–3.

41. If one pair of sides of a square were doubled and the other pair were halved, the perimeter of the resulting rectangle would be 20 in. What is the side of the square?

42. A piece of wire 60 in. long is to be made into the shape of a rectangle, of which the ratio of the length to the width is 3/2. Find the dimensions of the rectangle.

43. The power of one engine is 2 hp more than that of a second engine, which has 6 hp more than a third engine. The three engines have a total of 26 hp. What is the power of each?

44. A student got a score of 68 on his first test and a score of 81 on his second test. What score must he get on the third test to have an average of 80 for the three tests?

45. An engineering firm constructing a bridge requires a certain number of 50-ft steel girders to go the length of the span. If the girders were 46 ft long, 10 more would be necessary. How long is the bridge?

46. Eighty coins—nickels and dimes—have a total value of $5.30. How many of each coin are there?

47. A drawer contains 52 six-cent and ten-cent stamps which have a total face value of $3.96. How many of each are there?

48. Two cars, 540 mi apart, start toward each other, one at 30 mi/hr and the other at 42 mi/hr. When will they meet?

49. Two jets, 9000 mi apart, start toward each other and meet 3 hr later. One is going 300 mi/hr faster than the other. What is the speed of each?

50. The current in a river flows at 2 mi/hr. A motorboat can go 6 mi/hr in still water. It takes 2 hr longer to go upstream than it does to go downstream between the same two points. How far apart are the points?

51. How much water must be added to 15 qt of alcohol to make a solution which is 40% alcohol?

52. A chemist has 40 cm^3 of an 8% solution of sulfuric acid. How many cm^3 of a 20% solution must be added to get a 12% solution?

In Exercises 53 through 58, solve the given problems.

53. y varies directly as x and inversely as z; $y = 6$ when $x = 2$ and $z = 3$. Find the resulting equation relating y, x, and z, and solve for x.

54. s varies directly as the square of t and inversely as v; $s = 18$ when $t = 3$ and $v = 4$. Find the resulting equation relating s, v, and t and solve for v.

55. The weight w on the end of a spring varies directly as the length x that the spring stretches. A weight of 6 lb stretches a spring 2 in. What weight will stretch it 3 in.?

56. The cost C of using an electric appliance varies as the product of the wattage w of the appliance, the time t it is used, and the electric rate r. It costs 12¢ to operate a 400-watt color television set for 6 hr at a rate of 5¢/kw-hr. How much does it cost to operate a 75-watt electric light bulb for 10 hr at 6¢/kw-hr?

57. The period of a pendulum varies directly as the square root of its length. A pendulum 4.00 ft long has a period of 2.22 sec. What is the period of a pendulum 9.00 ft long?

58. The amount of heat H which passes through a wall t ft thick is proportional to the product of the area A of the wall and $T_2 - T_1$, the difference in temperature of the surfaces of the wall, and is inversely proportional to t. Express this as an equation and solve for T_2.

Introduction to Geometry 7

7–1 BASIC GEOMETRIC FIGURES

In Chapter 1 we introduced a few of the basic geometric figures. We employed the triangle, rectangle, and square to demonstrate uses of some of the arithmetic operations. In this chapter we shall formally present geometric terminology and formulas that are related to some of the elementary geometric figures. Other useful geometric concepts will be developed in Chapter 16.

Geometry deals with the properties and measurement of angles, lines, surfaces, and volumes, and the basic figures that are formed. In establishing the properties of the basic figures it is not possible to define every word and prove every statement. Certain words and concepts must be accepted without definition. In general, in geometry the concepts of a *point*, a *line*, and a *plane* are accepted as being known intuitively. This gives us a basic starting point and we can define other terms with the help of these.

Figure 7–1

If two lines meet at point P (see Fig. 7–1a), the amount of rotation necessary to bring one line together with the other is called the *angle* through which the first line was rotated. Notation and terminology associated with angles are illustrated in the following example.

Example A   In Fig. 7–1(b), the angle formed by lines AB and AC is denoted by $\angle BAC$. The *vertex* of the angle is the point A, and the *sides* of the angle are AB and AC.

One complete rotation (see Fig. 7–2a) of a line about a point is defined to be an angle of 360 *degrees*, written as 360°. A *straight angle* contains

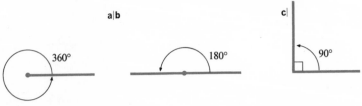

Figure 7–2

180°, (see Fig. 7–2b), and a *right angle* (denoted, as in Fig. 7–2c, by ∟)
contains 90°. If two lines meet so that the angle between them is a right
angle, the lines are said to be *perpendicular*.

A device that can be used to measure angles approximately is a
protractor (see Fig. 7–3).

When it is necessary to measure angles more accurately than is
possible in terms of degrees, decimal parts of a degree are sometimes used.
However, the more common way to express such angles is to divide each
degree into 60 equal parts, called *minutes*, and to divide each minute into
60 equal parts, called *seconds*. It is rather common for surveyors and
astronomers to measure angles to the nearest second.

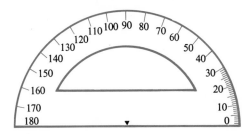

Figure 7–3

Example B

An angle equal to 36 degrees, 42 minutes, and 12 seconds is denoted as
36°42′12″.

An angle of 68°18′ = 68.3°, since $1' = (\frac{1}{60})°$ and $18' = (\frac{18}{60})° = (\frac{3}{10})°$.

A *triangle* is a plane figure having three sides and therefore three
interior angles. In an *equilateral triangle* the three sides are equal, and
the three angles are also equal, each being 60° (see Fig. 7–4a). In an
isosceles triangle two of the sides are equal, as are the two *base angles*
(the angles opposite the equal sides) (see Fig. 7–4b). In a *scalene triangle*,
no two sides are equal, and none of the angles is a right angle (see Fig.

Figure 7–4

7–4c). In a *right triangle* one of the angles is a right angle. The side opposite the right angle is called the *hypotenuse* (see Fig. 7–4d).

Example C   In Fig. 7–5, triangle *ABC*, denoted △*ABC*, is an isosceles right triangle. Both designations are used because it contains two equal sides and a right angle. The equal sides are *AC* and *BC*. The hypotenuse is *AB*. The base angles are ∠*ABC* and ∠*CAB*.

Figure 7–5

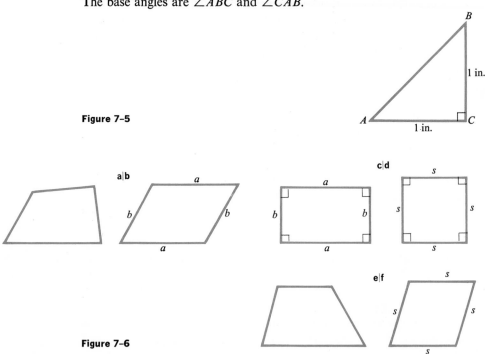

Figure 7–6

A *quadrilateral* is a plane figure having four sides and therefore four interior angles (see Fig. 7–6a). A *parallelogram* is a quadrilateral with opposite sides *parallel* (extensions of the sides will not intersect). Also opposite sides and opposite angles of a parallelogram are equal (see Fig. 7–6b). A *rectangle* is a parallelogram with intersecting sides perpendicular, which means that all four angles are right angles (see Fig. 7–6c). It also means that opposite sides of a rectangle are equal and parallel. A *square* is a rectangle all sides of which are equal (see Fig. 7–6d). A *trapezoid* is a quadrilateral with two of the sides parallel (see Fig. 7–6e).

These parallel sides are called the *bases* of the trapezoid. A *rhombus* is a parallelogram all four sides of which are equal (see Fig. 7–6f).

In Fig. 7–7, parallelogram $ABCD$ is given with $AD = 6$ in., $DC = 10$ in., $\angle DAB = 50°$ and $\angle ADC = 130°$. Since we know that the figure is a parallelogram, we know that opposite sides are equal. This means that $BC = 6$ in. and $AB = 10$ in. Also opposite angles are equal. This means that $\angle DCB = 50°$ and $\angle CBA = 130°$.

Example D

When we are identifying quadrilaterals, more than one designation may be strictly correct. For example, a square can also be considered a rectangle (four right angles) or a rhombus (four equal sides). However, only a square has both properties, and the word "square" should be used to identify the figure. It must also be kept in mind that a square has all the properties of a rectangle and a rhombus.

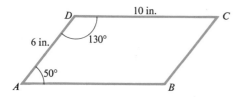

Figure 7–7

The last basic geometric figure we shall discuss in this section is the *circle*. All the points on a circle are the same distance from a fixed point in the plane (see Fig. 7–8). This point O is the *center* of the circle. The distance ON (or OM) from the center to a point on the circle is the *radius* of the circle. The distance MN between two points on the circle and on a line passing through the center of the circle is the *diameter* of the circle. Thus the diameter is twice the radius.

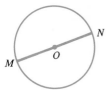

Figure 7–8

Figure 7–9

For the circle in Fig. 7–9, the radius is 6 in. This means that the diameter is 12 in.

Example E

EXERCISES   In Exercises 1 through 4, use a protractor to measure the angles given in Fig. 7–10 to the nearest degree.

Figure 7–10

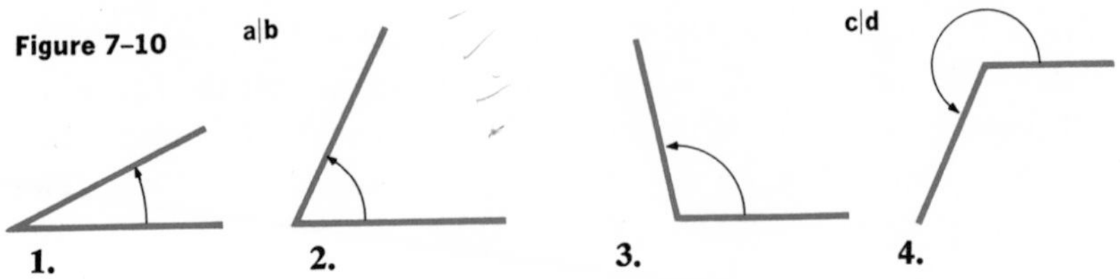

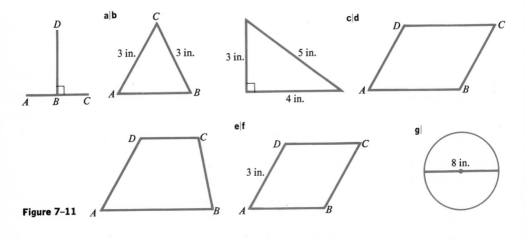

In Exercises 5 through 8, convert the given angles to decimal form.

5. 17°6′   **6.** 56°21′   **7.** 73°54′30″   **8.** 128°12′15″

In Exercises 9 through 16, answer the given questions about the figures in Fig. 7–11.

Figure 7–11

9. In Fig. 7–11(a), identify any right angles.

10. In Fig. 7–11(a), identify any straight angles.

11. In Fig. 7–11(b), if $\angle CAB = 65°$, what is $\angle CBA$?

12. In Fig. 7–11(c), what is the length of the hypotenuse?

13. In the parallelogram in Fig. 7–11(d), if $\angle ABC = 135°$, what is $\angle CDA$?

14. What are the bases of the trapezoid in Fig. 7–11(e)?

15. What is the length of side DC of the rhombus in Fig. 7–11(f)?

16. What is the radius of the circle in Fig. 7–11(g)?

Using a protractor and ruler, construct the figures required in Exercises 17 through 24.

17. An equilateral triangle of side 2 in.

18. An isosceles triangle with equal sides of 3 in. and base angles of 75°.

19. A right triangle with hypotenuse of 4 in. and one of the other sides of 2 in.

20. A parallelogram with sides of 4 in. and 2 in. and one interior angle of 60°.

21. A rectangle with sides of 4 in. and 2 in.

22. A trapezoid with bases of 4 in. and 3 in.

23. A rhombus with sides of 3 in. and an interior angle of 30°.

24. A quadrilateral with interior angles of 35°, 122°, and 95°.

Answer the questions given in Exercises 25 through 30.

25. a) Is a square always a parallelogram?   b) Is a parallelogram always a square?

26. a) Is an equilateral triangle always an isosceles triangle?   b) Is an isosceles triangle always an equilateral triangle?

27. Suppose that two opposite vertices of a rhombus are joined by a straight line. What are the figures into which it is divided?

28. Suppose that the opposite vertices of a figure are joined by a straight line, and the figure is divided into two equilateral triangles. What is the figure?

29. The angle between a ray of light and a line perpendicular to a mirror is 36°. What is the angle between the ray of light and the plane of the mirror?

30. The earth moves in an orbit that is approximately circular. The diameter of the orbit is 186,000,000 mi. How far is the earth from the sun?

7–2 PERIMETER

One of the basic concepts associated with a plane figure is that of its *perimeter*. As we mentioned in Chapter 1, the perimeter of a plane figure is the distance around it. In order to find the perimeter of any figure, one should use the definition directly when possible.

To find the perimeter of the figure in Fig. 7–12, we simply add the lengths of the individual sides, even though the figure may appear to be somewhat complicated. In this case we find that the perimeter p is   Example A

$$p = 10 + 6 + 5 + 3 + 4 + 2 = 30 \text{ in.}$$

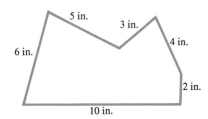

Figure 7-12

From the definition of perimeter we can derive formulas for the perimeters of many plane figures. However, if we remember the definitions of the figures and that of perimeter, we do not have to memorize most of these perimeter formulas, for the meaning of perimeter can be used directly. Consider the formulas in the following example.

Example B   For the given figures, we have the following perimeter formulas.

Figure	Perimeter
1. Triangle with sides a, b, c	$p = a + b + c$
2. Equilateral triangle with side s	$p = 3s$
3. Quadrilateral with sides a, b, c, d	$p = a + b + c + d$
4. Parallelogram, or rectangle, with sides a and b	$p = 2a + 2b$
5. Square of side s	$p = 4s$

The perimeter of a circle, called the *circumference*, cannot be found directly from the definition. Therefore the number π, equal to about 3.14 (to five significant digits, $\pi = 3.1416$), is defined such that the circumference c is

$$c = 2\pi r,$$

where r is the radius of the circle. Another formula for the circumference is

$$c = \pi d,$$

where d is the diameter of the circle.

Example C   The circumference of a circle of radius 3.00 in. is

$$c = 2\pi(3.00) = (6.00)\pi = 18.8 \text{ in.}$$

The circumference of a circle of diameter 8.00 ft is

$$c = \pi(8.00) = 25.1 \text{ ft.}$$

By employing the definition of perimeter, we can find the perimeters of geometric figures that are combinations of basic figures. Consider the following examples.

A Norman window is one whose shape is a rectangle surmounted by a semicircle (half a circle). See Fig. 7–13. Find the perimeter of a Norman window, given that its vertical side h is 3.00 ft and the radius r of the circular part is 1.00 ft.

Example D

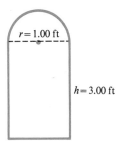

r = 1.00 ft

h = 3.00 ft

Figure 7–13

Let us first find a formula for the perimeter in terms of h and r. The perimeter will be the sum of the lengths of the two vertical sides, the base, and the semicircular portion at the top. Each of the two vertical sides is h; the base is equal to the diameter of the circle at the top, or $2r$; the semicircular portion at the top is $2\pi r/2$, since it is half a circle. Thus

$$p = 2h + 2r + \frac{2\pi r}{2} = 2h + 2r + \pi r.$$

Since, in this case, $h = 3.00$ ft and $r = 1.00$ ft, we have

$$p = 2(3.00) + 2(1.00) + (3.14)(1.00) = 6.00 + 2.00 + 3.14 = 11.14 \text{ ft.}$$

A certain machine part is a square with a quarter circle removed. See Fig. 7–14. The side of the square is 3.00 in. The perimeter of the part is to be coated with a special metal costing 25¢ per in. What is the cost of coating this part?

Example E

$$p = 2s + \frac{2\pi s}{4} = 2s + \frac{\pi s}{2},$$

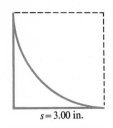

Figure 7-14

$s = 3.00$ in.

where s is the side of the square as well as the radius of the circular part. Letting $s = 3.00$ in., we have

$$p = 2(3.00) + \frac{(3.14)(3.00)}{2}$$

$$= 6.00 + 4.71 = 10.71 \text{ in.}$$

Since the coating costs 25¢ per in., the cost is

$$c = 25p = 25(10.71) = 268¢ = \$2.68.$$

EXERCISES   In Exercises 1 through 16, evaluate the perimeters of the indicated figures for the given values.

1. The figure shown in Fig. 7-15(a).

2. The figure shown in Fig. 7-15(b). All angles are right angles.

3. The figure shown in Fig. 7-15(c). All angles are right angles.

4. The figure shown in Fig. 7-15(d). All angles are right angles.

5. A triangle with sides 6 ft, 8 ft, and 11 ft.

6. A quadrilateral with sides 3 in., 4 in., 6 in., and 9 in.

7. An isosceles triangle whose equal sides are 3 yd long and whose third side is 4 yd long.

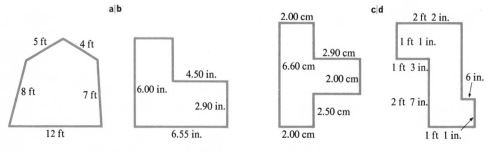

Figure 7-15

8. An equilateral triangle whose sides are 7 ft long.

9. A rectangle 5.14 in. long and 4.09 in. wide.

10. A square of side 8.18 cm.

11. A rhombus of side 15.6 m.

12. A trapezoid whose bases are 17.8 in. and 7.4 in., and whose other sides are each 8.1 in.

13. A circle of radius 10.0 ft.

14. A circle of diameter 7.06 cm.

15. The figure shown in Fig. 7–16(a). A square is surmounted by a parallelogram.

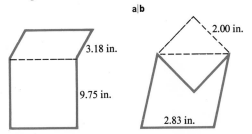

a|b

3.18 in.

9.75 in.

2.00 in.

2.83 in.

Figure 7–16

16. The figure shown in Fig. 7–16(b). Half of a square has been removed from a rhombus.

In Exercises 17 through 24, find a formula for the perimeter of the given figures.

17. An isosceles triangle with equal sides s and a third side a.

18. A rhombus with side s.

19. The semicircular figure shown in Fig. 7–17(a).

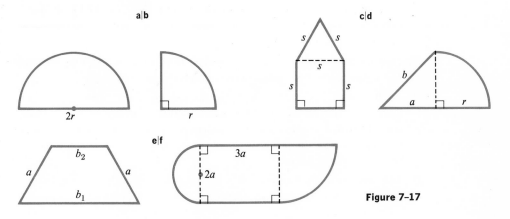

a|b   c|d

2r   r

s s

s

s s

b

a r

e|f

b_2

a a

b_1

3a

2a

Figure 7–17

20. The quarter-circular figure shown in Fig. 7–17(b).

21. The figure shown in Fig. 7–17(c). A square is surmounted by an equilateral triangle.

22. The figure shown in Fig. 7–17(d). A quarter-circle is attached to a triangle.

23. The isosceles trapezoid shown in Fig. 7–17(e).

24. The figure shown in Fig. 7–17(f). A semicircle and a quarter-circle are attached to a rectangle.

In Exercises 25 through 30, solve the required perimeter formulas for the given letters.

25. A triangle with sides a, b, and c, for a.

26. A square with side s, for s.

27. A circle with radius r, for r.

28. An isosceles triangle with equal sides s and third side a, for s.

29. The figure in Fig. 7–17(d), for b.

30. The figure in Fig. 7–17(e), for a.

In Exercises 31 through 38, solve the given problems.

31. The floor of a room is in the shape of a square 12 ft on a side. The room has two doors 3 ft wide. How many feet of floor moulding are required for this room?

32. A certain machine part has the shape of a square with equilateral triangles attached to two sides (see Fig. 7–18a). The side of the square is 2 cm. What is the perimeter of the machine part?

33. Rug binding costs 15¢ per ft. What would be the cost of the binding for a rug 12 ft by 18 ft?

34. A certain flower bed is made up of semicircular areas attached to a square (see Fig. 7–18b). The side of the square is 4.00 ft. What is the perimeter of the flower bed?

35. How much fencing is required to enclose the area shown in Fig. 7–18(c)? The figure consists of two rectangles attached to a quarter-circle.

36. To prevent a basement from being flooded, drainage pipe is to be put around the outside of a building whose outline is shown in Fig. 7–18(d), consisting of 3 rectangles and a semicircle. How much drainage pipe is required (neglect the fact that the pipe is slightly away from the walls) to go around the building?

37. The area within a racetrack is a rectangle with semicircles at each end (see Fig. 7–18e). The radius of the circular parts is 30.0 yd, and the perimeter

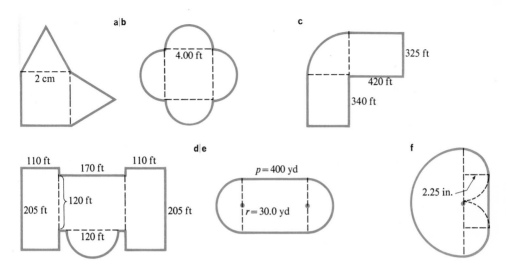

Figure 7–18

of the area within the track is 400 yd. How long is each straight section of the track?

38. To help resist wear, the edge of the cam in Fig. 7–18(f) is to be coated with a special metal strip. The strip costs $0.75 per inch. How much will it cost to put the strip on the cam? The figure consists of a semicircle, two quarter-circles, and a rectangle.

7–3 AREA AND VOLUME

In this section we shall develop additional formulas from geometry. These will involve the concept of *area* (introduced in Chapter 1) of the geometric figures given earlier in this chapter. We shall also discuss the formula for the volume of a basic solid figure.

The concept of area is an intuitive one, but we can easily define the measure of an area. We begin by defining the area of a parallelogram, and find that formulas for the areas of many other geometric figures follow easily. Thus the area of a parallelogram is defined as

$$A = bh,$$

where b is the length of one side, the *base*, and h is the perpendicular distance, called the *height*, between the base and the opposite side. See Fig. 7–19.

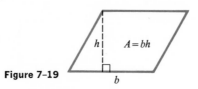

Figure 7–19

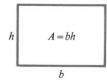

Figure 7–20

Since the sides of a rectangle intersect at right angles, its area is the product of the lengths of a pair of its intersecting sides. See Fig. 7–20.

When we join opposite vertices (points of intersection of two sides) of a parallelogram, we see that two equal triangles are formed. Thus the area of a triangle is

$$A = \frac{bh}{2}.$$

See Fig. 7–21.

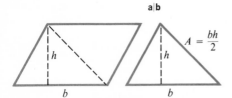

Figure 7–21

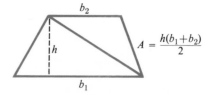

Figure 7–22

When we join opposite vertices of a trapezoid, we see that two triangles are formed. See Fig. 7–22. The area of the lower triangle is $b_1h/2$ and that of the upper triangle is $b_2h/2$. The sum of these areas is equal to

$$A = \frac{h(b_1 + b_2)}{2},$$

which is the required formula for the area of the trapezoid.

Example A The area of a parallelogram of base 6.0 in. and height 4.0 in. is

$$A = (6.0)(4.0) = 24 \text{ in}^2.$$

The area of a triangle of base 12 ft and height 7.0 ft is

$$A = \frac{(12)(7.0)}{2} = 42 \text{ ft}^2.$$

The area of a trapezoid of bases 3.0 yd and 4.0 yd and height 6.0 yd is

$$A = \frac{(6.0)(3.0 + 4.0)}{2} = 21 \text{ yd}^2.$$

A painter charges 20¢ per ft² for painting house exteriors. One side of   Example B
a house is a rectangle surmounted by a triangle. The base of the rectangle
is 30.0 ft, the height of the rectangle is 9.00 ft, and the height of the
triangle is 7.00 ft. What would his charge for this part of the job be?
There are three windows, each 2.0 ft by 3.0 ft in the side of the house
(see Fig. 7–23).

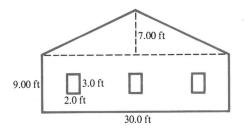

9.00 ft   7.00 ft
                3.0 ft
            2.0 ft
                                                        Figure 7–23
        30.0 ft

The area of the side of the house to be painted is the area of the
rectangle plus that of the triangle minus the area of the windows. Thus

$$A = (30.0)(9.00) + \frac{(30.0)(7.00)}{2} - 3(2.0)(3.0)$$
$$= 270 + 105 - 18 = 357 \text{ ft}^2.$$

The charge, in cents, is

$$c = 20A = 20(357) = 7140¢ \quad \text{or} \quad c = \$71.40.$$

The area of a circle cannot be found directly from the area of a
parallelogram. It is expressed in terms of π, as is the circumference.
The area of a circle is

$$A = \pi r^2.$$

The area of a circle of radius 3.85 ft is   Example C

$$A = \pi(3.85)^2 = (3.14)(14.8) = 46.5 \text{ ft}^2.$$

The area of a semicircle of radius 5.00 in. is

$$A = \frac{\pi(5.00)^2}{2} = \frac{(3.14)(25.0)}{2} = 39.3 \text{ in}^2.$$

The volume of a *rectangular solid*, one that has six rectangular faces
or sides, is

$$V = lwh,$$

where l is its length, w its width, and h its height (see Fig. 7–24). This is one of the basic solid figures, since many common objects have this shape. We mentioned this volume in Chapter 2 when we were discussing units.

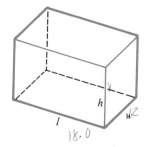

Figure 7–24

Example D   The volume of a room of length 18.0 ft, width 12.0 ft, and height 8.00 ft is

$$V = (18.0)(12.0)(8.00) = 1730 \text{ ft}^3.$$

Also associated with the rectangular solid is its *surface area*. This is the total area of the six faces. In general this area is given by

$$A = 2lw + 2lh + 2wh.$$

Observe Fig. 7–24 and note the pairs of like faces on opposite sides of the solid.

Example E   The surface area of the room of Example D is

$$A = 2(18.0)(12.0) + 2(18.0)(8.00) + 2(12.0)(8.00)$$
$$= 432 + 288 + 192 = 912 \text{ ft}^2.$$

One special type of rectangular solid is the *cube*. The six faces of a cube are squares, and therefore all the edges of a cube are equal. Thus its volume is

$$V = e^3,$$

where e is the length of one of its edges. Also its surface area is

$$A = 6e^2.$$

Example F   The volume of an ice cube 2.1 cm on an edge is

$$V = (2.1)^3 = 9.3 \text{ cm}^3.$$

The surface area of this cube is

$$A = 6(2.1)^2 = 26 \text{ cm}^2.$$

The volumes and surface areas of other figures are discussed in Chapter 16.

In Exercises 1 through 8, evaluate the areas of the given figures for the given values.   **EXERCISES**

1. A parallelogram of base 7.0 in. and height 4.0 in.
2. A rectangle of base 8.2 ft and height 2.5 ft
3. A triangle of base 6.3 yd and height 4.1 yd
4. A triangle of base 14.2 cm and height 6.83 cm
5. A trapezoid of bases 3.0 ft and 9.0 ft and height 4.0 ft
6. A trapezoid of bases 18.5 in. and 26.3 in. and height 10.5 in.
7. A circle of radius 7.00 in.
8. A semicircle of diameter 8.24 ft

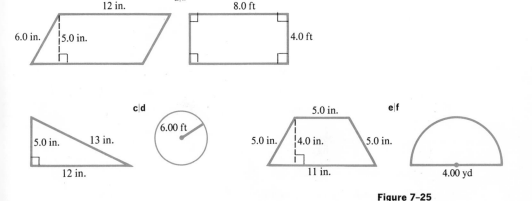

Figure 7–25

In Exercises 9 through 14, evaluate (a) the perimeter and (b) the area of the figures.

9. The figure in Fig. 7–25(a)   10. The figure in Fig. 7–25(b)
11. The figure in Fig. 7–25(c)   12. The figure in Fig. 7–25(d)
13. The figure in Fig. 7–25(e)   14. The figure in Fig. 7–25(f)

In Exercises 15 through 18, evaluate the volume of the given figures for the given values.

15. A rectangular solid of length 9.00 ft, width 6.00 ft, and height 4.00 ft

16. A cube of edge 7.15 ft

17. A rectangular solid with a square base, 6.10 in. on a side, and a height of 4.55 in.

18. A cubical volume 18.0 ft on an edge, from which a rectangular solid 4.00 ft by 3.55 ft by 6.25 ft has been removed.

In Exercises 19 through 24, find a formula for the area of the figures listed.

19. The figure in Fig. 7–26(a)   **20.** The figure in Fig. 7–17(b)

21. The figure in Fig. 7–17(d)   **22.** The figure in Fig. 7–13

23. The figure in Fig. 7–26(b)   **24.** The figure in Fig. 7–26(c)

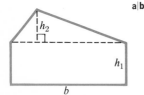
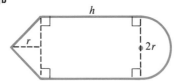
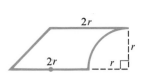

Figure 7–26

In Exercises 25 through 28, solve the required formula for the indicated letter.

25. The volume of a rectangular solid of length l, width w, and height h, for l.

26. The area of a trapezoid with bases b_1 and b_2 and height h, for b_1.

27. The area of the Norman window in Fig. 7–13, for h.

28. The area of the figure in Fig. 7–26(b), for h.

In Exercises 29 through 40, solve the given problems.

29. A man wishes to put screening in a window frame which has a square opening 2 ft 2 in. on a side. He must put a 1-in.-wide strip under the moulding. How many square inches of screening does he need?

30. A gallon of paint will cover 300 ft². How much paint is required to paint the walls of a room 12 ft by 16 ft by 8.0 ft, given that the room has three windows 2.0 ft by 3.0 ft and two doors 3.0 ft by 6.5 ft?

31. Land fill costs $2.00 per yd³. How much will it cost to fill in a rectangular hole 6.0 ft by 9.0 ft by 12 ft?

32. A rectangular brass bar is 6.0 in. long, 2.5 in. wide, and 2.0 in. high. Brass weighs 510 lb/ft^3. What is the weight of the bar?

33. What is the area of the flower bed in Fig. 7–18(b)?

34. How many pipes 1.00 in. in radius are required to carry as much water as a pipe 3.00 in. in radius?

35. Atmospheric pressure is approximately 14.7 lb/in^2 in all directions. What is the total atmospheric pressure on the outside of a box 5.25 in. by 8.50 in. by 12.0 in.?

36. It costs 10¢/yd^2 to grass an area. How much would it cost to grass in the area within the racetrack of Fig. 7–18(e)?

37. A flat steel ring 14.5 in. in diameter has a hole 3.50 in. in diameter in the center. What is the area of one face of the ring?

38. A swimming pool is 3.00 ft deep at one end and slopes uniformly to a depth of 10.5 ft at the other end. The pool is 45.0 ft long. What is the area of a wall that runs the length of the pool?

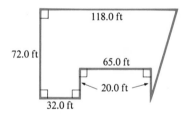

72.0 ft   118.0 ft

65.0 ft

20.0 ft

32.0 ft

Figure 7–27

39. A lawn area has the shape shown in Fig. 7–27. How many gallons of water fall on the lawn in a 0.75 in. rainfall? (1 ft^3 = 7.48 gal)

40. What is the side of a square which has the same area as that of a circle of 5.00 ft radius?

7–4 REVIEW EXERCISES

In Exercises 1 through 8, find the perimeter of each of the given figures.

1. A rectangle of length 18.0 ft and width 8.00 ft

2. The parallelogram of Fig. 7–28(a)

3. An isosceles triangle whose equal sides are 17 ft, whose base is 16 ft, and whose height is 15 ft

4. A right triangle whose hypotenuse is 20 in. and whose other sides are 12 in. and 16 in.

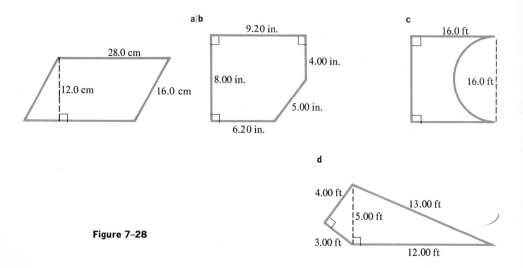

Figure 7–28

5. A circle of radius 12.0 yd

6. The figure shown in Fig. 7–28(b) (a rectangle with a triangular part removed)

7. The figure shown in Fig. 7–28(c) (a square with a semicircle removed)

8. The figure shown in Fig. 7–28(d) (two attached right triangles)

In Exercises 9 through 16, find the area of each of the given figures.

9. The rectangle of Exercise 1   10. The parallelogram of Exercise 2

11. The triangle of Exercise 3   12. The triangle of Exercise 4

13. The circle of Exercise 5   14. The figure of Exercise 6

15. The figure of Exercise 7   16. The figure of Exercise 8

In Exercises 17 through 20, find the indicated volumes and surface areas.

17. Find the volume and surface area of a cube of edge 22.0 cm.

18. Find the volume and surface area of a rectangular solid 28.0 in. long, 15.5 in. wide, and 12.3 in. high.

19. Find the volume of the figure shown in Fig. 7–29.

20. Find the surface area of the figure shown in Fig. 7–29.

In Exercises 21 through 28, set up the required formula.

21. The perimeter of the figure shown in Fig. 7–30(a) (an equilateral triangle within an isosceles triangle)

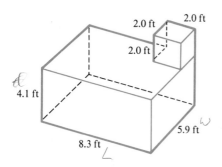

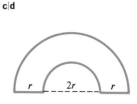

Figure 7-29

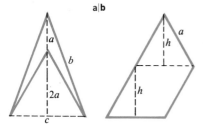

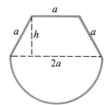

Figure 7-30

22. The perimeter of the figure shown in Fig. 7–30(b) (a trapezoid made up of a rhombus and an equilateral triangle)

23. The perimeter of the figure shown in Fig. 7–30(c) (a trapezoid on a semi-circle)

24. The perimeter of the figure shown in Fig. 7–30(d) [two concentric (same center) semicircles]

25. The area of the figure shown in Fig. 7–30(a)

26. The area of the figure shown in Fig. 7–30(b)

27. The area of the figure shown in Fig. 7–30(c)

28. The area of the figure shown in Fig. 7–30(d)

In Exercises 29 through 45, solve the given problems.

29. How many feet of fencing are required to enclose a rectangular field 60 yd by 90 yd?

30. A sidewalk 3 ft wide goes around a rectangular area 75 ft by 125 ft. What is the perimeter around the inside of the sidewalk? What is the perimeter around the outside of the sidewalk?

31. How long must a label be if it is to fit tightly around a can 4.25 in. in diameter, allowing 0.25 in. for pasting?

32. An automobile traveled 100 mi (assume correct to 3 significant digits). The radius of its tire is 14.0 in. How many revolutions did the tire make?

33. The two nonparallel sides and one of the bases of a trapezoid are equal. Given that the other base is 3 in. longer and the perimeter is 23 in., how long are the sides?

34. One of the equal sides of an isosceles triangle is $\frac{4}{3}$ as long as the base. The perimeter is 33 ft. What is the length of the base?

35. The circumference of a circle exceeds its diameter by 22.3 in. What is the diameter of the circle?

36. The length of a rectangle is twice the side of a square. The width of the rectangle is 2 in. less than the side of the square. What are the dimensions of each figure, given that the areas are the same?

37. Calculate the area of the roof, the top view of which is shown in Fig. 7–31.

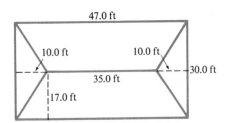

Figure 7–31

38. A rectangular box is to be used to store radioactive materials. The inside dimensions of the box are 12 in., 14 in., and 20 in., and it is to be lined with sheet lead 0.25 in. thick. Lead weighs 690 lb/ft^3. What is the weight of the lead used?

39. Calculate the total force on the bottom of a cylindrical tank (circular bottom), given that the diameter is 8.25 ft and the pressure is 575 lb/ft^2.

40. How many circular air ducts, 8.00 in. in diameter have (at least) the same cross-sectional area as one rectangular duct of dimensions 24.0 in. by 36.0 in.?

41. Gold weighs 0.69 lb/in^3. What is the weight of a cube of gold 3.0 in. on an edge?

42. A certain metal container, rectangular solid in shape, is to be made of sheet metal costing 20¢ per in^2 for the top and bottom and 15¢ per in^2 for the sides. The container is 6.2 in. long, 4.0 in wide, and 3.5 in. high. What is its cost?

43. A roll of paper 7.50 in. in diameter is wound tightly on a cylinder 1.25 in. in diameter. The paper is 0.0075 in. thick. What is the length of the paper on the roll?

44. What is the length of a belt connecting two pulleys 12.0 in. in diameter, given that the pulleys are 40.0 in. apart, center to center?

45. The radius of the earth is 3960 mi. An artificial satellite is traveling around the earth in a circular orbit at an altitude of 180 mi. How far does the satellite travel in going one-fourth of the way around the earth? How far apart are two cities on the equator which are one-fourth of the way around the earth from each other?

8 Basic Algebraic Operations

8–1   ALGEBRAIC ADDITION AND SUBTRACTION

In Section 5–3 we introduced the basic operations in algebra. We have used these operations a great deal in the last two chapters in working with equations and formulas from algebra and geometry. By this time the reader should have a good working knowledge of them. We are now in a position to develop the general use of these operations with algebraic expressions.

We recall from Section 5–3 that in the addition of algebraic expressions, we may *combine* only like terms, whereas for unlike terms we can only *indicate* the sum. Also, we showed the use of parentheses for grouping terms. The following example illustrates algebraic addition.

Add $4xy + 3a - x$ and $2xy - 5a + 2x$.

Example A

This addition may be written as

$$
\begin{aligned}
4xy + 3a - {}& x \\
2xy - 5a + {}& 2x \\
\hline
6xy - 2a + {}& x
\end{aligned}
$$

where the sum is $6xy - 2a + x$. We were able to combine only the like terms. We also note that the sum of $3a$ and $-5a$ is $-2a$. A commoner method of expressing addition in algebra is by means of parentheses. Thus, for the sum given above, we write

$$(4xy + 3a - x) + (2xy - 5a + 2x).$$

It is not possible to proceed with the addition until we write an equivalent expression without parentheses. Only then are we able to combine the like terms. Removing the parentheses from this expression, we have

$$4xy + 3a - x + 2xy - 5a + 2x.$$

Combining like terms, we have $6xy - 2a + x$, which is the above result. Thus we may state that

$$(4xy + 3a - x) + (2xy - 5a + 2x) = 4xy + 3a - x + 2xy - 5a + 2x$$
$$= 6xy - 2a + x.$$

Generalizing on the results of this example, we see that:

When parentheses are preceded by a plus sign, and the parentheses are removed, the sign of each term within the parentheses is retained.

From Section 4–2 we recall that when we subtract a signed number, we may change the sign of the number and proceed as in addition. This principle is important for the subtraction of one algebraic expression from another. The following example illustrates the use of this principle in the subtraction of algebraic expressions.

Example B   Subtract $2xy - 5a + 2x$ from $4xy + 3a - x$.

This subtraction may be written as

$$\begin{array}{r} 4xy + 3a - x \\ 2xy - 5a + 2x \\ \hline 2xy + 8a - 3x \end{array}$$

where the difference is $2xy + 8a - 3x$. In this subtraction, we may consider three separate subtractions. The first is $4xy - 2xy$, which results in $2xy$. The second is $(+3a) - (-5a)$, which, by the principle of subtracting signed numbers, becomes

$$(+3a) + (+5a) = 3a + 5a = 8a.$$

The third subtraction is $(-x) - (+2x)$, which becomes

$$(-x) + (-2x) = -x - 2x = -3x.$$

The combination of these three differences gives the result shown above. Using parentheses to indicate the subtraction, we have

$$(4xy + 3a - x) - (2xy - 5a + 2x),$$

again a more common algebraic type of expression. Since in each individual subtraction shown above, it is necessary to change the sign of the number being subtracted, we remove the second parentheses here and also change the sign of each term within them. This leads to

$$4xy + 3a - x - 2xy + 5a - 2x = 2xy + 8a - 3x,$$

which agrees with the above result.

Generalizing on the results of this example, we see that:

When parentheses are preceded by a minus sign, and the parentheses are removed, the sign of each term within the parentheses is changed.

$$4a - (a - 3x + 2y) + (-4x + y) = 4a - a + 3x - 2y - 4x + y \qquad \text{Example C}$$
$$= 3a - x - y.$$

Brackets [ ] and *braces* { } are also used to group terms, particularly when a group of terms is contained within another group. (Another symbol of grouping, the *bar* or *vinculum* $^-$, is used, especially for radicals and fractions. The expression $\sqrt{a + b}$ means the square root of the *quantity* $a + b$, and

$$\frac{c}{a + b}$$

means c divided by the quantity $a + b$.) In simplifying expressions containing more than one type of grouping symbols, we may remove the symbols one at a time. In general, it is better to remove the innermost symbols first. Consider the illustrations in the following example.

Simplify the expression $5a - [2a - (3a + 6)]$.   Example D

We shall start by removing the parentheses, and then we shall remove the brackets. This leads to

$$5a - [2a - (3a + 6)] = 5a - [2a - 3a - 6]$$
$$= 5a - 2a + 3a + 6$$
$$= 6a + 6.$$

In simplifying the expression $18 - \{[-(a - 1) + 3a] - 4a\}$, we shall remove the parentheses, brackets, and braces in that order:

$$18 - \{[-(a - 1) + 3a] - 4a\} = 18 - \{[-a + 1 + 3a] - 4a\}$$
$$= 18 - \{-a + 1 + 3a - 4a\}$$
$$= 18 + a - 1 - 3a + 4a$$
$$= 17 + 2a.$$

Algebraic addition and subtraction and the associated use of symbols of grouping are often encountered in equations. Consider the following example.

Solve the equation $2 - (3a - 4x) = 2x + (7 - a)$ for x.   Example E

In this case, we shall first remove the parentheses, then collect terms with x on the left and the other terms on the right. This leads to the following solution:

$$2 - (3a - 4x) = 2x + (7 - a),$$
$$2 - 3a + 4x = 2x + 7 - a,$$
$$4x - 2x = 7 - a - 2 + 3a,$$
$$2x = 5 + 2a,$$
$$x = \frac{5 + 2a}{2}.$$

EXERCISES   In Exercises 1 through 4, add the given expressions.

1. $2s - 3xy + 5a$
   $\underline{s + 2xy - 6a}$

2. $3t^2 - 4as - p$
   $\underline{-9t^2 - 5as + 2h}$

3. $5y - 2x + 4a - 8xy$
   $\underline{4y - x - 8a - xy}$

4. $8u - rs + 2y - 3s$
   $\underline{-2u - 3rs - 7y - 6s}$

In Exercises 5 through 8, subtract the lower expression from the upper expression.

5. $5x - 6xy$
   $\underline{2x - 8xy}$

6. $4as - 9py - s$
   $\underline{6as + 2py + 4s}$

7. $4x^2 - 6xy - 4s$
   $\underline{7x^2 - 9xy - 2s}$

8. $-7y + 2w - 5u + 7uy$
   $\underline{6y - 3w - 4u - 8uy}$

In Exercises 9 through 20, remove the symbols of grouping and simplify the given expressions.

9. $4a + (3 - 2a)$

10. $6x + (-5x + 4)$

11. $3 - (4x + 7)$

12. $9y - (4y - 8)$

13. $(4s - 9) + (8 - 2s)$

14. $(5x - 2 + 3y) + (4 - 3x)$

15. $(t - 7 + 3y) - (2 - y + t)$

16. $-(6b^3 - 3as + 4x^2) - (2s - 3b^3 - 6x^2)$

17. $4 + [6x - (3 - 4x)]$

18. $-(5 - x) - [(5x - 7) - (2 - 3x + b)]$

19. $(t - 5x) - \{[(6p^2 - x) - 9] - (6t + p^2 - x)\}$

20. $8 - \{6xy - [7 - (2xy - 5)] - [6 - (xy - 8)]\}$

In Exercises 21 through 28, solve the given equations for x.

21. $5 - 7x = 2 - (5x - 1)$

22. $6 - (3 - x) = (5 + 4x) - (x - 1)$

23. $2x - (4 - x) = 6 + (x - 7)$

24. $-(x - 8) = 2x - (5 - 7x)$

25. $4a + (2x - a) = 5 - (a - x)$

26. $ax - (b - 2c) = c + (3b - 5ax)$

27. $(t - x) - (x + t) = (2x - 1) - (5 - x)$

28. $-(2a - x) - (4x - 5) = -[5x - (3 - x)]$

In Exercises 29 through 36, solve the given problems.

29. Twice a number equals six more than the number subtracted from three. Find the number.

30. Three less than a number subtracted from six equals twice the number plus fifteen. Find the number.

31. When one is analyzing the forces on a certain beam, one encounters the expression

$$3M - 10(3.5M + 141) + 140.$$

Simplify this expression.

32. When we are applying a basic equation in electricity to a particular circuit, the expression

$$1 + 0.5(I_1 - I_2) - 0.3(I_2 - I_3)$$

arises. Simplify this expression.

33. In physics, when studying momentum, one encounters the equation

$$I = -(mv - mv_0).$$

Solve for v.

34. The net loss L that a firm had on the sale of an item can be expressed as

$$L = C - (P_2 - P_1),$$

where C is the overhead cost, P_2 is the selling price, and P_1 is the cost to the firm. Solve for P_2.

35. In electricity, when one is analyzing the voltage in a certain type of circuit, one finds the equation

$$V = i(R + r) - (E - E_1).$$

Solve for E_1.

36. The width of a rectangle is two feet less than the length. Four times the length less the width equals the perimeter. Find the dimensions.

8–2 ALGEBRAIC MULTIPLICATION

In Chapter 5 we introduced the multiplication of algebraic expressions. We also noted that the use of exponents is directly associated with multiplication. We shall now show a general expression for multiplication of powers of a number.

The expression a^n is read as "a to the nth power," where n is the exponent and a is called the *base*. The following example leads us to a conclusion regarding the multiplication of factors with the same base.

Example A $(a^3)(a^4) = (a \cdot a \cdot a)(a \cdot a \cdot a \cdot a) = a^7$. However, $a^{3+4} = a^7$. We see that we can multiply a^3 by a^4 as follows:

$$(a^3)(a^4) = a^{3+4} = a^7.$$

Generalizing on the results of Example A, we see that if we multiply a^m by a^n, a^m has m factors of a, a^n has n factors of a, and therefore

$$(a^m)(a^n) = a^{m+n}. \tag{8-1}$$

Another result which is important to our work with exponents is the result we encounter when we raise a power of a number to a power. Consider the following example.

Example B
$$(a^3)^4 = (a^3)(a^3)(a^3)(a^3)$$
$$= (a \cdot a \cdot a)(a \cdot a \cdot a)(a \cdot a \cdot a)(a \cdot a \cdot a) = a^{12}.$$

However, $a^{3\times4} = a^{12}$. We see that we can raise a^3 to the fourth power by writing

$$(a^3)^4 = a^{3\times4} = a^{12}.$$

Generalizing on the results of Example B, we see that if we raise a^m to the nth power, we have

$$(a^m)^n = a^{mn}. \tag{8-2}$$

The distinction between the meaning of Eqs. (8–1) and (8–2) should be carefully noted and understood. These equations will be of considerable importance in our future work, since they will be of direct use on numerous occasions.

To multiply terms containing more than one base, the exponents of like bases are combined, respectively. The following example demonstrates this.

$$(a^3b^2)(a^2b^4) = a^3b^2a^2b^4 = a^3a^2b^2b^4 = a^{3+2}b^{2+4} = a^5b^6.$$ Example C

We can only indicate the multiplication of a^5 and b^6 as shown. It is not possible to simplify further, just as the addition of algebraic expressions is complete when like terms have been combined.

The power of a product leads to another important result in operating with exponents. The following example will enable us to develop a general expression for this case.

$$(xy)^4 = (xy)(xy)(xy)(xy) = x^4y^4$$ Example D
$$(3c^2d^5)^3 = (3c^2d^5)(3c^2d^5)(3c^2d^5) = 27c^6d^{15}$$

Also $3^3(c^2)^3(d^5)^3 = 27c^6d^{15}$.

We see from Example D that if a product of factors is raised to a power n, the result is the product of each factor raised to the power n. Generalizing this result, we have

$$(ab)^n = a^nb^n.$$ 8-3

When we multiply monomials we use the notation of exponents and the rules for multiplying signed numbers. We first multiply the numerical coefficients and then the literal factors. The product of the new numerical coefficient and the literal factors is the required product.

$$2ab^3(3a^2bc) = (2 \cdot 3)(a \cdot a^2 \cdot b^3 \cdot b \cdot c) = 6a^3b^4c,$$ Example E
$$-2x^2y^3(4ax^2y) = -8ax^4y^4,$$
$$(-p^2q)(3pq^2r)(-2qrs) = 6p^3q^4r^2s.$$

To multiply a monomial and a multinomial, we make use of the distributive law (see Section 5–3), which states that we must multiply each term of the multinomial by the monomial. Also, we must be careful to assign the correct sign to each term of the result in accordance with the rules for multiplication of signed numbers.

$$5ab^2(-3ac - 2b^3x) = 5ab^2(-3ac) + 5ab^2(-2b^3x)$$ Example F
$$= -15a^2b^2c - 10ab^5x,$$
$$2xy^2(3x + y - 4x^2y) = 2xy^2(3x) + 2xy^2(y) + 2xy^2(-4x^2y)$$
$$= 6x^2y^2 + 2xy^3 - 8x^3y^3.$$

To multiply one multinomial by another we multiply each term of one by each term of the other, again using the rules outlined above. This comes about as a result of the distributive law.

Example G

$$(x^2 - 2xy)(ab + a^2) = x^2(ab) + x^2(a^2) + (-2xy)(ab)$$
$$+ (-2xy)(a^2)$$
$$= abx^2 + a^2x^2 - 2abxy - 2a^2xy.$$

$$(2a + 4)(2a^2 + 3a - b) = (2a)(2a^2) + (2a)(3a) + (2a)(-b) + (4)(2a^2)$$
$$+ (4)(3a) + (4)(-b)$$
$$= 4a^3 + 6a^2 - 2ab + 8a^2 + 12a - 4b$$
$$= 4a^3 + 14a^2 - 2ab + 12a - 4b.$$

$$(a + 2b)^2 = (a + 2b)(a + 2b)$$
$$= a(a) + a(2b) + 2b(a) + 2b(2b)$$
$$= a^2 + 2ab + 2ab + 4b^2$$
$$= a^2 + 4ab + 4b^2.$$

EXERCISES   In Exercises 1 through 38, perform the indicated multiplications.

1. x^3x^7 **2.** n^2n^6 **3.** y^5y^2y **4.** $p^2p^3p^5$

5. $(x^3)^7$ **6.** $(n^2)^6$ **7.** $(y^2y)^5$ **8.** $(p^2p^3)^5$

9. $(3ax)(-2a^2xy)$ **10.** $(-6yrs^2)(-3xy^2r^3)$

11. $(-5act^2)(9at^5)$ **12.** $(8dr^3s^2)(-4drs^4)$

13. $(-4rs)(-3st^3)(-7rt)$ **14.** $(-2axy^3)(7ay^4)(-ax^4y)$

15. $(-2st^3x)^3$ **16.** $(-3axt^7)^4$

17. $2a(a + 3x)$ **18.** $3x(2x - 5)$

19. $(-2st)(sx - t^2y)$ **20.** $(-8y)(8y + t^2)$

21. $(-3xy)(x^2y - 3axy^6)$ **22.** $(-5y^6)(-uy^7 - hpy)$

23. $(x + 1)(2x - 1)$ **24.** $(3a - 2)(5a + 4)$

25. $(a - x)(a - 2x)$ **26.** $(x + 2y)(x - y)$

27. $(2x - 5t)(x + 9)$ **28.** $(4x - 9uy)(2 + 3uy)$

29. $(2a - 9py)(2a + 9py)$ **30.** $(s - 3xu^2)(-xu^2 - 8s)$

31. $(a - x)(a + 2xy - 3x)$ **32.** $(2 - x)(5 + x - x^2)$

33. $(x - 2)(x + 3)(x - 4)$ **34.** $(2x - 3)(x + 1)(3x - 4)$

35. $(x + 2y)^2$ **36.** $(2a - 3b)^2$ **37.** $(x + 1)^3$ **38.** $(2a - x)^3$

In Exercises 39 through 46, solve the given problems.

39. The sum of two numbers x and y is multiplied by the difference between the numbers. Find an expression for this product.

40. In determining the focal length of a lens, one encounters the expression

$$(u - 1)(r_2 - r_1).$$

Multiply out this expression.

41. Under specified conditions, the velocity v of an object in terms of the time t is given by the formula

$$v = 6(t - 2)(t - 4).$$

Multiply out the right side of this equation.

42. In finding the force on a parabolic plate due to liquid pressure, the expression

$$w(1 - y)(4 - y^2)$$

arises. Multiply out this expression.

43. By multiplication, show that $(2x - y)(2x + y) = 4x^2 - y^2$. Then show by substitution that the same value is obtained for each side for the values $x = 3$ and $y = -4$.

44. By multiplication, show that $(a - b)(a^2 + ab + b^2) = a^3 - b^3$. Then show by substitution that the same value is obtained for each side for the values $a = -2$ and $b = -3$.

45. When one is dealing with the electron, one finds the expression $m(v_2 - v_1)(v_2 + v_1)$. Multiply out this expression.

46. The length of a rectangle is 6 in. more than the side of a square. The width of the rectangle is 4 in. less than the side of the square. What are the dimensions of each figure if the areas are the same?

8–3 ALGEBRAIC DIVISION

In division, as in multiplication, the use of exponents plays an important role. The following example leads us to the basic formula for the use of exponents in division.

Divide a^5 by a^2.   **Example A**

We may express this division as a fraction, as stated in Section 5–2. This gives us

$$\frac{a^5}{a^2}.$$

Now we use the principle stated in that section, namely, that if a fraction has a factor common to the numerator and denominator, this factor may be divided out. We note the common factor of a^2 in the numerator and the denominator, or

$$\frac{a^5}{a^2} = \frac{a^2 a^3}{a^2}.$$

Dividing out this factor of a^2, we have

$$\frac{a^5}{a^2} = a^3.$$

However, $a^{5-2} = a^3$. We see that we can divide a^5 by a^2 as follows:

$$\frac{a^5}{a^2} = a^{5-2} = a^3.$$

Let us now divide a^2 by a^5. This is expressed as a fraction, and then the common factor of a^2 is divided out. This leads to

$$\frac{a^2}{a^5} = \frac{a^2}{a^2 a^3} = \frac{1}{a^3}.$$

Here we see that

$$\frac{a^2}{a^5} = \frac{1}{a^{5-2}} = \frac{1}{a^3}.$$

Generalizing on the results of Example A, we see that if we divide a^m by a^n, we have

$$\frac{a^m}{a^n} = a^{m-n} \qquad \text{if } m > n, \qquad\qquad \textbf{8–4a}$$

and

$$\frac{a^m}{a^n} = \frac{1}{a^{n-m}} \qquad \text{if } n > m. \qquad\qquad \textbf{8–4b}$$

Example B
$$\frac{x^4}{x^3} = x, \qquad \frac{x^3}{x^4} = \frac{1}{x}; \qquad \frac{3c^6}{c^2} = 3c^4, \qquad \frac{c^2}{3c^6} = \frac{1}{3c^4}.$$

To divide one monomial by another, we use the basic principle introduced in Section 5–3 and divide out any factor common to numerator and denominator. As in multiplication, we can combine only those exponents which have the same base.

Example C

$$-16a^2b \div 4a = \frac{-16a^2b}{4a} = -4ab,$$

$$36a^2b^3 \div (-12ab) = \frac{36a^2b^3}{-12ab} = -3ab^2,$$

$$-18x^3y \div (-12xy^4) = \frac{-18x^3y}{-12xy^4} = \frac{3x^2}{2y^3},$$

$$-8ab^2x^5 \div (-14a^2b^2x) = \frac{-8ab^2x^5}{-14a^2b^2x} = \frac{4x^4}{7a}.$$

Note that in the first two illustrations, the exponents in the numerator are larger than those in the denominator. In the third illustration the exponent of x is larger in the numerator, and thus we use Eq. (8–4a) for x; the exponent of y is larger in the denominator, and hence we use Eq. (8–4b) for y. In the fourth illustration, b^2 appears as part of the common factor, and therefore b does not appear in the final result.

We may draw from the arithmetic of fractions to show how a multinomial is to be divided by a monomial. When adding fractions, say $\frac{2}{7}$ and $\frac{3}{7}$, we have

$$\frac{2}{7} + \frac{3}{7} = \frac{2+3}{7}.$$

Considering the right-hand side of this equation, we have the sum of two numbers divided by one number, and this equals, reading right to left, the sum obtained by dividing each of the numbers of the numerator separately by the number of the denominator. Since algebraic expressions represent numbers, we have the following method of dividing a multinomial by a monomial. Divide each term of the multinomial by the monomial and add the resulting terms algebraically to obtain the quotient.

Example D

$$(28a^3b^3 + 35a^2b^2) \div (-7ab^2) = \frac{28a^3b^3 + 35a^2b^2}{-7ab^2}$$

$$= \frac{28a^3b^3}{-7ab^2} + \frac{35a^2b^2}{-7ab^2} = -4a^2b - 5a.$$

$$(axy^2 + ax^3 - 4a^3x^2) \div (-ax) = \frac{axy^2 + ax^3 - 4a^3x^2}{-ax}$$

$$= \frac{axy^2}{-ax} + \frac{ax^3}{-ax} + \frac{-4a^3x^2}{-ax}$$

$$= -y^2 - x^2 + 4a^2x.$$

In dividing algebraic expressions of more than one term by another such expression, we shall deal exclusively with *polynomials*. A polynomial in x is an expression wherein every term contains x only in the numerator, and all powers of x are positive integers. The expression $x^2 + 1/x$ is not a polynomial due to the x in the denominator of the second term, whereas $x^2 + x$ is a polynomial. These restrictions do not apply to the term multinomial.

To divide one polynomial by another we arrange both the dividend and the divisor in descending powers of the same literal factor. Then we divide the first term of the dividend by the first term of the divisor. The result of this division is the first term of the quotient. We then multiply the entire divisor by the first term of the quotient and subtract this product from the dividend. Now we repeat these operations by dividing the first term of the divisor into the first term of the difference just obtained. The result of this division is the second term of the quotient. We multiply the entire divisor by this second term and subtract the result from the first difference. We repeat this process until the difference is either zero or a quantity whose *degree* is less than that of the divisor (that is, the exponent of the literal factor must be less than the highest exponent of the literal factor in the divisor).

Example E The expression $5x^2 + 7y^2 - 8xy + 2$ in descending powers of x is $5x^2 - 8xy + 7y^2 + 2$. The same expression in descending powers of y is $7y^2 - 8xy + 5x^2 + 2$.

Example F Divide $3x^2 - 4x + x^3 - 12$ by $x + 2$.

The dividend is arranged in descending powers of x, and the division proceeds as shown.

$$
\begin{array}{r}
x^2 + x - 6 \text{ (quotient)} \\
(\text{divisor}) \quad x + 2\overline{)x^3 + 3x^2 - 4x - 12} \text{ (dividend)} \\
\underline{x^3 + 2x^2} \text{(subtract)} \\
x^2 - 4x - 12 \\
\underline{x^2 + 2x} \text{(subtract)} \\
- 6x - 12 \\
\underline{- 6x - 12} \text{(subtract)} \\
0 \text{ (remainder)}
\end{array}
$$

That is, the division is exact.

The division may be checked by multiplication. In this case

$$(x + 2)(x^2 + x - 6) = x^3 + x^2 - 6x + 2x^2 + 2x - 12$$
$$= x^3 + 3x^2 - 4x - 12.$$

Divide $4y^3 + 6y^2 + 1$ by $2y - 1$.   **Example G**

Since no first-power term in y appears in the dividend, we shall insert one with a zero coefficient to simplify the division.

$$
\begin{array}{r}
2y^2 + 4y + 2 \\
2y - 1 \overline{)4y^3 + 6y^2 + 0(y) + 1} \\
4y^3 - 2y^2 \qquad\qquad \text{(subtract)} \\
\hline
8y^2 + 0(y) + 1 \\
8y^2 - 4y \qquad\qquad \text{(subtract)} \\
\hline
4y + 1 \\
4y - 2 \qquad\qquad \text{(subtract)} \\
\hline
+ 3 \quad \text{(remainder)}
\end{array}
$$

The quotient in this case is

$$2y^2 + 4y + 2 + \frac{3}{2y - 1}.$$

Note how the remainder is expressed as part of the quotient.

The solution of equations uses a combination of the basic operations. The following example illustrates such a solution.

Solve the equation $2(3 - x) = 8 - 4(x - a)$ for x.   **Example H**

The solution proceeds as follows:

$$2(3 - x) = 8 - 4(x - a),$$
$$6 - 2x = 8 - 4x + 4a,$$
$$4x - 2x = 8 + 4a - 6,$$
$$2x = 2 + 4a,$$
$$x = \frac{2 + 4a}{2} = \frac{2}{2} + \frac{4a}{2} = 1 + 2a.$$

In Exercises 1 through 32, perform the indicated divisions.   **EXERCISES**

1. $x^7 \div x^4$ **2.** $x^2 \div x^8$ **3.** $\dfrac{a^5}{a^4}$ **4.** $\dfrac{y^9}{y^3}$

5. $p^3 \div p^{13}$ **6.** $p \div p^7$ **7.** $\dfrac{8n^4}{2n}$ **8.** $\dfrac{9m}{6m^8}$

9. $(a^2x) \div (-a)$ **10.** $(-x^4y^3) \div (x^2y)$

11. $(-4ca^2t^4) \div (-2c^3a)$ **12.** $(9c^3yp^4) \div (-12cy^6p)$

13. $(-5x^2yr) \div (20xyr^3)$ **14.** $(-rst^4) \div (-rs^4t^2)$

15. $\dfrac{-7yt^3u}{-6yt}$ **16.** $\dfrac{9abc^4ds}{15bc^4d^4}$

17. $(a^3x^4 - a^2x^3) \div (-ax^2)$ **18.** $(-2xy^6 - 4x^2y^5) \div (2xy^3)$

19. $(3xy^4 - 6x^2y^5) \div (3xy^2)$ **20.** $(-14p^3q^5 + 49p^4q^2) \div (-7p^2q^2)$

21. $\dfrac{a^2b^2c^3 - a^3b^4c^6 - 2a^3bc^2}{a^2bc^2}$ **22.** $\dfrac{8rs^2t^5 - 18r^3st^4 - 16rst^3}{-2rst^2}$

23. $\dfrac{a^2b^3 - 2a^3b^4 - ab - ab^2}{-ab}$ **24.** $\dfrac{5m^2n^2y - 30mn^2 + 35m^2n^8}{-5mn^2}$

25. $(x^2 - 2x - 3) \div (x + 1)$ **26.** $(x^2 + 3x - 10) \div (x - 2)$

27. $(2x^2 - 5x - 3) \div (x - 3)$ **28.** $(3x^2 + 4x - 5) \div (x + 2)$

29. $(5x - 5x^2 + 2x^3 - 6) \div (x - 2)$

30. $(1 - x^2 + 6x^3) \div (1 + 2x)$

31. $\dfrac{6x^4 - 5x^3 + 7x^2 + x - 3}{3x - 1}$ **32.** $\dfrac{xy + 2x^2 - 6y^2}{x + 2y}$

In Exercises 33 through 38, solve the given equations for x.

33. $2(2 - x) = 7 + x$ **34.** $2(x - 3) = -4(6 - x)$

35. $(x - 2)(3 - 2x) = -2x(x + 5)$ **36.** $6(2 - x) = 9 - 3(x - 2a)$

37. $(a - 1)x = a^2 + 4a - 5$ **38.** $(3b - 1)x = 3b^3 - b^2 + 3b - 1$

In Exercises 39 through 42, solve the given problems.

39. When dealing with the resistance of a certain type of electric circuit, one encounters the expression

$$\frac{R_2R_3 + R_1R_3 + R_1R_2}{R_1R_2R_3}.$$

Perform the indicated division.

40. The revenue R obtained from selling x units at a price of p is related to x and p by the formula $R = px$. Under certain conditions, $R = p_0x - kx^2$, where p_0 is the highest price and k is a constant depending on the economic conditions. Substitute this expression for R and solve the resulting equation for p.

41. One number is three larger than another number. If two more than the product of these numbers is divided by one less than the larger number, the result is seven. Find the numbers.

42. Under certain conditions, when dealing with the electronics of coils, one may encounter the expression

$$\frac{60r^2}{6r + 1.2}.$$

Perform the indicated division.

8–4 REVIEW EXERCISES

In Exercises 1 through 36, simplify the given expressions by performing the indicated operations.

1. $a - (x - 2a)$ **2.** $-(y + 2s) - (5s - y)$

3. $-2 + (n + 4) - (6 - n)$ **4.** $t - (5 + 2t) + (t - 7)$

5. $2(x - 5y) - (3y - 7x)$ **6.** $-8x + 4r - 2(-r - 3x)$

7. $5 - [x - (3 - 4x)]$ **8.** $3y + [(5y - 2) - 6y]$

9. $2x + [(2x - a) - (a - x)]$

10. $-(3xy - y) - 2[2x - y - (y - xy)]$

11. $-\{2b - [b - (4 - 5b)] + (6 - b)\}$

12. $2x - y - 2\{3x - [y - (3y - 4x)]\}$

13. $(-2xy^2z)(-7xy^3z^5)$ **14.** $(-2)(-5aby^5)(4ab^4)$

15. $(3ab^2)^3$ **16.** $(2a^4c)^4$

17. $-2a(a^2x - at)$ **18.** $3a^2j(-3j^4 + 4a - aj)$

19. $(2x - 5)(x + 2)$ **20.** $(3 - 7y)(4y - 1)$

21. $(2a - 5b)(3a + 2b)$ **22.** $-(2x - y)(y - 5x)$

23. $2(2 - x)(x^2 - x - 4)$ **24.** $-3(xy - q)(x - 2y + 3q)$

25. $(-8a^2px^4) \div (2apx)$ **26.** $(-18rs^3t^5) \div (-24r^4st^6)$

27. $(2x^3y^5 - 3x^6y^2) \div (-x^3y^2)$

28. $(-6a^2b^3 - 9a^3b^4 + 12ab^5) \div (-3ab^2)$

29. $\dfrac{h^2j^4 - 3hj^6 - 6h^4j^7}{hj^4}$ **30.** $\dfrac{-18f^3g^2k^2 + 24f^2gk^6 - 36fgk^4}{-6fgk^2}$

31. $(x^2 + x - 12) \div (x - 3)$ **32.** $(6x^2 - 7x - 5) \div (2x + 1)$

33. $\dfrac{2x^3 + x^2 - x - 8}{2x + 3}$

34. $\dfrac{6x^4 + x^3 + 5x^2 + 2}{2x^2 - x + 1}$

35. $\dfrac{3x^2 + 5xy - 2y^2}{3x - y}$

36. $\dfrac{-a^2 b - 2b^2 + 3a^4}{a^2 - b}$

In Exercises 37 through 44, solve the given equations for x.

37. $3 - (2x - 7) = -(5 - x)$ **38.** $2(x - 4) - (5 - 3x) = 6$

39. $9 - 2(6 - x) = 6 + (7 - x)$ **40.** $a - 2(x - a) = 3x - (5 - 4a)$

41. $(x - 1)(x - 2) = -x(6 - x)$ **42.** $ax - 3 - a(2 - x) = 3(4a - 1)$

43. $(a^2 - 1)x = a^4 - 1$

44. $b(x - 3b) - (b^2 - x) = x - b(1 - b)$

In Exercises 45 through 56, solve the given problems.

45. When finding the center of mass of a particular area, one encounters the expression

$$(2x - x^2) - (3x^2 - 6x).$$

Simplify this expression.

46. In optics, the expression

$$\frac{lD}{d}(n + \tfrac{1}{2}) - \frac{lD}{d}(n - \tfrac{1}{2})$$

is found. Simplify this expression.

47. In the mathematics dealing with geometric progressions, the equation

$$S(1 - r) = a(1 + r + r^2 + r^3) - a(r + r^2 + r^3 + r^4)$$

may be used. Solve for S.

48. In the theory dealing with the expansion of a surface when it is heated, one finds the expression

$$lh(1 + at)^2.$$

Perform the indicated multiplication.

49. When one is studying the interference of light from a double source, the expression

$$(2x + d)^2 - (2x - d)^2$$

arises. Simplify this expression.

50. In transistor theory, the expression

$$[r_1 + (1 - a)r_2](1 - a)$$

is found. Perform the indicated multiplication.

51. The area of a certain rectangle is $2a^2 + 11a + 14$ and one side is $a + 2$. Find an expression for the length of the other side.

52. A rectangular box is to be made from a piece of cardboard 8 in. by 10 in. by cutting out a square of side x from each corner and turning up the sides. Show that the volume of the box is $V = x(8 - 2x)(10 - 2x)$, and then perform the indicated multiplication.

53. A car traveled a distance of $6x^2 - x - 2$ mi in $2x + 1$ hr, traveling at an average rate of 43 mi/hr. Determine the actual distance traveled.

54. Find the value of a, given that $x^2 - 6x + a$ is divisible by $x - 2$, with no remainder.

55. The longest side of a triangle is 3 in. longer than the shortest side. The third side is 2 in. longer than the shortest side. Twice the difference of eight times the shortest side and three times the longest side is 12 in. more than the perimeter. Find the sides of the triangle.

56. The height of a triangle is 4 in. longer than the side of a square. The base of the triangle is 3 in. less than the side of the square. Find the dimensions of each figure if the area of the square is twice that of the triangle.

9 Factoring

In the preceding chapter we discussed the basic operations of algebra. Among these essential operations was multiplication, which is performed when we wish to determine the product of two or more algebraic expressions. Many times, however, we find that we have an algebraic expression and wish to determine which expressions, when multiplied together, equal the given expression. We know that when an algebraic expression is the product of two or more quantities, each of these quantities is known as a factor of the expression. Therefore determining these factors is known as *factoring*. We shall find this process important to the work on fractions in the next chapter, as well as to the work in later sections.

Since $x^2 - 4 = (x - 2)(x + 2)$, the quantities $x - 2$ and $x + 2$ are   **Example A**
factors of $x^2 - 4$. Since $2ax - a^2x = ax(2 - a)$, the quantities ax and $2 - a$ are factors of $2ax - a^2x$. In fact, ax itself has factors of a and x, which means that we could state that the factors of $2ax - a^2x$ are a, x, and $2 - a$.

As we see in the above example, there are times when the factors of a given expression may be stated in different ways. When we recall our work in Section 1–5 when we determined the prime factors of numbers, we realize that factors of natural numbers also show this point. It should also be stated that $+1$ or -1 may always be stated as a factor of a given expression. Consider the various possibilities shown in the following example.

$$
\begin{aligned}
24 &= (+1)(+24) & 24 &= (+3)(-1)(-8) \\
&= (-1)(-24) & &= (-3)(-1)(+8) \\
&= (+2)(+12) & &= (+4)(+6)(+1) \\
&= (+2)(-1)(-12) & &= (-1)(-2)(-2)(-6). \\
&= (+2)(+2)(+2)(+3).
\end{aligned}
$$

         Example B

(Innumerable other possibilities also exist.)

In our work on factoring we shall consider only the factoring of polynomials (which include the integers), all terms of which will have integers as coefficients. Also, all factors will have integral coefficients and will contain no radicals such as $\sqrt{2}$, for example. When we extend the meaning of a prime number as stated in Section 1–5, and include the possibility of signed numbers, we can call a polynomial *prime* if it contains no factors other than $+1$ or -1, or plus or minus itself. We then say that an expression is *factored completely* if it is expressed as a product of its prime factors.

Example C $12 = (2)(2)(3)$. Here the factors of 12 are seen to be 2, 2, and 3 (any given factor may appear more than once). Since neither 2 nor 3 may be expressed as the product of any other pair of integers not including 1, they are prime. If we factored 12 as $12 = (6)(2)$, we have not factored it completely, since $6 = (2)(3)$.

Similarly $24 = (2)(2)(2)(3)$ is the complete factoring of 24. Again, $24 = (6)(4)$ is not the complete factorization of 24, since $6 = (2)(3)$ and $4 = (2)(2)$. When we factor $6ab^2$, we have $6ab^2 = (2)(3)(a)(b)(b)$ as the complete factorization.

Now $x^2 - 1 = (x - 1)(x + 1)$ represents the complete factorization of the expression $x^2 - 1$. However, even though $x - 1 = (\sqrt{x} - 1)(\sqrt{x} + 1)$, we do not include this type of factoring, since it includes radicals in the factors. In the same sense, $x^2 - 3$ is not factorable, even though

$$(x - \sqrt{3})(x + \sqrt{3}) = x^2 - 3.$$

We shall not attempt to develop any specific method for determining whether or not a factor is prime. For the restricted factoring we shall encounter, a knowledge of basic algebraic multiplication is sufficient, for any set of factors may be checked by multiplication.

Example D   The expressions $x - 1$, $x^2 + 1$, $x^2 - 5$, and $a^2 - ax + x$ are prime. The expressions $2x - 2$, $x^2 - 4$, and $a^2 - 2ax + x^2$ are not prime, since

$$2x - 2 = 2(x - 1),$$
$$x^2 - 4 = (x - 2)(x + 2),$$

and

$$a^2 - 2ax + x^2 = (a - x)^2.$$

Methods of determining factors such as those in Example D will be discussed in the sections which follow, although we must be able to recognize prime factors when they occur.

In Exercises 1 through 6, factor the given integers into a product of prime
integers.

1. 10   **2.** 18   **3.** 28

4. 54   **5.** 96   **6.** 210

In Exercises 7 through 12, state the prime factors of the indicated products.

7. $2(x - 1)(x + 3)$ **8.** $2a(x - 8)$

9. $15a^2c$ **10.** $36xy^3$

11. $9c^2(ax - b)(cx + d)$ **12.** $abc(c - a)(b + d)$

In Exercises 13 through 16, determine whether or not the given expressions have
been factored completely.

13. $5x - 25x^2 = 5x(1 - 5x)$ **14.** $2x^2 - 7x - 4 = (2x + 1)(x - 4)$

15. $2x^2 - 8x = 2(x^2 - 4x)$ **16.** $2x^2 - 2x - 4 = (2x + 2)(x - 2)$

In Exercises 17 through 20, determine whether or not the given expressions have
been correctly factored.

17. $x^2 + 4 = (x + 2)(x + 2)$ **18.** $2x^2 - x = 2x(x - 1)$

19. $2x^2 - 5x - 3 = (2x - 1)(x - 3)$
20. $3a^2b + 6ab - 3a = 3a(ab + 2b)$

In Exercises 21 through 26, determine the quantity that must be used to multiply
the first expression so that the product is the second expression given.

21. $x - 5, 3x - 15$ **22.** $x - b, 2bx - 2b^2$

23. $x - y + 2, 4x - 4y + 8$ **24.** $2 + x^2, 6ax + 3ax^3$

25. $x - 3, x^2 - 9$ **26.** $x + 1, x^2 + 2x + 1$

In Exercises 27 through 30, determine which of the given expressions are prime.

27. $x + 1, x^2 + 2, x^2 + ax + 1$ **28.** $3x - 8, 4x - 8, 3x - 9$
29. $ax + x^2, a + x^2, a^2x + x^2$ **30.** $2x^2 + 4x + 6, 2x^2 + 4x + 7$

9-2 COMMON MONOMIAL FACTORS

Often an algebraic expression contains a monomial that is common to
each term of the expression. The first step in factoring any expression is
to determine whether there is such a *common monomial factor*. If there is,
then the expression is written as the product of the common monomial
factor and the quotient obtained by dividing the expression by the
monomial factor.

Example A

Factor $3ax^2 + 3x^3y - 6x^2z$.

The numerical factor 3 and the literal factor x^2 are common to each term of the polynomial and they are common monomial factors. Normally monomial factors are not reduced to prime factors, and therefore we say that $3x^2$ is the common monomial factor. The quotient obtained by dividing the above polynomial by $3x^2$ is $a + xy - 2z$. Therefore the factoring of $3ax^2 + 3x^3y - 6x^2z$ is expressed as

$$3ax^2 + 3x^3y - 6x^2z = 3x^2(a + xy - 2z).$$

There is a systematic method of finding common monomial factors. When each of the terms of a polynomial is expressed as the product of its prime factors, the highest common factor is the product of the factors common to all terms. The following example illustrates this technique.

Example B

Factor $4x^3 + 8x^2y - 24xy^2$.

Expressing each of the terms as the product of prime factors, we have

$$4x^3 = 2 \cdot 2 \cdot x \cdot x \cdot x, \qquad 8x^2y = 2 \cdot 2 \cdot 2 \cdot x \cdot x \cdot y,$$
$$-24xy^2 = -1 \cdot 2 \cdot 2 \cdot 2 \cdot 3 \cdot x \cdot y \cdot y.$$

We now note that 2 appears twice in each of the products and x appears once in each. Even though 2 appears three times in each of the second and third terms, it appears only twice in the first term; hence we may use only two factors of 2 in the highest common factor. Similar arguments may be given for x and y. Therefore the highest common factor is $2 \cdot 2 \cdot x = 4x$. The remaining factors of the first term give the product x^2; those of the second term give $2xy$, and those of the third term give $-6y^2$. Therefore

$$4x^3 + 8x^2y - 24xy^2 = 4x(x^2 + 2xy - 6y^2).$$

In practice, one determines the common monomial factor of a given polynomial by inspection. The method of finding the highest common factor as in Example B is a general technique which can be followed regardless of the nature of the terms. However, it is rarely necessary to actually write out the factors of the individual terms. The factors of each term can be seen by inspection, and the common monomial factor is thereby found. The following example gives several illustrations of factoring problems done by inspection.

$$2x - 2y = 2(x - y), \qquad 2x^2 + 4y = 2(x^2 + 2y),$$

Example C

$$3ax + 6a^2 = 3a(x + 2a), \qquad 6p^2q - 18pq^2 = 6pq(p - 3q),$$

$$4x^2 - 8xy - 20xy^2 = 4x(x - 2y - 5y^2),$$

$$6a^2b^3c - 9a^3bc^2 + 3a^2bc = 3a^2bc(2b^2 - 3ac + 1).$$

Note the presence of the 1 in the last illustration. Since each of the factors of this term is common to all other terms, we must include the factor of 1. We can also recognize that this inclusion is necessary by multiplying the right-hand side as a check. Also we find the polynomial in parentheses by dividing the polynomial on the left by $3a^2bc$, and the division of the last term gives 1.

In Exercises 1 through 24, factor the given expressions by determining any common monomial factors which may exist.

1. $5x + 5y$ **2.** $3x^2 - 3y$ **3.** $2x^2 - 4x$ **4.** $7a^2 - 14bc$

5. $a^2 + 2a$ **6.** $3ab - 3ac$ **7.** $4p - 6pq$ **8.** $5h + 10h^2$

9. $3a^2b + 9ab$ **10.** $6xy^3 - 9xy^2$ **11.** $a^2bc^2f - 4acf$ **12.** $2rs^2t - 8r^2st^2$

13. $5x^2 + 15xy - 20y^3$ **14.** $4rs - 14s^2 - 16rs^2$

15. $12pq^2 - 8pq - 28pq^3$ **16.** $18x^2y^2 - 24x^2y^3 + 54x^3y$

17. $35a^3b^4c^2 + 14a^2b^5c^3 - 21a^3b^2$ **18.** $15x^2yz^3 - 45x^3y^2z^2 + 16x^2y^2z$

19. $6a^2b - 3a + 9ab^2 - 12a^2b^2$ **20.** $4r^2s - 8r^3s^2 + 16r^4s - 4r^2s^3$

21. $51pqrs - 34qrst - 17rstu - 68stuv$

22. $5a^2c - 25a^2b + 125a^2x - 10a^2bcx$

23. $3(a - b)^2 + 6x(a - b)$

24. $2xy(x - y) + (x - y)^3$

In Exercises 25 through 29, factor the indicated expressions.

25. The total surface area A of a rectangular solid is given by the formula

$$A = 2lw + 2lh + 2hw,$$

where l, w, and h are the length, width, and height of the solid. Factor the right-hand side of this formula.

26. Under certain circumstances, the distance s which an object is above the surface of the earth is given by the formula $s = 128 + 64t - 16t^2$, where t is the time. Factor the right-hand side of this formula.

27. In computing the value of a 6-month loan on which payments of R dollars per month are made, we use the equation $P = Rv + Rv^2 + Rv^3 + Rv^4 + Rv^5 + Rv^6$, where v is a factor involving the interest which is paid. Factor the right-hand side of this equation.

28. Under certain circumstances, in discussing magnetic fields, the equation

$$H = 2iMAC + 2iMBC - 10iMDC$$

could be used. Factor the right-hand side of this equation.

29. When determining the deflection of a certain beam, of length L, at a distance x from one end, the expression

$$wx^4 - 2wLx^3 + wL^3x$$

is encountered. Here w is the weight per unit length of the beam. Factor this expression.

9–3 THE DIFFERENCE BETWEEN TWO SQUARES

If we multiply $(x + y)$ by $(x - y)$, the product is $x^2 - y^2$. This product contains two perfect squares, x^2 and y^2. In general, a *perfect square* is any quantity which is an exact square of a rational quantity.

Example A The number 4 is a perfect square, since $4 = 2^2$, The quantity $9y^2$ is a perfect square, since $9y^2 = (3y)^2$. The quantity $25a^4$ is a perfect square, since $25a^4 = (5a^2)^2$. Other perfect squares are 16, $49x^2$, x^2y^2, b^4, p^2y^4, and $36x^8y^2$.

The number 7 is not a perfect square, since there is no rational number which, when squared, equals 7. The quantity x^3 is not a perfect square, since there is no integral power of x which, when squared, equals x^3.

Having noted that

$$(x + y)(x - y) = x^2 - y^2, \qquad \text{9–1}$$

we see that the multiplication results in the *difference* between the *squares* of the two terms which appear in the binomials. Therefore we can easily recognize the factors of the binomial $x^2 - y^2$, which are $(x + y)$ and $(x - y)$. It will be necessary to recognize the perfect squares represented by x^2 and y^2 when we factor expressions of this type. We can now apply the result of Eq. (9–1) to the problem of factoring the difference between any two squares.

$$x^2 - 9 = x^2 - 3^2 = (x + 3)(x - 3), \qquad \text{Example B}$$
$$9 - 4y^2 = 3^2 - (2y)^2 = (3 + 2y)(3 - 2y),$$
$$36p^2 - 49q^2 = (6p)^2 - (7q)^2 = (6p + 7q)(6p - 7q),$$
$$4s^4 - 25t^4 = (2s^2)^2 - (5t^2)^2 = (2s^2 + 5t^2)(2s^2 - 5t^2),$$
$$16y^4x^2 - p^6 = (4y^2x)^2 - (p^3)^2 = (4y^2x + p^3)(4y^2x - p^3).$$

In actually writing down the result of the factoring, we do not usually need to write the middle step shown in this example. Thus the first illustration would be written simply as $x^2 - 9 = (x + 3)(x - 3)$. The middle steps are given here to indicate the perfect squares which are used.

Equation (9–1) can be used to perform certain multiplications very rapidly. The following example demonstrates how this is done.

To multiply 49 by 51, we may express the product as   Example C

$$(49)(51) = (50 - 1)(50 + 1) = (50)^2 - 1^2 = 2500 - 1 = 2499.$$

In Eq. (9–1) we are letting $x = 50$ and $y = 1$.

Other illustrations of this method of multiplication are:

$$(32)(28) = (30 + 2)(30 - 2) = (30)^2 - 2^2 = 900 - 4 = 896,$$
$$(104)(96) = (100 + 4)(100 - 4) = (100)^2 - 4^2 = 10,000 - 16 = 9984,$$
$$(43)(57) = (50 - 7)(50 + 7) = (50)^2 - 7^2 = 2500 - 49 = 2451.$$

The major value of performing multiplication in this way is to attain facility in working with the difference between squares. It is not too often that one comes across the type of product which may be obtained in this manner, for it must be of a special form.

As indicated previously, if it is possible to factor out a common monomial factor, this should be done first. If the resulting factor is the difference between squares, the factoring is not complete until this difference is also factored. This illustrates that *complete factoring* often requires more than one step. Also, when you are writing the result in complete factoring, be sure to include *all* factors.

In factoring $3x^2 - 12$, we note that there is a common factor of 3 in   Example D
each of the terms. Therefore $3x^2 - 12 = 3(x^2 - 4)$. However, the
factor $x^2 - 4$ is itself the difference between two perfect squares. There-

fore $3x^2 - 12$ is completely factored as

$$3x^2 - 12 = 3(x^2 - 4) = 3(x + 2)(x - 2).$$

In factoring $x^4 - 16$, we note that we have the difference between squares. Therefore $x^4 - 16 = (x^2 + 4)(x^2 - 4)$. However, the factor $x^2 - 4$ is again the difference between squares. Therefore

$$x^2 - 16 = (x^2 + 4)(x^2 - 4) = (x^2 + 4)(x - 2)(x + 2).$$

The factor $x^2 + 4$ is prime.

This product and its factors, Eq. (9-1), should become very familiar, for the product of the sum and the difference between two terms appears frequently in algebra.

EXERCISES In Exercises 1 through 4, determine which of the given quantities are perfect squares.

1. 9, 25, $4x^2$, $9x$ **2.** 18, 121, $8x^2$, x^8

3. a^2b^4, x^2yz^4, $16xy^2$ **4.** $9r^6$, $s^2t^5x^2$, $36d^4y^{10}$, $81r^{12}s$

In Exercises 5 through 10, determine the products by direct multiplication.

5. $(x + y)(x - y)$ **6.** $(a - 2)(a + 2)$

7. $(2a - b)(2a + b)$ **8.** $(3xy + 1)(3xy - 1)$

9. $(7ax^2 + p^3)(7ax^2 - p^3)$ **10.** $(5x^2 - 6y^5)(5x^2 + 6y^5)$

In Exercises 11 through 14, perform the indicated multiplications by means of Eq. (9-1). Check by direct multiplication.

11. $(21)(19)$ **12.** $(78)(82)$

13. $(210)(190)$ **14.** $(144)(156)$

In Exercises 15 through 30, factor the given expressions completely.

15. $a^2 - b^2$ **16.** $x^2 - 4$

17. $16 - x^2$ **18.** $25x^2 - y^2$

19. $4x^4 - y^2$ **20.** $64 - x^2y^2$

21. $a^2b^2 - 9y^2$ **22.** $4q^2 - (rs)^2$

23. $81x^4 - 4y^6$ **24.** $49b^6 - 25c^4$

25. $4x^2 - 100y^2$ **26.** $24x^2y^2 - 54a^4$

27. $x^4 - 1$ **28.** $a^4 - 81b^4$

29. $4x^2 + 36y^2$ **30.** $75a^2x^2 + 27b^4y^4$

In Exercises 31 through 34, solve the given problems.

31. In discussing the energy of a moving object, one encounters the expression $mv_1^2 - mv_2^2$. Factor this expression.

32. Find the area of a rectangle whose sides are 37 and 43 in. by performing the multiplication by the method of this section.

33. Set up and then factor the expression for the difference in volumes of a cube of side x and a rectangular solid of sides x, y, and y.

34. The difference of the energy radiated by an electric light filament at temperature T_2 and that radiated by a filament at temperature T_1 is given by the formula

$$R = kT_2^4 - kT_1^4.$$

Factor the right-hand side of the formula.

9–4 FACTORING TRINOMIALS

In this section we shall discuss the factoring of trinomials of the form $ax^2 + bx + c$. As we stated in Section 9–1, we shall consider only those cases in which a, b, and c are integers. Such a trinomial may or may not be factorable into two binomial factors, the coefficients of which are integers.

We shall first discuss the trinomial $x^2 + bx + c$, that is, the case in which $a = 1$. The binomial factors of this trinomial (if they exist) will be of the form $(x + p)$ and $(x + q)$. That is, we shall determine whether factors exist such that

$$x^2 + bx + c = (x + p)(x + q).$$

Multiplying out the right-hand side of this equation, we obtain

$$(x + p)(x + q) = x^2 + px + qx + pq = x^2 + (p + q)x + pq.$$

We now see that $b = p + q$ and $c = pq$. It is therefore necessary to find two integers p and q whose sum is b and whose product is c. The quantities p and q are readily found by inspection.

In order to factor the trinomial $x^2 + 5x + 4$, we must find two integers such that their product is $+4$ and their sum is $+5$. The possible factors of $+4$ are: $+2$ and $+2$, -2 and -2, $+4$ and $+1$, and -4 and -1. Of these possibilities, only $+4$ and $+1$ have a sum of $+5$. Hence the   *Example A* required factors are $(x + 4)$ and $(x + 1)$. Therefore

$$x^2 + 5x + 4 = (x + 4)(x + 1).$$

When we factor $x^2 - 5x + 4$, an examination of the possible factors of $+4$, which are indicated above, reveals that the only factors whose sum is -5 are -4 and -1. Therefore the factors are $(x - 4)$ and $(x - 1)$. Hence

$$x^2 - 5x + 4 = (x - 4)(x - 1).$$

When we factor $x^2 + 3x + 4$, an examination of the possible factors of $+4$, which are indicated in the first part of this example, reveals that none of the combinations has a sum of $+3$. Therefore, $x^2 + 3x + 4$ is prime.

Example B   In order to factor $x^2 + x - 6$ we must find two integers whose product is -6 and whose sum is $+1$. The possible factors of -6 are -1 and $+6$, $+1$ and -6, -2 and $+3$, and $+2$ and -3. Of these factors, only -2 and $+3$ have a sum of $+1$. Therefore

$$x^2 + x - 6 = (x - 2)(x + 3).$$

When we factor $x^2 - 5x - 6$, we see that the necessary factors of -6 are $+1$ and -6. Hence

$$x^2 - 5x - 6 = (x + 1)(x - 6).$$

When we factor $x^2 + 4x - 6$, we see that this expression is prime, since none of the pairs of factors of -6 has a sum of $+4$.

We shall now turn our attention to factoring the trinomial $ax^2 + bx + c$, where a does not equal 1. The binomial factors of this trinomial will be of the form $(rx + p)$ and $(sx + q)$. That is, we shall determine whether factors exist such that

$$ax^2 + bx + c = (rx + p)(sx + q).$$

Multiplying out the right-hand side of this equation, we obtain

$$(rx + p)(sx + q) = rsx^2 + rqx + spx + pq = rsx^2 + (rq + sp)x + pq.$$

We now see that $a = rs$, $b = rq + sp$, and $c = pq$. It is therefore necessary to find four such integers r, s, p, and q.

You probably realize that finding these integers is relatively easy as far as the ax^2 term and the c term are concerned. We simply need to find integers r and s whose product is a, and integers p and q whose product is c. However, we must find the right integers so that the bx term is correct. This is usually the most troublesome part of factoring trinomials. We must remember that the bx term will result from the *sum of two terms* when the factors are multiplied together.

The problem therefore is to determine factors of a and c, the sum of whose *cross products* is equal to b. We may determine the cross products $rq + sp$ in this manner: arrange the factors r, s, p, and q at the corners of an imaginary square, as

$$r \diagdown \diagup p$$
$$\times$$
$$s \diagup \diagdown q \,.$$

We find the product rq by multiplying the factors on the diagonal r—q, while we find sp by multiplying the factors on the diagonal s—p. We shall *always* take r and s to be positive if a is positive.

When we factor $2x^2 - 11x + 5$, we take the factors of 2 to be $+2$ and $+1$ (we shall take only the positive factors of a, since it is $+2$). The factors of $+5$ are $+1$ and $+5$, and -1 and -5. Since the sum of the cross products must equal -11, only negative factors can possibly be used (both p and q are of the same sign, and are to be multiplied by positive numbers). We now set up the factors to determine the cross product:
Example C

$$+2 \qquad -5$$
$$+1 \qquad -1 \,.$$

The sum of the cross products is $-2 - 5 = -7$. Since this arrangement of factors did not give us the sum of -11, we now try another arrangement:

$$+1 \qquad -5$$
$$+2 \qquad -1 \,.$$

This sum is

$$-1 - 10 = -11,$$

the required sum. The numbers in this arrangement are the required coefficients of the binomial factors. Thus

$$2x^2 - 11x + 5 = (x - 5)(2x - 1).$$

Example D
Factor $4y^2 + 7y + 3$.

The positive factors of $+4$ are $+1$ and $+4$, and $+2$ and $+2$. Since b is $+7$ and c is $+3$, both cross products must be formed from positive numbers, which means we are limited to the positive factors of $+3$. The positive factors of $+3$ are $+1$ and $+3$. We now set up our factors to determine the cross products:

$$\begin{matrix} +1 & +1 \\ +4 & +3 \end{matrix}.$$

The sum of the cross products is $+3 + 4 = +7$, the required value. Therefore

$$4y^2 + 7y + 3 = (y + 1)(4y + 3).$$

It is not necessary to try the other pair of factors $+2$ and $+2$.

Example E
Factor $6x^2 + 5x - 4$.

The positive factors of $+6$ are $+6$ and $+1$, and $+3$ and $+2$. The factors of -4 are $+4$ and -1, -4 and $+1$, and $+2$ and -2. Since b is $+5$, we know that the cross product of larger absolute value will be the product of positive numbers. This eliminates several of the possible combinations, such as

$$\begin{matrix} +6 & +1 \\ +1 & -4 \end{matrix}.$$

We find that the factors $+6$ and $+1$ do not work with any of the factors of -4. Trying the factors $+3$ and $+2$, we find that the combination

$$\begin{matrix} +3 & +4 \\ +2 & -1 \end{matrix}$$

has a sum of cross products of $-3 + 8 = +5$, the required value. Therefore

$$6x^2 + 5x - 4 = (3x + 4)(2x - 1).$$

As we mentioned in the previous sections, we must always be on the alert for a common monomial factor. A check should be made for such a factor first. Consider the following example.

Example F
Factor $2x^2 + 6x - 8$.

At first it might appear that we are to find the factors of $+2$ and -8. However, note that there is a common factor of 2 in each term. Therefore

we can write
$$2x^2 + 6x - 8 = 2(x^2 + 3x - 4).$$

It is now necessary only to factor $x^2 + 3x - 4$. The factors of this trinomial are $x + 4$ and $x - 1$. Therefore
$$2x^2 + 6x - 8 = 2(x + 4)(x - 1).$$

Many trinomials which are factorable by the methods of this section will contain a literal factor in each term of the binomial factors. The following example illustrates this type of problem.

Factor $4x^2 + 22xy - 12y^2$.   **Example G**

We first note that there is a common factor of 2 in each term. This means that $4x^2 + 22xy - 12y^2 = 2(2x^2 + 11xy - 6y^2)$. The problem now is to factor $2x^2 + 11xy - 6y^2$. Since the product of
$$(rx + py)(sx + qy) = rsx^2 + (rq + sp)xy + pqy^2,$$

we see that this is essentially the same as the problems previously encountered. The only difference is the presence of the xy in the middle term and the y^2 in the last term. However, the process of finding the values of r, s, p, and q is the same. We find that the arrangement:

$$+2 \qquad -1$$
$$+1 \qquad +6$$

works for this combination. Therefore
$$4x^2 + 22xy - 12y^2 = 2(2x - y)(x + 6y).$$

Much of the work done in factoring the trinomials in these examples can be done mentally. With experience, you will be able to write the factors of such expressions by inspection.

In Exercises 1 through 32, factor the given trinomials, when possible.   **EXERCISES**

1. $x^2 + 3x + 2$ 2. $x^2 - x - 2$

3. $x^2 + x - 12$ 4. $s^2 + 7s + 12$

5. $y^2 - 4y - 5$ 6. $x^2 - 3x - 8$

7. $x^2 + 10x + 25$ 8. $t^2 + 3t - 10$

9. $2q^2 + 11q + 5$ 10. $2a^2 - a - 3$

11. $3x^2 + x - 3$ 12. $3x^2 - 14x + 8$

13. $2s^2 - 13st + 15t^2$ **14.** $3x^2 - 17x - 6$

15. $5x^2 + 17x + 6$ **16.** $7n^2 - 16n + 2$

17. $4x^2 - 8x + 3$ **18.** $4x^2 + 33xy + 8y^2$

19. $6t^2 + 7tu - 10u^2$ **20.** $6x^2 + 19x - 7$

21. $8x^2 + 6x - 9$ **22.** $8y^2 + 5y - 3$

23. $12q^2 + 20q + 3$ **24.** $12x^2 - 7xy - 12y^2$

25. $2x^2 - 22x + 48$ **26.** $3x^2 - 12x - 15$

27. $4x^2 + 2xz - 12z^2$ **28.** $5x^2 + 15x + 25$

29. $2x^3 + 6x^2 + 4x$ **30.** $2x^4 + x^3 - 10x^2$

31. $10ax^2 + 23axy - 5ay^2$ **32.** $54a^2 - 45ab - 156b^2$

In Exercises 33 through 39, factor the indicated expression.

33. To find the side of a rectangle whose length is 6 in. longer than the width, and whose area is 40 in^2, it is necessary to factor the expression $x^2 - 6x - 40$. Factor this expression.

34. When one is determining the deflection of a certain beam, of length L, at a distance x from one end, the expression

$$x^2 - 3Lx + 2L^2$$

is found. Factor this expression.

35. To determine the speed of a train under certain circumstances, it is necessary to factor the expression $3s^2 + 30s - 9000$. Factor this expression.

36. To find the time that a projectile has been in the air, it is necessary to factor the expression $16t^2 - 128t - 320$. Factor this expression.

37. The resistance of a certain electric resistor varies with the temperature according to the equation $R = 10000 + 600T + 5T^2$. Factor the right-hand side of this equation.

38. An open box is made from a sheet of cardboard 12 in. square by cutting equal squares of side x from the corners and bending up the sides. Show that the volume of the box is given by the formula $V = 4x^3 - 48x^2 + 144x$. Factor the right-hand side of this formula.

39. A rectangular field bounded on one side by a river is to be fenced in. No fencing is required along the river and the area to be fenced in is 2500 ft^2. If the length of the side of the field that is perpendicular to the river is called x, and 225 ft of fencing are used, show that $225x - 2x^2 = 2500$ is the equation found by setting up the solution for x. The final solution requires that the equation be written as $2x^2 - 225x + 2500 = 0$. Factor the left-hand side of this equation.

In Exercises 1 through 48, factor the given expression, if possible.

1. $5a - 5c$ **2.** $4r + 8s$

3. $3a^2 + 6a$ **4.** $6t^3 - 8t^2$

5. $12a^2b + 4ab$ **6.** $15t^3y - 10ty^2$

7. $4x^2 - y^2$ **8.** $p^2 - 9u^2v^2$

9. $16y^4 - x^2$ **10.** $r^2s^2t^2 - 4x^2$

11. $x^2 + 2x + 1$ **12.** $x^2 - 2x - 3$

13. $x^2 - 7x + 6$ **14.** $x^2 + 2x - 63$

15. $ax^2 + 3a^2x - a^3$ **16.** $18r^2t - 9r^3t^2 - 6r^2t^3$

17. $2nm^3 - 4n^2m^2 + 6n^3m$ **18.** $8y^2 + 24y^3z - 32y^2z^4$

19. $4p^3t^2 - 12t^4 - 4t^2 + 4at^2$

20. $22r^2s^2t^2 - 121rst^2 - 22r^3st^2 + 33r^4s^2t^2$

21. $(4rs)^2 - 9y^2$ **22.** $49r^4t^4 - y^6$

23. $36w^2x^2 + y^4$ **24.** $(a + b)^2 - c^2$

25. $2x^2 + 9x + 7$ **26.** $3y^2 + y - 10$

27. $14t^2 - 19t - 3$ **28.** $5x^2 + x - 4$

29. $9x^2 + 6x + 1$ **30.** $8r^2 + 2r - 15$

31. $x^2 + 3xy + 2y^2$ **32.** $6a^2 - 17ab + 12b^2$

33. $10c^2 + 23cd - 5d^2$ **34.** $4p^2 - 12pq + 9q^2$

35. $88x^2 - 19x - 84$ **36.** $16y^2 + 56y + 49$

37. $2x^2 - 18y^2$ **38.** $4r^2t^2 - 36p^2q^2$

39. $8y^4x^6 - 32y^2x^4$ **40.** $3m^5n - 27mn^3$

41. $3ax^2 + 3ax - 36a$ **42.** $36c^2x - 34cx - 30x$

43. $54r^3 - 45r^2s - 156rs^2$ **44.** $8c^2x^2 + 52c^2x + 72c^2$

45. $48y^3 - 64y^4 + 16y^5$ **46.** $18a^2u^2 + 23a^2u - 6a^2$

47. $16x^4 - 1$ **48.** $x^8 - 1$

In Exercises 49 through 59, factor the indicated expressions.

49. When one is determining the number of teeth on a circular gear, one encounters the expression $PN + 2P$. Factor this expression.

50. When one is finding the voltage of a battery, one encounters the expression $iR_1 + iR_2 + ir$. Factor this expression.

51. When one is determining the velocity of a fluid flowing through a pipe, one may encounter the expression $kD^2 - 4kr^2$. Factor this expression.

52. When one is studying the pressure P and the volume V of a certain gas, the expression

$$CP(V_2 - V_1) + PR(V_2 - V_1)$$

is found, where C and R are constants. Factor this expression.

53. When one is considering the work done by a jet of fluid striking a surface, the expression

$$v_2^2 - 4v_1v_2 + 3v_1^2$$

is encountered. Factor this expression.

54. For a certain projectile fired from ground level, its distance s above the ground after t sec is given by the formula $s = 256t - 16t^2$. Factor the right-hand side of this formula.

55. When one is dealing with the theory of light reflection, one uses the expression

$$\frac{u^2 - 2u + 1}{u^2 + 2u + 1}.$$

Factor both the numerator and denominator of this expression.

56. In the theory of magnetism, the expression

$$b(x^2 + y^2) - 2by^2$$

may be used. Factor this expression.

57. If the length of a rectangle is 5 in. more than twice the width, show that the area A is given by the formula

$$A = 2x^2 + 5x,$$

where x is the width. In order to solve for x, it is necessary to write the formula as $2x^2 + 5x - A = 0$. If $A = 52$ in^2, factor the left-hand side of this equation.

58. The edge of one cube is 2 in. longer than the edge of a second cube. Let $x = $ the edge of the smaller cube and set up the expression for the difference between the volumes. Perform any necessary algebraic operations and factor the resulting expression.

59. At an altitude of h ft above sea level, the boiling point of water is lower by a certain number of degrees than the boiling point at sea level, which is 212°F. The difference is given by the approximate equation $T^2 + 520T - h = 0$. Assuming that $h = 5300$ ft, factor the left-hand side of this equation.

Fractions 10

10–1 EQUIVALENT FRACTIONS

As we explained in Chapter 1, a fraction indicates the division of one number by another. In Chapter 1 we developed the basic operations with fractions in which the numerator and the denominator are natural numbers. Now in this chapter, we shall develop those operations for fractions in which the numerator and the denominator are algebraic expressions. Since algebraic expressions are representations of numbers, the basic operations on fractions from arithmetic form the basis of the algebraic operations.

In our previous discussion of fractions, we defined two fractions to be *equivalent* if the numerator and the denominator of one fraction can be multiplied, or divided, by the same number (not zero) in order to obtain the other fraction. This definition forms the basis of the operations with fractions, both arithmetic and algebraic.

Example A   From our work in Chapter 1, we know that if we multiply the numerator and denominator of the fraction $\frac{3}{4}$ by 2, we obtain the equivalent fraction $\frac{6}{8}$. Also, if we divide the numerator and denominator of the fraction $\frac{18}{24}$ by 6, we obtain the equivalent fraction $\frac{3}{4}$. Therefore $\frac{3}{4}$, $\frac{6}{8}$, and $\frac{18}{24}$ are equivalent. If we multiply the numerator and denominator of the fraction

$$\frac{3x^2}{5x^3}$$

by x^2, we obtain the equivalent fraction

$$\frac{3x^4}{5x^5}.$$

If we divide the numerator and denominator of the fraction

$$\frac{3x^2}{5x^3}$$

by x^2, we obtain the equivalent fraction

$$\frac{3}{5x}.$$

This can be seen by

$$\frac{(3x^2)(x^2)}{(5x^3)(x^2)} = \frac{3x^4}{5x^5} \qquad \text{and} \qquad \frac{\dfrac{3x^2}{x^2}}{\dfrac{5x^3}{x^2}} = \frac{3}{5x}.$$

Therefore $\dfrac{3x^2}{5x^3}$, $\dfrac{3x^4}{5x^5}$, and $\dfrac{3}{5x}$ are equivalent.

With an algebraic fraction, as with a fraction in arithmetic, one of the most important operations is reducing it to its lowest, or simplest, form. As in the case of an arithmetic fraction, we remove the factors which are common to both numerator and denominator by dividing both the numerator and denominator by the common factors. By finding the highest common factor of the numerator and denominator, and dividing each by this factor, we obtain the simplest form.

In simplifying the fraction $\frac{21}{28}$, we note that both numerator and de- **Example B**
nominator have a factor of 7. Therefore, dividing each by 7, we obtain $\frac{3}{4}$, or the simplest form of the fraction $\frac{21}{28}$.

In order to simplify the fraction

$$\frac{15x^2y^3z}{20xy^4z},$$

we note that the highest common factor of numerator and denominator is $5xy^3z$. Dividing both numerator and denominator by this highest common factor, we have

$$\frac{(15x^2y^3z) \div (5xy^3z)}{(20xy^4z) \div (5xy^3z)} = \frac{3x}{4y}.$$

When we are simplifying the fraction

$$\frac{x^2 - x - 2}{x^2 + 3x + 2},$$

we must first factor both numerator and denominator in order to determine whether there is a common factor. We obtain

$$\frac{x^2 - x - 2}{x^2 + 3x + 2} = \frac{(x - 2)(x + 1)}{(x + 2)(x + 1)} = \frac{x - 2}{x + 2}.$$

Here we see that the highest common factor is $(x + 1)$. We divide both numerator and denominator by this factor.

Special note: Remember that in simplifying fractions, we must *divide* both numerator and denominator by the common *factor*. This process is often called *cancellation*. However, many students are tempted to remove *terms* which appear in both numerator and denominator. This is an *incorrect* application of cancellation. The following example illustrates common errors in the simplification of fractions.

Example C   When simplifying the expression

$$\frac{x^2 - x - 2}{x^2 + 3x + 2},$$

many students would "cancel" the terms x^2 and 2, since they appear in both numerator and denominator. This is *incorrect*, for removing them in this way is equivalent to *subtracting* $x^2 + 2$ from the numerator and from the denominator, which violates the fundamental principle of fractions.

When simplifying the expression

$$\frac{2x + 3}{2(x - 1)(x + 3)},$$

many students tend to "cancel" the 3's and 2's. Again, this is *incorrect*. Actually, this expression cannot be further simplified, since there is no common *factor* in the numerator and the denominator. The 2 in the numerator is not a factor of the entire numerator.

There are cases, especially in the addition and subtraction of fractions, when a fraction in its simplest form must be changed to an *equivalent*, not the *simplest*, form. This is accomplished by the *multiplication* of both numerator and denominator by the same quantity.

When simplifying fractions, we shall often find that the numerator and denominator have factors which differ only in *sign*. We can show that

$$(a - b) = -(b - a), \qquad \qquad \textbf{10–1}$$

since $-(b - a) = -b + a = a - b$. This equation shows us that we may change all the signs of the terms of a factor, and not change the sign of the expression so long as we also introduce a factor of -1. The following example illustrates the simplification of fractions where a change of signs is necessary.

Example D   We may simplify the fraction

$$\frac{x - 3}{3 - x}$$

by expressing the denominator as $-(x - 3)$. This leads to

$$\frac{x - 3}{3 - x} = \frac{x - 3}{-(x - 3)} = \frac{1}{-1} = -1.$$

After rewriting the denominator, we divided out the common factor of $x - 3$.

The fraction

$$\frac{4 - x^2}{x^2 - 6x + 8} = \frac{(2 - x)(2 + x)}{(x - 2)(x - 4)}$$

is seen to have factors in the numerator and denominator which differ only in sign. Changing $(2 - x)$ to $-(x - 2)$, we have

$$\frac{(2 - x)(2 + x)}{(x - 2)(x - 4)} = \frac{-(x - 2)(2 + x)}{(x - 2)(x - 4)} = \frac{-(2 + x)}{x - 4}.$$

This result is one form of the simplest form of the original fraction. We can also express it as

$$\frac{2 + x}{4 - x}$$

by replacing $x - 4$ by $-(4 - x)$. Therefore acceptable forms of the simplest form are

$$\frac{-(2 + x)}{x - 4} = -\frac{2 + x}{x - 4} = \frac{2 + x}{-(x - 4)} = \frac{2 + x}{4 - x}.$$

Changing signs of factors of fractions often causes students difficulty. This need not be the case if Eq. (10–1) is understood and used correctly.

In Exercises 1 through 6, multiply the numerator and denominator of each of the given fractions by each of the two given factors and obtain the two equivalent fractions.   EXERCISES

1. $\frac{2}{3}$; 2, 5   **2.** $\frac{7}{5}$; 3, 6

3. $\frac{3ax}{b}$; $2a^2$, ab **4.** $\frac{5b}{3x}$; $2x$, $7b^2x$

5. $\frac{x - y}{x + y}$; $x - y$, $x + y$ **6.** $\frac{2(x - 2y)}{2x - y}$; $x + 2y$, $2x + y$

In Exercises 7 through 12, divide the numerator and denominator of each of the given fractions by the given factor and obtain an equivalent fraction.

7. $\frac{16}{28}$; 4   **8.** $\frac{27}{39}$; 3

9. $\dfrac{6a^2x}{9a^3x}$; $3ax$

10. $\dfrac{14r^2st}{28rst^2}$; $7rt$

11. $\dfrac{2x^2 + 5x - 3}{x^2 + 4x + 3}$; $x + 3$

12. $\dfrac{6x^2 - 11x + 3}{2x^2 - 3x}$; $2x - 3$

In Exercises 13 through 32, determine the simplest form of each of the given fractions.

13. $\frac{8}{36}$

14. $\frac{42}{63}$

15. $\dfrac{5a^2b}{20a}$

16. $\dfrac{12xyz^2}{21xyz^3}$

17. $\dfrac{18r^3st^2}{63r^5s^2t}$

18. $\dfrac{91a^3b^2c}{26ab^2c^5}$

19. $\dfrac{(x - 1)(x + 1)(x + 2)}{2(x - 1)(x + 3)}$

20. $\dfrac{3(x + 5)(2x - 1)(3x - 2)}{9(5x + 1)(3x - 2)(2x - 1)}$

21. $\dfrac{x^2 - 1}{x^2 - 2x + 1}$

22. $\dfrac{x^2 + 5x + 4}{x^2 + 3x - 4}$

23. $\dfrac{3x^2 - x}{3x^2 + 5x - 2}$

24. $\dfrac{4x^2 + 9x - 9}{4x^2 - 8x}$

25. $\dfrac{6x^2 - 19x + 10}{8x^2 - 14x - 15}$

26. $\dfrac{4x^2 + 10x + 6}{12x^2 + 8x - 4}$

27. $\dfrac{x^2 - 9y^2}{3xy - 9y^2}$

28. $\dfrac{5a^2 + 39ab - 8b^2}{5a^2 + 4ab - b^2}$

29. $\dfrac{(3x - 1)(5 - x)}{(x - 5)(3x + 1)}$

30. $\dfrac{(x - 2)(x - 3)(4 - x)}{(3 - x)(x - 4)(2x - 1)}$

31. $\dfrac{20 - 9x + x^2}{8 + 2x - x^2}$

32. $\dfrac{4ab - b^2}{b^2 - 16a^2}$

In Exercises 33 through 36, solve the given problems.

33. Evaluate the fraction

$$\frac{4a - 8}{4(a + 2)}$$

for the value $a = 5$ before and after reducing it to simplest form.

34. Evaluate the fraction

$$\frac{2x^2 + 5xy - 3y^2}{2x^2 + 3xy - 2y^2}$$

for the values $x = 2$ and $y = 3$ before and after reducing it to simplest form.

35. Evaluate the fraction

$$\frac{x - 2}{2 - x}$$

for the value $x = 7$ and compare it with the value obtained when it is reduced to lowest terms.

36. Which of the following fractions are in simplest form?

$$\frac{x - 2}{x + 2}, \qquad \frac{2x}{2x + 3}, \qquad \frac{3x + 1}{3x + 5}, \qquad \frac{x^2 - x + 2}{x^2 + 2}, \qquad \frac{x^2 + x + 4}{x^2(x + 4)}$$

10–2 MULTIPLICATION AND DIVISION OF FRACTIONS

From Chapter 1 we recall that the product of two fractions is a fraction whose numerator is the product of the numerators and whose denominator is the product of the denominators of the given fractions. Since algebra is a generalization of arithmetic, the same definition holds in algebra. Symbolically, we write this as

$$\frac{a}{b} \cdot \frac{c}{d} = \frac{ac}{bd} \qquad (b \text{ and } d \text{ not zero}). \qquad \qquad \textbf{10–2}$$

$$\frac{5}{6} \cdot \frac{7a^2}{9x} = \frac{(5)(7a^2)}{(6)(9x)} = \frac{35a^2}{54x}, \qquad\qquad \textbf{Example A}$$

$$\frac{3a}{b} \cdot \frac{x^2}{5b} = \frac{(3a)(x^2)}{(b)(5b)} = \frac{3ax^2}{5b^2}.$$

Closely associated with the multiplication of fractions is the power of a fraction. To find $(a/b)^n$ we would have n factors of (a/b), which would result in a numerator of a^n and a denominator of b^n. Therefore

$$\left(\frac{a}{b}\right)^n = \frac{a^n}{b^n} \qquad (b \text{ not zero}). \qquad\qquad \textbf{10–3}$$

$$\left(\frac{2}{3}\right)^3 = \frac{2^3}{3^3} = \frac{8}{27}, \qquad\qquad \textbf{Example B}$$

$$\left(\frac{2a^2}{x}\right)^4 = \frac{(2a^2)^4}{x^4} = \frac{(2^4)(a^2)^4}{x^4} = \frac{16a^8}{x^4}.$$

To divide one fraction by another, we recall the procedure developed for arithmetic fractions. We invert the divisor (the fraction in the denominator) and multiply the dividend (the fraction in the numerator) by the inverted fraction. We can explain this procedure on the basis of multiplying the numerator and denominator by the same quantity. If we want to divide a/b by c/d, we multiply the numerator and denominator by d/c. This may be written as

$$\frac{\dfrac{a}{b}}{\dfrac{c}{d}} = \frac{\dfrac{a}{b}\cdot\dfrac{d}{c}}{\dfrac{c}{d}\cdot\dfrac{d}{c}} = \frac{\dfrac{ad}{bc}}{\dfrac{cd}{dc}} = \frac{\dfrac{ad}{bc}}{1} = \frac{ad}{bc}.$$

Therefore, showing the division of fractions symbolically, we have

$$\frac{\dfrac{a}{b}}{\dfrac{c}{d}} = \frac{ad}{bc} \qquad (b,\ c, \text{ and } d \text{ not zero}).\qquad\qquad \text{10-4}$$

Example C

$$\frac{2x}{5} \div \frac{3}{7c} = \frac{\dfrac{2x}{5}}{\dfrac{3}{7c}} = \frac{2x}{5}\cdot\frac{7c}{3} = \frac{(2x)(7c)}{(5)(3)} = \frac{14cx}{15},$$

$$\frac{\dfrac{4xy}{3b}}{\dfrac{7b}{xyz}} = \frac{4xy}{3b}\cdot\frac{xyz}{7b} = \frac{(4xy)(xyz)}{(3b)(7b)} = \frac{4x^2y^2z}{21b^2}.$$

Another mathematical term which we previously introduced in connection with the division of fractions is *reciprocal*. Recalling that the reciprocal of a number is 1 divided by that number, we see that the reciprocal of a is $1/a$ (a not zero). Also, since

$$\frac{1}{\dfrac{a}{b}} = 1\cdot\frac{b}{a} = \frac{b}{a},$$

we recall that the reciprocal of the fraction a/b is the inverted fraction b/a. This result is consistent with that found in Chapter 1.

Example D The reciprocal of $2a$ is $1/2a$. The reciprocal of $1/b$ is $b/1$, or b. The reciprocal of $8x/3n$ is $3n/8x$. The reciprocal of the negative fraction $-xy/a$ is the negative fraction $-a/xy$. When we are finding the reciprocal, the sign of the fraction is unaltered.

One immediate use of the term reciprocal is in an alternative definition of the division of one fraction by another. We may state that when we divide one fraction by another we multiply the dividend by the reciprocal of the divisor.

As we brought out in Section 10–1, results which are fractions are usually expressed in simplified form. Due to the process of multiplying fractions, it is usually a relatively simple matter to simplify the product or quotient of two fractions. Remember that in simplifying a fraction, we must divide the numerator and denominator by factors which are common to both. Therefore, if we factor the numerators and denominators of the fractions being multiplied or divided, and then *indicate* the appropriate product, we can readily determine any common factors. If this is not done, it is very possible that the result obtained by multiplying out the fractions will be a fraction containing expressions which are extremely difficult to factor. This, in turn, will make the simplification difficult. The following examples illustrate the multiplication and division of algebraic fractions.

Multiply   *Example E*

$$\frac{8x^2y^3}{21abc} \quad \text{by} \quad \frac{15ax^2}{16b^2y^2} :$$

$$\frac{8x^2y^3}{21abc} \cdot \frac{15ax^2}{16b^2y^2} = \frac{(8)(15)ax^4y^3}{(21)(16)ab^3cy^2} .$$

Now we see that the highest common factor of the numerator and denominator is $(8)(3)ay^2$. Dividing numerator and denominator by this factor, we have $5x^4y/14b^3c$. Therefore

$$\frac{8x^2y^3}{21abc} \cdot \frac{15ax^2}{16b^2y^2} = \frac{5x^4y}{14b^3c} .$$

Perform the multiplication   *Example F*

$$\frac{x^2 - y^2}{x + 2y} \cdot \frac{3x + 6y}{x - y} .$$

If we perform the multiplication directly, by multiplying numerators together and denominators together, we obtain

$$\frac{3x^3 + 6x^2y - 3xy^2 - 6y^3}{x^2 + xy - 2y^2} .$$

Although the numerator is factorable, it is not of a simple form for factoring. The numerator is not factorable by methods we have developed. However, if we only *indicate* the multiplication as

$$\frac{x^2 - y^2}{x + 2y} \cdot \frac{3x + 6y}{x - y} = \frac{(x^2 - y^2)(3x + 6y)}{(x + 2y)(x - y)},$$

the numerator is already partially factored and the denominator is completely factored. The additional work now required is considerably less than that required after direct multiplication. Completing the factoring of the numerator, since $x^2 - y^2 = (x + y)(x - y)$ and $3x + 6y = 3(x + 2y)$, we have

$$\begin{aligned}
\frac{x^2 - y^2}{x + 2y} \cdot \frac{3x + 6y}{x - y} &= \frac{(x^2 - y^2)(3x + 6y)}{(x + 2y)(x - y)} \\
&= \frac{3(x - y)(x + y)(x + 2y)}{(x + 2y)(x - y)} \\
&= 3(x + y).
\end{aligned}$$

Here we see that the highest common factor of the numerator and denominator is $(x - y)(x + 2y)$.

Example G   Perform the division

$$\frac{b^2 - 2b + 1}{9b^2 - 1} \div \frac{5b - 5}{12b - 4}.$$

We shall first indicate the product of the dividend and the reciprocal of the divisor. We then factor both the numerator and denominator. Next we divide out the highest common factor. These steps lead to

$$\begin{aligned}
\frac{b^2 - 2b + 1}{9b^2 - 1} \div \frac{5b - 5}{12b - 4} &= \frac{(b^2 - 2b + 1)(12b - 4)}{(9b^2 - 1)(5b - 5)} \\
&= \frac{(b - 1)(b - 1)(4)(3b - 1)}{(3b + 1)(3b - 1)(5)(b - 1)} \\
&= \frac{4(b - 1)}{5(3b + 1)}.
\end{aligned}$$

The highest common factor which was divided out was $(b - 1)(3b - 1)$. The result has been left in factored form. Although it would be perfectly correct to multiply out each of the numerator and denominator, the factored form is often more convenient. Therefore it is definitely permissible to leave the result in factored form.

In Exercises 1 through 6, find the reciprocal of each expression.   **EXERCISES**

1. $8n$

2. $\dfrac{1}{13s}$

3. a^2b

4. $\dfrac{a}{3b}$

5. $-\dfrac{2x^2}{3y}$

6. $-\dfrac{5cd}{3ax}$

In Exercises 7 through 36, perform the indicated multiplications and divisions, expressing all answers in simplest form.

7. $\dfrac{2}{9} \cdot \dfrac{3a}{5}$

8. $\dfrac{6x}{13} \cdot \dfrac{7}{a}$

9. $\dfrac{17rs}{12t} \cdot \dfrac{3t^2}{51s}$

10. $\dfrac{24xy^2}{5z} \cdot \dfrac{125z^2}{8y^3}$

11. $\left(\dfrac{3}{4}\right)^4$

12. $\left(\dfrac{7}{5}\right)^3$

13. $\left(\dfrac{a^2}{2x}\right)^5$

14. $\left(\dfrac{4xy^4}{8z^2}\right)^5$

15. $\dfrac{6x}{17} \div \dfrac{7}{68m}$

16. $\dfrac{15}{8z} \div \dfrac{25}{18y}$

17. $\dfrac{3x}{25y} \div \dfrac{27x^2}{5y^2}$

18. $\dfrac{3a^2x}{4ay^2} \div \dfrac{6ax}{5a^3x^2}$

19. $\dfrac{9a^2b^2}{10ab^3} \div \dfrac{72a^3b^4}{40}$

20. $\dfrac{4x}{3x^2y^2} \div \dfrac{20xy}{9y^3}$

21. $\dfrac{a - 5b}{a + b} \cdot \dfrac{a + 3b}{a - 5b}$ $\dfrac{a + 3b}{a + b}$

22. $\dfrac{5n + 10}{3n - 9} \cdot \dfrac{n - 3}{15}$

23. $\dfrac{x^2 - y^2}{14x} \cdot \dfrac{35x^2}{3x + 3y}$

24. $\dfrac{a + b}{4a} \cdot \dfrac{3a^2}{(a + b)^2}$

25. $\dfrac{x^2 + 2x - 3}{x^2 - 4} \cdot \dfrac{x^2 - x - 6}{x^2 - 5x + 4}$

26. $\dfrac{3x^2 + 10x - 8}{36x^2 - 16} \cdot \dfrac{9x^2 + 15x + 6}{x^2 + 3x - 4}$

27. $\dfrac{3a^2 - 3b^2}{a^2 - 4b^2} \div \dfrac{a^2 + 2ab + b^2}{a + 2b}$

28. $\dfrac{20x}{x^2 - 8x + 15} \div \dfrac{10x}{x^2 - 2x - 15}$

29. $\dfrac{s^2 - 5s - 14}{s^2 - 9s - 36} \div \dfrac{s^2 + 4s - 77}{s^2 + 10s + 21}$

30. $\dfrac{p^2 + 5pq + 6q^2}{2p^2 + pq - q^2} \div \dfrac{p^2 - 9q^2}{(p + q)^2}$

31. $\dfrac{4x^2 - 4}{3x^2 - 13x - 10} \div \dfrac{4x + 4}{x^2 - 6x + 5}$

32. $\dfrac{y^2 - y - 2}{2y^2 + y - 10} \div \dfrac{6y^2 - y - 7}{12y^2 + 16y - 35}$

33. $\dfrac{3a - 3b}{6a} \cdot \dfrac{(a + b)^2}{a^2 - b^2} \cdot \dfrac{4a^2}{2a^2 - ab - b^2}$

34. $\left(\dfrac{2x^2 + x - 15}{4x^2 - 5x - 21} \cdot \dfrac{x^2 - 6x + 9}{x^2 - 9}\right) \div \dfrac{4x^2 - 25}{4x + 7}$

35. $\left[\dfrac{1}{a^2(x - y)^3} \cdot a^3(3x - 3y)\right] \div \dfrac{1}{3^3(4x^2 - 9y^2)}$

36. $\left[(3x + 7)\left(\dfrac{1}{8x^2 - 10x - 25}\right)\right] \cdot [(14 - x - 3x^2) \div (x^2 - 4)]$

In Exercises 37 through 39, solve the given problems.

37. In order to find the focal length of a lens in terms of the object distance p and the image distance q, it is necessary to find the reciprocal of the expression $(p + q)/pq$. Find this reciprocal.

38. The current in a simple electric circuit is the voltage in the circuit divided by the resistance. Given that the voltage changes with time according to the formula

$$V = \frac{3t}{t + 2}$$

and the resistance changes with time according to the formula

$$R = \frac{t^2 + 4}{t^2 + 4t + 4},$$

what is the formula for the current i in terms of t?

39. In the development of the theory of relativity, one encounters the expression

$$\left[\frac{c^2 - V^2}{\dfrac{c^2(c^2 - v^2)^2 - (c^2 - v^2)^2 V^2}{(c^2 + v^2)^2}} \right] \left(\frac{c^2 - v^2}{c^2 + v^2} \right)^2$$

Show that this expression equals 1.

10-3 THE LOWEST COMMON DENOMINATOR

From Chapter 1 we recall that the sum of a set of fractions, all having the same denominator, is the sum of the numerators divided by the denominator. The reason for this is reviewed in the following example.

Example A   When we determine the sum $\frac{2}{7} + \frac{4}{7}$, we are finding the total number of one-sevenths of a unit. The first fraction represents two and the second fraction represents four of the one-sevenths of the unit. Thus the total is six one-sevenths. This we represent as

$$\frac{2}{7} + \frac{4}{7} = \frac{2 + 4}{7} = \frac{6}{7}.$$

Therefore we know that finding the sum of a set of fractions having the same denominator is a relatively easy task. However, if the fractions do not all have the same denominator, we also know that we must first change each to an equivalent fraction such that each resulting fraction has the same denominator. Since this step is of utmost importance in the addition and subtraction of fractions, and since it is also the step which causes the most difficulty with algebraic fractions, we shall devote this entire section to finding the common denominator of a given set of fractions. In the following section we shall discuss the complete method for the addition and subtraction of algebraic fractions.

From our previous work with fractions, we know that the most convenient and useful denominator for a set of fractions is the *lowest common denominator*. We recall that this is the denominator that contains the smallest number of prime factors of the given denominators and which is exactly divisible by each denominator. For algebraic fractions it is the simplest expression into which all given denominators will divide evenly.

When we are finding the sum $\frac{3}{8} + \frac{5}{16}$, we know that the lowest common   **Example B**
denominator of these fractions is 16. That is, 16 is the smallest number into which both 8 and 16 divide evenly.

When we are finding the sum

$$\frac{3}{8a} + \frac{5}{16a},$$

we note that both $8a$ and $16a$ will divide evenly into $16a$, which is therefore the lowest common denominator. If we used $16a^2$ as the common denominator, we would not have the simplest possible expression for the common denominator.

With algebraic fractions, just as with arithmetic fractions, in order to determine the lowest common denominator of a set of fractions, we first find all the prime factors of each denominator. We then form the product of these prime factors, giving each factor the largest exponent it has in any of the given denominators.

When we are finding the lowest common denominator of $\frac{5}{24}$ and $\frac{7}{36}$,   **Example C**
we first factor 24 and 36 into their prime factors. This gives

$$24 = 2 \cdot 2 \cdot 2 \cdot 3 = 2^3 \cdot 3 \quad \text{and} \quad 36 = 2 \cdot 2 \cdot 3 \cdot 3 = 2^2 3^2.$$

The prime factors to be considered are 2 and 3. The largest exponent to which 2 appears is 3. The largest exponent to which 3 appears is 2. Therefore the lowest common denominator is $2^3 3^2 = 72$. No number smaller than 72 is divisible evenly by 24 and 36.

When we are finding the lowest common denominator of

$$\frac{1}{4x^2y} \quad \text{and} \quad \frac{7a}{6xy^4},$$

we factor the denominators into their prime factors. This gives

$$4x^2y = 2^2x^2y \quad \text{and} \quad 6xy^4 = 2 \cdot 3 \cdot xy^4.$$

The prime factors to be considered are 2, 3, x, and y. The largest exponent of 2 is 2; the largest exponent of 3 is 1; the largest exponent of x is 2; and the largest exponent of y is 4. Therefore the lowest common denominator is $2^2 \cdot 3 \cdot x^2y^4 = 12x^2y^4$. This is the simplest expression into which $4x^2y$ and $6xy^4$ both divide evenly.

When we are finding the lowest common denominator of a set of algebraic fractions, and when some of the factors are binomials, we *indicate* the multiplication of the necessary factors but do not multiply out the product. This prevents us from losing the identity of the several factors, and therefore makes the process of finding the appropriate equivalent fractions much easier. The reasoning for this will be shown in the following section when we actually add and subtract algebraic fractions. The following examples illustrate the procedure for finding the lowest common denominator for given sets of algebraic fractions.

Example D   Find the lowest common denominator of the fractions

$$\frac{x-9}{x^2+x-6} \quad \text{and} \quad \frac{x+2}{x^2-5x+6}.$$

Factoring the denominators, we have

$$x^2+x-6 = (x+3)(x-2), \quad x^2-5x+6 = (x-2)(x-3).$$

The necessary factors are $(x-2)$, $(x-3)$, and $(x+3)$. Since the highest power to which each appears is 1, the lowest common denominator is

$$(x-2)(x-3)(x+3).$$

The product of these three factors is $x^3 - 2x^2 - 9x + 18$. It is readily apparent that we would lose the identity of the factors in the multiplication. In forming the equivalent fractions, we would have to actually divide this expression by each of the individual denominators. This would create a great deal of extra work, since in the factored form

this division can be done by inspection.   Therefore the form
$(x - 2)(x - 3)(x + 3)$ is preferable.

Find the lowest common denominator of the fractions   Example E

$$\frac{2}{5x^2}, \quad \frac{3x}{10x^2 - 10}, \quad \frac{5}{x^2 - x}.$$

Factoring the denominators, we have

$$5x^2 = 5x^2,$$
$$10x^2 - 10 = 10(x^2 - 1) = 2 \cdot 5(x - 1)(x + 1),$$
$$x^2 - x = x(x - 1).$$

The prime factors of the lowest common denominator are 2, 5, x, $x - 1$,
and $x + 1$. Each appears to the first power except x, which appears to
the second power.   Therefore the lowest common denominator is
$2 \cdot 5x^2(x - 1)(x + 1) = 10x^2(x - 1)(x + 1)$. (Here we have multiplied
the numerical factors in the coefficient. However, the others have been
left in factored form.)

Find the lowest common denominator of the fractions   Example F

$$\frac{3x}{x^2 + 4x + 4}, \quad \frac{5}{x^2 - 4}, \quad \frac{x}{6x + 12}.$$

Factoring the denominators, we have

$$x^2 + 4x + 4 = (x + 2)(x + 2) = (x + 2)^2,$$
$$x^2 - 4 = (x - 2)(x + 2),$$
$$6x + 12 = 6(x + 2) = 2 \cdot 3(x + 2).$$

The prime factors of the lowest common denominator are 2, 3, $x + 2$,
and $x - 2$. All appear to the first power except $x + 2$, which appears
to the second power. Therefore the lowest common denominator is

$$2 \cdot 3(x + 2)^2(x - 2) = 6(x + 2)^2(x - 2).$$

   The lowest common denominator of many simpler fractions, especially
arithmetic fractions, can be determined by inspection. However, whenever the *lowest* common denominator is not obvious, the method outlined
above should be followed.

EXERCISES   In the following exercises, find the lowest common denominator of each of the given sets of fractions.

1. $\dfrac{1}{4a}, \dfrac{1}{6a}$

2. $\dfrac{7}{15x}, \dfrac{8}{25x}$

3. $\dfrac{5}{18}, \dfrac{11}{45y}$

4. $\dfrac{7}{40}, \dfrac{7}{72n}$

5. $\dfrac{9}{60ax}, \dfrac{9}{28a}$

6. $\dfrac{3a}{8rst}, \dfrac{9b}{20st}$

7. $\dfrac{36}{125ax^2}, \dfrac{7}{15ax}$

8. $\dfrac{9}{16a^2b^2}, \dfrac{1}{12a^2b}$

9. $\dfrac{1}{25a^2}, \dfrac{7}{3a^3}$

10. $\dfrac{5}{4x^5}, \dfrac{9}{8x^2}$

11. $\dfrac{15}{32ab^3}, \dfrac{11}{12a^3b^2}$

12. $\dfrac{8}{27abc^5}, \dfrac{7x}{3a^2bc^4}$

13. $\dfrac{27}{4acx^3}, \dfrac{5}{12a^2cx}, \dfrac{13b}{20acx}$

14. $\dfrac{4}{25p^2q}, \dfrac{8}{15q^2r}, \dfrac{16}{27prs^2}$

15. $\dfrac{5}{4x-4}, \dfrac{3}{8x}$

16. $\dfrac{7}{6y^3-12y^2}, \dfrac{3y}{4y-8}$

17. $\dfrac{5}{3a^2x-9ax}, \dfrac{7x}{6a^2-18a}$

18. $\dfrac{9}{8a^2x^3+2a^3x^2}, \dfrac{26}{12x+3a}$

19. $\dfrac{3x}{2x-2y}, \dfrac{5}{x^2-xy}, \dfrac{7x}{6x^2-6y^2}$

20. $\dfrac{1}{x^4-x^3}, \dfrac{3}{4x^2-4}, \dfrac{a}{x^3+x^2}$

21. $\dfrac{a+3b}{a^2-ab-2b^2}, \dfrac{a+b}{a^2-4b^2}$

22. $\dfrac{x-5}{x^2-3x+2}, \dfrac{x}{2x^2-4x+2}$

23. $\dfrac{x-1}{4x^2-36}, \dfrac{x+7}{3x^2+18x+27}$

24. $\dfrac{7}{2t^2-5t-12}, \dfrac{5t}{2t^2+10t+6}$

25. $\dfrac{x-7y}{3x^2-7xy-6y^2}, \dfrac{x+y}{x^2-9y^2}, \dfrac{7}{2x-6y}$

26. $\dfrac{5}{6x^4-6y^4}, \dfrac{x+y}{4x^2+4y^2}, \dfrac{2x-5y}{3x^2-6xy+3y^2}$

10-4 ADDITION AND SUBTRACTION OF FRACTIONS

Now that we have discussed the basic method of finding the lowest common denominator of a set of fractions, we are in a position to perform the operations of addition and subtraction of algebraic fractions. As we have pointed out, if we want to add or subtract fractions whose denominators are the same, we place the sum of numerators over the denominator. If the denominators differ, we must first change the fractions to equivalent ones with a common denominator equal to the lowest common denominator. We then combine the numerators of the equivalent fractions algebraically, placing this result over the common denominator. The following examples illustrate the method.

Combine
$$\frac{7}{5ax} + \frac{3b}{5ax} - \frac{4b}{5ax}.$$
Example A

Since the denominators are the same for each of the fractions, we need only to combine the numerators over the common denominator. We therefore have

$$\frac{7}{5ax} + \frac{3b}{5ax} - \frac{4b}{5ax} = \frac{7 + 3b - 4b}{5ax} = \frac{7 - b}{5ax}.$$

Note that the signs of the terms of the numerator are the same as those of the fractions from which they were obtained.

Combine
$$\frac{3}{ax} + \frac{x}{2a^2} - \frac{7}{2x}.$$
Example B

By looking at the denominators, we see that the factors necessary in the lowest common denominator are 2, a, and x. Both 2 and x appear only to the first power and a appears squared. Thus the lowest common denominator is $2a^2x$. We now wish to write each of the fractions in an equivalent form with $2a^2x$ as denominator. Since the denominator of the first fraction contains factors of a and x, it is necessary to introduce additional factors of 2 and a, or, in other words, we must multiply the numerator and denominator of the first fraction by $2a$. For similar reasons, we must multiply the numerator and denominator of the second fraction by x, and the numerator and denominator of the third fraction by a^2. This leads to

$$\frac{3}{ax} + \frac{x}{2a^2} - \frac{7}{2x} = \frac{3(2a)}{(ax)(2a)} + \frac{x(x)}{(2a^2)(x)} - \frac{7(a^2)}{(2x)(a^2)}$$

$$= \frac{6a}{2a^2x} + \frac{x^2}{2a^2x} - \frac{7a^2}{2a^2x} = \frac{6a + x^2 - 7a^2}{2a^2x}.$$

Combine
$$\frac{4}{x + 3} + \frac{3}{x + 2}.$$
Example C

Since there is only one factor in each of the denominators, and they are different, the lowest common denominator of these fractions is the product $(x + 3)(x + 2)$. This in turn means that we must multiply the numerator and denominator of the first fraction by $x + 2$, and those of the second fraction by $x + 3$ in order to make equivalent fractions with $(x + 3)(x + 2)$ as the denominator. Therefore, performing the addition, we have

$$
\begin{aligned}
\frac{4}{x + 3} + \frac{3}{x + 2} &= \frac{4(x + 2)}{(x + 3)(x + 2)} + \frac{3(x + 3)}{(x + 2)(x + 3)} \\
&= \frac{4(x + 2) + 3(x + 3)}{(x + 3)(x + 2)} \\
&= \frac{4x + 8 + 3x + 9}{(x + 3)(x + 2)} \\
&= \frac{7x + 17}{(x + 3)(x + 2)} .
\end{aligned}
$$

Example D   Combine

$$
\frac{x}{x + y} - \frac{2y^2}{x^2 - y^2} .
$$

Factoring the denominator of the second fraction, we have $x^2 - y^2 = (x + y)(x - y)$. Since the factor $x + y$ appears in the first fraction, and there is no other (third) factor, the lowest common denominator is $(x + y)(x - y)$. Therefore we must multiply the numerator and denominator of the first fraction by $x - y$, whereas the second fraction remains the same. This leads to

$$
\begin{aligned}
\frac{x}{x + y} - \frac{2y^2}{x^2 - y^2} &= \frac{x}{x + y} - \frac{2y^2}{(x + y)(x - y)} \\
&= \frac{x(x - y)}{(x + y)(x - y)} - \frac{2y^2}{(x + y)(x - y)} \\
&= \frac{x^2 - xy - 2y^2}{(x + y)(x - y)} \\
&= \frac{(x + y)(x - 2y)}{(x + y)(x - y)} \\
&= \frac{x - 2y}{x - y} .
\end{aligned}
$$

We note here that when the numerators were combined, the result was factorable. One of the factors also appeared in the denominator, which means it was possible to reduce the resulting fraction. Remember, we must express the result in simplest form.

Combine   Example E

$$\frac{5}{a^2 - a - 6} + \frac{1}{a^2 - 5a + 6} - \frac{2}{a^2 - 4a + 4}.$$

Factoring the denominators, we have

$$a^2 - a - 6 = (a - 3)(a + 2),$$
$$a^2 - 5a + 6 = (a - 3)(a - 2),$$
$$a^2 - 4a + 4 = (a - 2)(a - 2) = (a - 2)^2.$$

The prime factors of the lowest common denominator are $a - 3$, $a + 2$, and $a - 2$, where $a - 2$ appears to the second power. The lowest common denominator is therefore $(a - 3)(a + 2)(a - 2)^2$. To have equivalent fractions with the lowest common denominator, it is necessary to multiply the numerator and the denominator of the first fraction by $(a - 2)^2$, those of the second fraction by $(a - 2)(a + 2)$, and those of the third fraction by $(a + 2)(a - 3)$. This leads to

$$\frac{5}{a^2 - a - 6} + \frac{1}{a^2 - 5a + 6} - \frac{2}{a^2 - 4a + 4}$$

$$= \frac{5}{(a - 3)(a + 2)} + \frac{1}{(a - 3)(a - 2)} - \frac{2}{(a - 2)^2}$$

$$= \frac{5(a - 2)^2}{(a - 3)(a + 2)(a - 2)^2} + \frac{1(a - 2)(a + 2)}{(a - 3)(a - 2)(a - 2)(a + 2)}$$
$$\quad - \frac{2(a + 2)(a - 3)}{(a - 2)^2(a + 2)(a - 3)}$$

$$= \frac{5(a - 2)^2 + (a - 2)(a + 2) - 2(a + 2)(a - 3)}{(a - 3)(a + 2)(a - 2)^2}$$

$$= \frac{5(a^2 - 4a + 4) + a^2 - 4 - 2(a^2 - a - 6)}{(a - 3)(a + 2)(a - 2)^2}$$

$$= \frac{5a^2 - 20a + 20 + a^2 - 4 - 2a^2 + 2a + 12}{(a - 3)(a + 2)(a - 2)^2}$$

$$= \frac{4a^2 - 18a + 28}{(a - 3)(a + 2)(a - 2)^2}$$

$$= \frac{2(2a^2 - 9a + 14)}{(a - 3)(a + 2)(a - 2)^2}.$$

Since $2a^2 - 9a + 14$ is not factorable, it is not possible to simplify the form of the result any further.

EXERCISES   In Exercises 1 through 8, change the indicated sum of fractions to an indicated sum of equivalent fractions with the proper lowest common denominator. Do not combine.

1. $\dfrac{5}{9a} - \dfrac{7}{12a}$

2. $\dfrac{1}{40ax} + \dfrac{5}{84a}$

3. $\dfrac{5}{ax} + \dfrac{1}{bx} - \dfrac{4}{a}$

4. $\dfrac{6}{a^3b} - \dfrac{5}{4ab} - \dfrac{1}{6a^2}$

5. $\dfrac{4}{x^2 - x} - \dfrac{3}{2x^3 - 2x^2}$

6. $\dfrac{5b}{3ab - 6ac} - \dfrac{7c}{3b^2 - 12c^2}$

7. $\dfrac{x}{2x - 4} + \dfrac{5}{x^2 - 4} - \dfrac{3x}{x^2 + 4x + 4}$

8. $\dfrac{a - 1}{3a - 3} - \dfrac{8}{a^2 - 5a + 4} - \dfrac{1}{9}$

In Exercises 9 through 28, combine the given fractions, expressing all results in simplest form.

9. $\dfrac{1}{2} - \dfrac{5}{8b} + \dfrac{3}{20}$

10. $\dfrac{11}{12} + \dfrac{13}{40} - \dfrac{4}{15s}$

11. $\dfrac{8}{by} - \dfrac{1}{y^2}$

12. $\dfrac{5}{p^2q} - \dfrac{1}{6pq}$

13. $\dfrac{2}{x} + \dfrac{5}{y} - \dfrac{3}{x^2y}$

14. $\dfrac{2}{a^2} - \dfrac{5}{6b} + \dfrac{3}{8ab}$

15. $\dfrac{7}{2x} - \dfrac{5}{4y} + \dfrac{1}{6z}$

16. $\dfrac{1}{6pq} + \dfrac{7}{3p} - \dfrac{9}{2p}$

17. $\dfrac{x}{2x - 6} - \dfrac{3}{4x + 12}$

18. $\dfrac{b}{a^2 - ab} + \dfrac{2}{a^3 + a^2b}$

19. $\dfrac{y - 1}{3y + 9} + \dfrac{2}{y - 3} - \dfrac{8}{3y - 9}$

20. $\dfrac{3}{4x - 16} - \dfrac{x}{4 - x} - \dfrac{1}{4x}$

21. $\dfrac{x - 1}{4x + 6} + \dfrac{2x}{6x + 9} - \dfrac{5}{6}$

22. $\dfrac{c + d}{5c - 2d} - \dfrac{c - d}{5c + 2d} - \dfrac{4c}{15c - 6d}$

23. $\dfrac{4}{4 - 9x^2} - \dfrac{x - 5}{2 + 3x}$

24. $\dfrac{q - 3}{q^2 - q - 12} + \dfrac{q + 1}{q^2 - 4q}$

25. $\dfrac{3x}{x^2 - 4} + \dfrac{2}{x - 2} - \dfrac{5x}{x + 2}$

26. $\dfrac{4}{x} - \dfrac{1}{3x - 1} + \dfrac{x + 1}{3x + 1}$

27. $\dfrac{p + 2q}{2p^2 - 20pq + 50q^2} + \dfrac{7p}{4p - 20q} - \dfrac{7}{8}$

28. $\dfrac{2}{x^2 + 2x - 15} + \dfrac{1}{x^2 - 9} - \dfrac{7}{x^2 + 8x + 15}$

In Exercises 29 through 36, solve the given problems.

29. Find the area of a trapezoid whose height is $\frac{16}{5}$ in. and whose bases are $\frac{7}{12}$ in. and $\frac{32}{15}$ in.

30. Find the total surface area of a rectangular solid whose sides are $\frac{5}{8}$, $\frac{7}{12}$, and $\frac{5}{6}$ ft.

31. When one is analyzing noise in an electronic vacuum tube, the expression

$$\frac{1}{g_m} + \frac{8}{g_m^2}$$

is found. Combine and simplify.

32. Under certain conditions, the equation of the curve for the cable of a bridge is

$$y = \frac{wx^2}{2T_0} + \frac{kx^4}{12T_0}.$$

Combine and simplify the terms on the right side.

33. In the theory dealing with the motion of the planets, one finds the expression

$$\frac{p^2}{2mr^2} - \frac{gmM}{r}.$$

Combine and simplify.

34. In the study of the stress and strain of deformable objects, one encounters the expression

$$a\left(l - \frac{l^2}{l + u} + 2u\right).$$

Combine and simplify.

35. In the theory dealing with a pendulum, one encounters the expression

$$\frac{P_1^2 + P_2^2}{2(h_1 + h_2)} + \frac{P_1^2 - P_2^2}{2(h_1 - h_2)}.$$

Combine and simplify.

36. In determining the characteristics of a specific optical lens, one uses the expression

$$\frac{2n^2 - n - 4}{2n^2 + 2n - 4} + \frac{1}{n - 1}.$$

Combine and simplify.

10–5 EQUATIONS INVOLVING FRACTIONS

Many important equations in technology and science have fractions in them. The solution of such equations still involves the use of the basic operations as outlined in Chapter 6. However, there is a basic procedure which can be used to eliminate the fractions and thereby help lead to the solution.

   If we *multiply each term of the equation by the lowest common denominator*, the resulting equation will not involve fractions and can be solved by methods previously discussed. The following examples illustrate the method.

Example A   Solve
$$\frac{x}{12} - \frac{x-3}{6} = \frac{3}{4} \quad \text{for } x.$$

We first note that the lowest common denominator of the terms of the equation is 12. We therefore now indicate the multiplication of each term by 12. This gives

$$\frac{12(x)}{12} - \frac{12(x-3)}{6} = \frac{12(3)}{4}.$$

We now reduce each term of the equation to its lowest terms. When this is done, no fractions remain, and the resulting equation is then solved.

$$x - 2(x - 3) = 3(3),$$
$$x - 2x + 6 = 9,$$
$$-x = 3,$$
$$x = -3,$$

Checking *in the original equation*, we have

$$\frac{-3}{12} - \frac{-3-3}{6} \overset{?}{=} \frac{3}{4}, \qquad -\frac{1}{4} - (-1) \overset{?}{=} \frac{3}{4}, \qquad -\frac{1}{4} + 1 = \frac{3}{4}.$$

Therefore the solution checks.

Example B   Solve
$$\frac{x}{a} - \frac{1}{2b} = \frac{3x}{ab} \quad \text{for } x.$$

The lowest common denominator of the terms of the equation is *2ab*. We therefore multiply each term of the equation by *2ab* and proceed with the solution.

$$\frac{(2ab)x}{a} - \frac{2ab(1)}{2b} = \frac{2ab(3x)}{ab},$$
$$2bx - a = 6x,$$
$$2bx - 6x = a.$$

In order to isolate x, we must factor x from each term on the left. This leads to

$$x(2b - 6) = a,$$
$$x = \frac{a}{2b - 6}.$$

Checking will lead to the expression

$$\frac{3}{2b(b - 3)}$$

on each side of the original equation.

Solve for x: $\dfrac{3}{x} + \dfrac{2}{x - 2} = \dfrac{4}{x^2 - 2x}$ **Example C**

Factoring the denominator of the term on the right, $x^2 - 2x = x(x - 2)$, we find that the lowest common denominator of the terms of the equation is $x(x - 2)$. Therefore we have

$$\frac{3x(x - 2)}{x} + \frac{2x(x - 2)}{x - 2} = \frac{4x(x - 2)}{x(x - 2)},$$
$$3(x - 2) + 2x = 4,$$
$$3x - 6 + 2x = 4,$$
$$5x = 10,$$
$$x = 2.$$

Substituting this value in the original equation, we obtain

$$\tfrac{3}{2} + \tfrac{2}{0} = \tfrac{4}{0}.$$

Since division by zero is an undefined operation (see Section 4–3), the value $x = 2$ cannot be a solution. Therefore there is no solution to this equation.

Example C points out well that we must check our solutions in the original equation. Another important conclusion from this example is that whenever we multiply through by a lowest common denominator *which contains the unknown* it is possible that a solution will be introduced into the resulting equation which is not a solution of the original equation. Such a solution is termed *extraneous*. Only certain equations will lead to extraneous solutions, but we must be careful to identify them when they occur.

Example D   Solve for y:
$$\frac{1}{2} - \frac{4}{3y - 6} = \frac{5}{y - 2}.$$

First we determine that the lowest common denominator of the terms of the equation is $6(y - 2)$. Multiplying each term by this expression and proceeding with the solution, we have

$$\frac{6(y - 2)}{2} - \frac{4(6)(y - 2)}{3(y - 2)} = \frac{5(6)(y - 2)}{y - 2},$$
$$3(y - 2) - 8 = 30,$$
$$3y - 6 - 8 = 30,$$
$$3y = 44,$$
$$y = \tfrac{44}{3}.$$

Checking this solution in the original equation, we have

$$\frac{1}{2} - \frac{4}{3(\frac{44}{3}) - 6} \overset{?}{=} \frac{5}{\frac{44}{3} - 2},$$
$$\frac{1}{2} - \frac{4}{44 - 6} \overset{?}{=} \frac{5}{\frac{44 - 6}{3}},$$
$$\tfrac{1}{2} - \tfrac{4}{38} \overset{?}{=} 5(\tfrac{3}{38}),$$
$$\tfrac{15}{38} = \tfrac{15}{38}.$$

Therefore the solution checks. No extraneous solutions were introduced.

A number of stated problems lead to equations which involve fractions. The following example illustrates such a problem.

Example E   A motorboat that can travel at 5 mi/hr in still water travels 14 mi upstream in the same time that it takes to go 26 mi downstream in a certain river. Find the rate of the stream.

Let $x =$ the rate of the stream. Therefore the rate of the boat when it is going upstream is $5 - x$ mi/hr, since the current of the stream is in the opposite direction. The rate of the boat when going downstream is $5 + x$ mi/hr.

The basis for finding the equation is distance $=$ rate $\times$ time, $d = rt$. Since we are told that the *time* is the same for the trips in opposite directions, we equate the time upstream to the time downstream. The time is expressed as the ratio of the distance to the rate. Therefore

$$\frac{14}{5-x} = \frac{26}{5+x}$$

is the required equation. Proceeding with the solution, we note that the lowest common denominator is $(5-x)(5+x)$. Therefore

$$\frac{14(5-x)(5+x)}{5-x} = \frac{26(5-x)(5+x)}{5+x},$$

$$14(5+x) = 26(5-x),$$

$$70 + 14x = 130 - 26x,$$

$$40x = 60,$$

$$x = 1.5 \text{ mi/hr.}$$

Checking the solution with the original statement, we see that the rate of the boat when it is traveling upstream is 3.5 mi/hr and the rate when it is traveling downstream is 6.5 mi/hr. Dividing 14 mi by 3.5 mi/hr, we find that it took 4 hr to travel upstream. Dividing 26 mi by 6.5 mi/hr, we see that it also took 4 hr to travel downstream. Therefore the solution checks.

In Exercises 1 through 20, solve the given equations and check the results.   **EXERCISES**

1. $\dfrac{x}{2} + 3 = x$ **2.** $\frac{1}{3} - 2x = \frac{5}{6}$

3. $\dfrac{6}{7} - \dfrac{y}{3} = \dfrac{5}{42}$ **4.** $\dfrac{x}{5} - \dfrac{5}{6} = \dfrac{4}{15}$

5. $\dfrac{x}{2} - \dfrac{x-5}{6} = 4$ **6.** $\dfrac{2t-3}{6} - \dfrac{2}{9} = \dfrac{5}{18}$

7. $3 - \dfrac{s}{6} = \dfrac{1-5s}{10}$ **8.** $\dfrac{1}{35} - \dfrac{7-x}{25} = \dfrac{4}{7}$

9. $\dfrac{2}{x} + \dfrac{7}{2} = 4$ **10.** $4 - \dfrac{6}{z} + \dfrac{2}{3z} = 0$

11. $4 - \dfrac{6-n}{n} + \dfrac{3}{7} = 0$ **12.** $\dfrac{x+1}{2x} = 3 + \dfrac{7}{4x}$

13. $\dfrac{2}{x} = \dfrac{6}{x-4}$ **14.** $\dfrac{12}{y-2} = 4$

15. $\dfrac{1}{2r-8} + \dfrac{2}{r-4} = 5$ **16.** $\dfrac{5}{3x+9} + \dfrac{x}{2x+6} = \dfrac{1}{6}$

17. $\dfrac{1}{x} + \dfrac{1}{x-1} = \dfrac{1}{x(x-1)}$ **18.** $\dfrac{4}{v-4} - \dfrac{1}{v-2} = \dfrac{v}{v^2 - 6v + 8}$

19. $\dfrac{10}{2x - 3} = \dfrac{6x + 7}{4x^2 - 9} + \dfrac{23}{2x + 3}$

20. $\dfrac{7}{2x - 1} - \dfrac{3}{4x - 2} = \dfrac{5x}{2x^2 - 3x + 1}$

In Exercises 21 through 32, solve for the indicated letter.

21. $3 + \dfrac{1}{a} = \dfrac{1}{b}$, for a

22. $\dfrac{3}{a} - \dfrac{2}{c} = \dfrac{7}{ac}$, for c

23. $\dfrac{x}{n} + \dfrac{3}{4n} = \dfrac{x}{2}$, for x

24. $\dfrac{7}{p^2} = t - \dfrac{3}{2p} + \dfrac{t}{p}$, for t

25. $\dfrac{x + 5}{a + 1} + 1 - \dfrac{2}{a - 1} = x$, for x

26. $\dfrac{2p}{c^2 - 5c} = \dfrac{3}{c^2} + \dfrac{p}{c - 5}$, for p

27. In optics, an important equation for a lens is

$$\frac{1}{p} + \frac{1}{q} = \frac{1}{f},$$

where p is the distance of the object from the lens, q is the distance of the image from the lens, and f is the focal length of the lens. Solve for q.

28. In electricity, if resistors R_1 and R_2 are connected in parallel, their combined resistance R is given by the equation

$$\frac{1}{R} = \frac{1}{R_1} + \frac{1}{R_2}.$$

Solve for R.

29. A formula relating the number of teeth N of a gear, the outside diameter D_0 of the gear, and the pitch diameter D_p is

$$D_p = \frac{D_0 N}{N + 2}.$$

Solve for N.

30. An equation found in the thermodynamics of refrigeration is

$$\frac{W}{Q_1} = \frac{T_2}{T_1} - 1,$$

where W is the work input, Q_1 is the heat absorbed, T_1 is the temperature within the refrigerator, and T_2 is the external temperature. Solve for T_2.

31. In hydrodynamics, one encounters the equation

$$\frac{p}{d} = \frac{P}{d} - \frac{m^2}{2\pi^2 r^2}.$$

Solve for d.

32. An equation which arises in the study of the motion of a projectile is

$$m^2 - \frac{2v^2m}{gx} + \frac{2v^2y}{gx^2} + 1 = 0.$$

Solve for g.

In Exercises 33 through 36, solve the given stated problems.

33. The perimeter of a rectangular metal plate whose width is two-thirds of its length is 80 in. Find the dimensions of the plate.

34. Two electric resistances are 3.0 ohms and 5.0 ohms, respectively. By how much must each resistance be increased in order that their ratio be 3/4?

35. The current in a certain river flows at 2.0 mi/hr. A man can row downstream 13 mi in the same time that it takes him to row 5.0 mi upstream. What is his rate of rowing in still water?

36. A jet travels 1500 mi between two cities. It then travels 1800 mi at the same speed in $\frac{1}{2}$ hr more than the first trip. What was the time required to travel between the first two cities?

10–6 REVIEW EXERCISES

In Exercises 1 through 12, reduce the given fractions to simplest form.

1. $\dfrac{9rst^6}{3s^4t^2}$

2. $\dfrac{-14y^2z^3}{84y^5z^2}$

3. $\dfrac{2a^2bc}{6ab^2c^3}$

4. $\dfrac{76x^3yz^3}{19xz^5}$

5. $\dfrac{4x + 8y}{x^2 - 4y^2}$

6. $\dfrac{a^2x - a^2y}{ax^2 - ay^2}$

7. $\dfrac{p^2 + pq}{3p + 2p^3}$

8. $\dfrac{4a - 12ab}{5b - 15b^2}$

9. $\dfrac{2a^2 + 2ab - 2ac}{4ab + 4b^2 - 4bc}$

10. $\dfrac{p^2 - 3p - 4}{p^2 - p - 12}$

11. $\dfrac{6x^2 - 7xy - 3y^2}{4x^2 - 8xy + 3y^2}$

12. $\dfrac{2y^2 - 14y + 20}{7y - 2y^2 - 6}$

In Exercises 13 through 36, perform the indicated operations.

13. $\dfrac{2x}{3a} \cdot \dfrac{5a^2}{x^3}$

14. $\dfrac{5b^3}{6c} \cdot \dfrac{3c^5}{10b}$

15. $\dfrac{3x^2}{4y^3} \cdot \dfrac{5y^4}{x^3}$

16. $\dfrac{7p}{12q^3} \cdot \dfrac{20q^4}{35p^3}$

17. $\dfrac{3a}{4} \div \dfrac{a^2}{8}$

18. $\dfrac{ab^3}{bc} \div a^2c$

19. $\dfrac{au^2}{4bv^2} \div \dfrac{a^2u}{8b^2v}$

20. $\dfrac{20m^3n^2}{12mn^4} \div \dfrac{27mn}{8m^2n^3}$

21. $\dfrac{2}{a^2} - \dfrac{3}{5ab}$

22. $\dfrac{3x}{4y} - \dfrac{5y}{6x}$

23. $\dfrac{5}{c} - \dfrac{3}{c^2d} + \dfrac{1}{2cd}$

24. $\dfrac{3}{2x^2} + \dfrac{1}{4x} - \dfrac{a}{6x^3}$

25. $\dfrac{x^2 - 2x - 15}{x^2 - 9} \cdot \dfrac{x^2 - 6x + 9}{4x - 12}$

26. $\dfrac{2x^2 - 14x + 24}{x^2 - 4x + 3} \cdot \dfrac{3x^2 - 27}{4x - 20}$

27. $(9x^2 - 4y^2) \div \dfrac{3x - 2y}{y - 2x}$

28. $\dfrac{6r^2 - rs - s^2}{4r^2 - 16s^2} \div \dfrac{2r^2 + rs - s^2}{r^2 + 3rs + 2s^2}$

29. $\dfrac{2x}{x - 2} - \dfrac{x^2 - 3}{x^2 - 4x + 4}$

30. $\dfrac{3}{3x + y} - \dfrac{7}{3x^2 - 5xy - 2y^2}$

31. $\dfrac{2x - 3}{2x^2 - x - 15} - \dfrac{3x}{x^2 - 9}$

32. $\dfrac{3}{8x + 16} - \dfrac{1 - x}{4x^2 - 16} + \dfrac{5}{2x - 4}$

33. $\left[\dfrac{2}{a - b} \cdot \dfrac{a + b}{5}\right] \div \left[\dfrac{a^2 + 2ab + b^2}{a^2 - b^2}\right]$

34. $\left[\dfrac{x^4 - 1}{(x - 1)^2} \div (x^2 + 1)\right] \cdot \left[\dfrac{x - 1}{x + 1}\right]$

35. $\left[\dfrac{1}{x - 2} \div \dfrac{3 + x}{x + 1}\right] \div \left[\dfrac{2 + x}{x^2 - x - 6}\right]$

36. $\left[\dfrac{2s}{s - 1} + \dfrac{s^2}{s^2 - 1}\right] \div \left[\dfrac{s^3}{s - 1}\right]$

In Exercises 37 through 44, solve the given equations.

37. $\dfrac{1}{2} - \dfrac{x}{6} + 3 = \dfrac{2x}{9}$

38. $\dfrac{6}{7} - \dfrac{x}{4} = 2x - \dfrac{5}{14}$

39. $\dfrac{bx}{a} - \dfrac{1}{4} = x + \dfrac{3}{2a}$, for x

40. $\dfrac{4(x - y)}{5b} - \dfrac{x}{b^2} = \dfrac{y}{5b}$, for x

41. $\dfrac{5}{x + 1} - \dfrac{3}{x} = \dfrac{-5}{x(x + 1)}$

42. $\dfrac{20}{y^2 - 25} - \dfrac{1}{y + 5} = \dfrac{2}{y - 5}$

43. $\dfrac{5x}{x^2 + 2x} + \dfrac{1}{x} = \dfrac{3}{4x + 8}$

44. $\dfrac{2}{2t + 1} - \dfrac{t - 1}{4t^2 - 4t - 3} = \dfrac{1}{2t - 3}$

In Exercises 45 through 57, solve the given problems.

45. In the study of the conduction of electrons in metals, one finds the expression

$$\frac{1}{2}\left(\frac{eE}{m}\right)(ne)\left(\frac{l}{v}\right).$$

Perform the indicated multiplication.

46. In the study of the resistance that a pipe gives to a liquid flowing through it, one finds the expression

$$(p_1 - p_2) \div \left[\frac{(p_1 - p_2)\pi a^4}{8lu}\right].$$

Perform the indicated division.

47. A sphere of radius r floats in a liquid. When one is determining the height h which the sphere protrudes above the surface, the expression

$$\frac{1}{4r^2} - \frac{h}{12r^3}$$

is found. Combine and simplify.

48. When one is considering the impedance of an electronic amplifier, the expression

$$1 - \frac{2Z_1}{Z_1 + Z_2}$$

is encountered. Combine and simplify.

49. In the theory of electricity, one finds the expression

$$L^2\omega^2 - \frac{2L}{C} + \frac{1}{C^2\omega^2}$$

(ω is the Greek letter omega). Combine these fractions and factor the resulting numerator for the final answer.

50. In the study of the velocity of light, one finds the expression

$$\frac{2d}{c}\left(1 + \frac{v^2}{2c^2} + \frac{3v^4}{4c^4}\right).$$

Combine and simplify.

51. In the study of the convection of heat, the equation

$$\frac{1}{U} = \frac{x}{k} + \frac{1}{h}$$

is used. Solve for x.

52. In photography, when one is analyzing the focusing of cameras, one uses the equation

$$\frac{q_2 - q_1}{d} = \frac{f + q_1}{D}.$$

Solve for q_1.

53. Under certain circumstances, the combined capacitance of three electric capacitors is given by

$$\frac{1}{C} = \frac{1}{C_2} + \frac{1}{C_1 + C_3}.$$

Solve for C_1.

54. In the study of the motion of the planets, one finds the equation

$$\frac{mv^2}{2} - \frac{kmM}{r} = -\frac{kmM}{2a}.$$

Solve for r.

55. When one is considering the amplification of a vacuum tube, the equation

$$A = \left[\left(\frac{\mu}{\mu + 1} \right) R \right] \div \left[\frac{r}{\mu + 1} + R \right]$$

(μ is the Greek letter mu) is found. Simplify the right side of this equation.

56. The radius of one pulley is 6.0 in. more than the radius of a second pulley. If each radius is increased by 5.0 in., their ratio is 2/3. Find the radius of the smaller pulley.

57. One river flows at the rate of 2 mi/hr and a second river at the rate of 4 mi/hr. It takes a motorboat as long to go 15 mi downstream in the first river as it does to go 18 mi downstream in the second river. Calculate the rate of the boat in still water.

Exponents, Roots and Radicals

11

11–1 ZERO AND NEGATIVE EXPONENTS

Before we can develop some of the topics which will arise in future chapters, we need to complete some of the basic concepts associated with exponents, roots, and radicals. Primarily we shall show their relationship to negative numbers and fractions.

In our discussion of algebraic division in Section 8–3, we determined that, when we are dividing powers of the same base, we must subtract exponents. Equations (8–4a) and (8–4b) give the results for two cases: (a) the exponent in the numerator is larger, and (b) the exponent in the denominator is larger. No mention was made of the case in which they are equal, although we have been able to deal with this situation. In this section we shall generalize the results of Eqs. (8–4a) and (8–4b) in such a way that we may include negative integers and zero as exponents. Including them is occasionally found to be convenient in work with fractions, but it will become essential in the following section when we discuss scientific notation and in Chapter 13 when we discuss logarithms.

If we apply Eq. (8–4a) to the case in which the exponent in the denominator is larger, we have the quantity $m - n$ as a negative integer. This is illustrated in the following example.

Example A   Applying Eq. (8–4a) to the fraction a^3/a^5, we have

$$\frac{a^3}{a^5} = a^{3-5} = a^{-2}.$$

Using Eq. (8–4b) leads to the result

$$\frac{a^3}{a^5} = \frac{1}{a^{5-3}} = \frac{1}{a^2}.$$

If these results are to be consistent, it must be that

$$\frac{1}{a^2} = a^{-2}.$$

We find that if we define

$$a^{-n} = \frac{1}{a^n}, \qquad\qquad \textbf{11–1}$$

then all results obtained by the use of Eqs. (8–4a), (8–4b), and (11–1) are consistent. Therefore Eq. (11–1) shows us that we may use negative integers as exponents. Also, we see that we may move a *factor* from the numerator to the denominator or from the denominator to the numerator by changing the sign of its exponent. Consider the illustrations of the following example.

In the division $b^4 \div b^7$, we may express the result as either $1/b^3$ or as b^{-3}.

Any number a can be expressed as $a^1 = a^{-(-1)} = 1/a^{-1}$. In the same sense, $a^{-1} = 1/a$.

In reducing the fraction

$$\frac{x^2 y z^3}{x y^4 z^2}$$

to its simplest form, we may place all factors in the numerator, by the use of negative exponents, and combine exponents of the same base in order to determine the result. This leads to

$$\frac{x^2 y z^3}{x y^4 z^2} = x^2 x^{-1} y y^{-4} z^3 z^{-2} = x^{2-1} y^{1-4} z^{3-2} = x y^{-3} z = \frac{xz}{y^3}.$$

In general, negative exponents are not used in the expression of a final result, with certain specific exceptions. They are, however, used in intermediate steps in many operations.

In dividing a^m by a^n, where $m = n$, we have the case in which we are dividing a given quantity by itself. This division must then give the result 1. That is, $a^m/a^m = 1$. Using Eq. (8–4a), we have $a^m/a^m = a^{m-m} = a^0$. Since a has not been specified,

$$a^0 = 1,$$

for any a not zero. This equation states that any algebraic expression which is not zero and which is raised to the zero power is 1.

Example C

$$5^0 = 1, \qquad\qquad x^0 = 1,$$
$$(rs)^0 = 1, \qquad\qquad (ax - p)^0 = 1,$$
$$(9x^2 - 8x - 3)^0 = 1, \qquad \left(\frac{ax - b}{cx + d}\right)^0 = 1.$$

Zero and negative exponents may be used in the other laws of exponents just as any positive exponent. For reference, we now list the laws of exponents we have encountered:

$$(a^m)(a^n) = a^{m+n} \qquad\qquad\qquad \text{8–1}$$

$$(a^m)^n = a^{mn} \qquad\qquad\qquad \text{8–2}$$

$$(ab)^n = a^n b^n \qquad\qquad\qquad \text{8–3}$$

$$\frac{a^m}{a^n} = a^{m-n} \quad (a \text{ not zero}) \qquad\qquad \text{8–4}$$

$$\left(\frac{a}{b}\right)^n = \frac{a^n}{b^n} \quad (b \text{ not zero}) \qquad\qquad \text{10–3}$$

$$a^{-n} = \frac{1}{a^n} \quad (a \text{ not zero}) \qquad\qquad \text{11–1}$$

$$a^0 = 1 \quad (a \text{ not zero}) \qquad\qquad \text{11–2}$$

Example D

$$(a^5)(a^0) = a^{5+0} = a^5,$$

$$(a^5)^0 = a^{5 \cdot 0} = a^0 = 1,$$

$$\frac{(x^2 y)^0}{x^3 y^2} = \frac{1}{x^3 y^2},$$

$$(a^{-5})(a^0) = a^{-5+0} = a^{-5} = \frac{1}{a^5},$$

$$\frac{x^{-2}}{x^{-7}} = x^{-2-(-7)} = x^{-2+7} = x^5$$

$$(x^{-2} y^3)^{-2} = x^{(-2)(-2)} y^{3(-2)} = x^4 y^{-6} = \frac{x^4}{y^6},$$

$$\left(\frac{p^{-1}}{q^3}\right)^2 = \frac{p^{(-1)(2)}}{q^{(3)(2)}} = \frac{p^{-2}}{q^6} = \frac{1}{p^2 q^6},$$

$$\frac{r^{-3} s^2 t^4}{r s^{-1} t^{-3}} = \frac{(s^2)(s)(t^4)(t^3)}{(r^3)(r)} = \frac{s^{2+1} t^{4+3}}{r^{3+1}} = \frac{s^3 t^7}{r^4}.$$

EXERCISES   In Exercises 1 through 32, express each of the given expressions in the simplest form which contains only positive exponents.

1. b^{-3} 2. c^{-5} 3. $\dfrac{1}{a^{-4}}$ 4. $\dfrac{1}{b^{-2}}$

5. $2b^{-1}$ 6. $(2b)^{-1}$ 7. $\dfrac{1}{2b^{-1}}$ 8. $\dfrac{1}{(2b)^{-1}}$

9. 8^0 10. $(10)^0$ 11. $(a - 5b)^0$ 12. $\dfrac{1}{(4x - 8)^0}$

13. $\dfrac{3}{3^{-5}}$ 14. $\dfrac{7^{-2}}{7^6}$ 15. $\dfrac{6^{-4}}{6^{-5}}$ 16. $\dfrac{9^{-5}}{9^{-4}}$

17. $a^2x^{-1}a^{-3}$ **18.** $b^{-2}c^{-3}b^5$ **19.** $2(c^{-2})^4$ **20.** $6(x^{-1})^{-1}$

21. $\dfrac{x^{-5}y^{-1}}{xy^{-3}}$ **22.** $\dfrac{3^{-1}a}{3a^{-1}}$ **23.** $\dfrac{2^{-2}x^{-2}y^{-4}}{2x^{-6}y^0}$ **24.** $\dfrac{(m^{-2}n)^0}{m^3n^{-4}}$

25. $\dfrac{(3a)^{-1}b^2}{3a^0b^{-5}}$ **26.** $\dfrac{(3p^0)^{-2}}{3p^2q^{-8}}$ **27.** $\left(\dfrac{2a^{-1}}{5b}\right)^2$ **28.** $\left(\dfrac{x^2}{y^{-1}z}\right)^{-2}$

29. $\dfrac{(xy^{-1})^{-2}}{x^2y^{-3}}$ **30.** $\dfrac{r^0st^{-2}}{(r^{-1}s^2t)^{-3}}$

31. $\dfrac{(3a^{-2}bc^{-1})^{-1}}{6a^{-3}(bc)^{-1}}$ **32.** $\dfrac{(axy^{-1})^{-2}}{(a^{-2}x^{-1}y)^{-3}}$

In Exercises 33 through 37, solve the given problems.

33. In the study of radioactivity the equation $N = N_0e^{-kt}$ is found. Express this equation without the use of negative exponents.

34. When you use scientific notation (see Section 11–2) and logarithms (see Chapter 13), you will find that negative and zero powers of 10 are important. Since $100 = 10^2$, $1/100 = 1/10^2 = 10^{-2}$. Similarly, express $1/10$ and $1/1000$ as negative powers of 10.

35. The impedance Z of a particular electronic circuit may be expressed as

$$Z = \left(h + \frac{1}{R}\right)^{-1}.$$

Express the right side as a simple fraction without negative exponents.

36. In the theory dealing with electricity, the expression $e^{-i(\omega t - ax)}$ (ω is the Greek omega) is encountered. Rewrite this expression so that it contains no minus signs in the exponent.

37. Negative exponents are often used to express the units of a quantity. For example, velocity can be expressed in units of ft/sec or ft $\cdot$ sec^{-1}. In this same manner, express the units of density in g/cm^3 by the use of negative exponents.

38. Find a value of n such that $(\tfrac{1}{2})^n = 4$.

11–2 SCIENTIFIC NOTATION

In technical and scientific work we often encounter numbers which are either very large or very small in magnitude. Illustrations of such numbers are given in the following example.

Television signals travel at about 30,000,000,000 cm/sec. The weight of the earth is about 6,600,000,000,000,000,000,000 tons. A typical   **Example A**

protective coating used on aluminum is about 0.0005 in. thick.   The
wavelength of some x-rays is about 0.000000095 cm.

Writing numbers such as these is inconvenient in ordinary notation,
as shown in Example A, particularly when the number of zeros needed
for the proper location of the decimal point is excessive.   However, a
convenient notation, known as *scientific notation*, is normally used to
represent such numbers.

A number written in scientific notation is expressed as the product
of a number between 1 and 10 and a power of 10.   Symbolically this can
be written as

$$P \times 10^k,$$

where P is between 1 and 10 (or possibly equal to 1), and k can take
on any integral value.   The following example illustrates how numbers
are written in scientific notation following the definition.

Example B

$$56{,}000 = 5.6(10{,}000) = 5.6 \times 10^4,$$

$$0.143 = \frac{1.43}{10} = 1.43 \times 10^{-1},$$

$$0.000804 = \frac{8.04}{10{,}000} = 8.04 \times 10^{-4},$$

$$2.97 = 2.97(1) = 2.97 \times 10^0.$$

From Example B we can establish a basic method of changing
numbers from ordinary notation to scientific notation. The decimal point
is moved so that only one nonzero digit is to its left.   The number of
places moved is the value of k.   It is positive if the decimal point is moved
to the left, and it is negative if it is moved to the right.   Consider the
illustrations in the following example.

Example C

$$\underset{\text{4 places}}{56000} = 5.6 \times 10^4,$$

$$\underset{\text{1 place}}{0.143} = 1.43 \times 10^{-1},$$

$$\underset{\text{4 places}}{0.000804} = 8.04 \times 10^{-4},$$

$$\underset{\text{0 places}}{2.97} = 2.97 \times 10^0.$$

Scientific notation is a very practical way to handle calculations involving numbers of very large or very small magnitude. This includes calculations made on the slide rule, particularly in the determination of the decimal point of the result. If all numbers are expressed in scientific notation, the laws of exponents are used to find the decimal point in the result. It is possible to leave the result in scientific notation.

In determining the result of   **Example D**

$$\frac{86,000,000}{0.306}, \quad \text{we may establish the result as} \quad \frac{9 \times 10^7}{3 \times 10^{-1}} = 3 \times 10^8$$

for purposes of determining the decimal point by estimation. The slide rule indicates the significant digits 281 for this division. Therefore the result is expressed as 2.81×10^8. The power of 10 here is sufficiently large that we would generally leave the result in its scientific-notation form.

In Exercises 1 through 6, change the given numbers from scientific notation to   **EXERCISES**
ordinary notation.

1. 4×10^6
2. 3.8×10^9
3. 8×10^{-2}

4. 7.03×10^{-11}
5. 2.17×10^0
6. 7.93×10^{-1}

In Exercises 7 through 18, change the given numbers from ordinary notation to scientific notation.

7. 3000
8. 700
9. 420000
10. 51000

11. 0.076
12. 0.0029
13. 0.704
14. 0.0108

15. 9.21
16. 1.05
17. 10.3
18. 25

In Exercises 19 through 28, perform the indicated calculations on a slide rule, making any necessary estimations by the use of scientific notation.

19. (6700)(23200)
20. (4510)(9700)

21. (0.0153)(0.608)
22. (79500)(0.00854)

23. $\dfrac{672000}{4050}$
24. $\dfrac{3740}{80500000}$

25. $\dfrac{0.000609}{0.276}$
26. $\dfrac{0.0186}{0.0000665}$

27. $\dfrac{(6.80)(8040000)}{4200000}$
28. $\dfrac{(0.0753)(73900)}{0.0000811}$

In Exercises 29 through 40, change any numbers in ordinary notation to scientific notation or change any numbers in scientific notation to ordinary notation.

29. A certain drill makes 350 rev/min.

30. The speed of many artificial satellites of the earth is about 17,500 mi/hr.

31. The area of the oceans of the earth is about 360,000,000 km^2.

32. The wavelength of red light is about 0.000065 cm.

33. The mass of an electron is 0.000000000000000000000000091 g.

34. A typical capacitor has a capacitance of 0.00005 farad.

35. The sun weighs about 4×10^{30} lb.

36. It takes about 5×10^4 lb of water to grow one bushel of corn.

37. Special boring machines can produce finishes to about 10^{-6} in.

38. Atmospheric pressure is about 1.013×10^6 dynes/cm^2.

39. The faintest sound which can be heard has an intensity of about 10^{-16} watt/cm^2.

40. Some computers can perform an addition in 1.5×10^{-6} sec.

In Exercises 41 and 42, perform the indicated calculations on a slide rule.

41. The transmitting frequency of a television signal is given by the formula

$$f = \frac{v}{\lambda},$$

where v is the velocity of the signal and λ (the Greek lambda) is the wavelength. Determine f if $v = 3.00 \times 10^{10}$ cm/sec and $\lambda = 4.95 \times 10^2$ cm.

42. The final length L of a pipe which has increased in length from L_0 due to an increase of temperature T is found by use of the formula

$$L = L_0(1 + \alpha T),$$

where α (the Greek alpha) depends on the material of the pipe. Find the final length of an iron steam pipe if $L_0 = 195.0$ ft, $T = 85°C$, and $\alpha = 9.8 \times 10^{-6}/°C$.

11-3 ROOTS OF A NUMBER

In Chapter 1 we introduced the idea of the root of a number. We also showed how the square root of a number could be determined. However, at that time the discussion was restricted primarily to the simple evaluation of square roots. In the work which follows in this chapter, we shall need a more thorough understanding of square roots and other roots of numbers, as well as of certain basic operations with them. Therefore this chapter is devoted to the further development of these topics.

We defined a square root of a given number to be one of two equal factors of the given number. Considering now our work in Chapter 4 with signed numbers, we see that there are actually two numbers which could be considered to be the square root of a given positive number. Also, there are no numbers among those we have discussed so far which could be the square root of a negative number.

Since $(+3)^2 = 9$ and $(-3)^2 = 9$, we see that, by the definition we have used up to this point, the square root of 9 can be either $+3$ or -3. Also, since the square of $+3$ and the square of -3 are both 9, we have no apparent result for the square root of -9. **Example A**

Since there are two numbers, one positive and the other negative, whose squares equal a given number, we define the *principal square root* of a positive number to be positive. That is,

$$\sqrt{N} = x,$$

where $\sqrt{N}$ is the principal square root of N and equals (positive) x. Also, of course, $x^2 = N$. This avoids the ambiguity of two possible answers for a square root.

$$\sqrt{16} = 4, \qquad \sqrt{25} = 5, \qquad \sqrt{121} = 11.$$ **Example B**

We do *not* accept answers such as $\sqrt{144} = -12$.

By defining the principal square root of a number in this way, we do not mean that problems involving square roots cannot have negative results. By $-\sqrt{N}$ we mean the negative of the principal value, which means therefore the negative of a positive signed number, and this is a negative number.

$$-\sqrt{16} = -(+4) = -4, \qquad -\sqrt{25} = -5, \qquad -\sqrt{121} = -11.$$ **Example C**

We do *not* accept answers such as $-\sqrt{144} = -(-12) = 12$.

Returning to the problem of the square root of a negative number, we find it necessary to define a new kind of a number to provide the required result. Thus we define

$$(bi)^2 = -b^2,$$

where *bi* is called an *imaginary number*. (The word *imaginary* is simply the name of the number; these numbers are not imaginary in the usual meaning of the word.) By this definition it can be seen that

$$i^2 = -1 \quad \text{or} \quad \sqrt{-1} = i.$$

Example D

$$\sqrt{-16} = 4i, \quad \sqrt{-25} = 5i,$$

$$-\sqrt{-121} = -(11i) = -11i, \quad \sqrt{-289} = 17i.$$

Also,

$$\sqrt{-144} = 12i \quad \text{and } not \quad -12i.$$

Furthermore,

$$(7i)^2 = -49, \quad (2i)^2 = -4, \quad (-3i)^2 = (-3)^2 i^2 = (9)(-1) = -9.$$

Most of our work with roots will deal with square roots, but we shall have some occasion to consider other roots of a number. In general, the principal *n*th root of a number N is designated as

$$\sqrt[n]{N} = x,$$

where $x^n = N$. (If $n = 2$, it is usually not written in, as we have already seen.) If N is positive, x is positive. If N is negative, and n is odd, x is negative. We shall not consider the case of N being negative and n being even and larger than 2.

Example E

$$\sqrt[3]{64} = 4 \quad (\text{since } 4^3 = 64),$$

$$\sqrt[3]{-64} = -4 \quad (\text{since } (-4)^3 = -64),$$

$$\sqrt[4]{81} = 3 \quad (\text{since } 3^4 = 81),$$

$$\sqrt[5]{32} = 2 \quad (\text{since } 2^5 = 32),$$

$$\sqrt[5]{-32} = -2 \quad (\text{since } (-2)^5 = -32).$$

If a negative sign precedes the radical sign, we express the result as the negative of the principal value. Consider the following example.

Example F

$$-\sqrt[3]{64} = -4, \quad -\sqrt[3]{-64} = -(-4) = 4,$$

$$-\sqrt[4]{16} = -2, \quad -\sqrt[5]{-32} = 2, \quad -\sqrt[7]{-128} = 2.$$

We shall conclude this section with a brief discussion of the type of number which the root of a number represents. In Section 4–3 we introduced the notion of rational numbers. If the root of a number can be found *exactly* in decimal form, the root is rational. Otherwise, it is *irrational*. By this we mean that it is possible to express certain roots as the ratio of one integer to another, but that many cannot be expressed in this way.

$\sqrt{4} = 2$ (an integer—therefore rational), $\sqrt[3]{0.008} = 0.2 = \frac{1}{5}$ (rational), $\sqrt{2}$ equals *approximately* 1.414, but it is not possible to find two *integers* whose ratio, one divided by the other, equals *exactly* $\sqrt{2}$. Thus $\sqrt{2}$ is irrational. For the same reason, $\sqrt[3]{7}$ and $\sqrt[5]{-39}$ are irrational.

Example G

Therefore we see that in discussing the roots of numbers, we are considering a set of numbers, many (in fact, most) of which are irrational.

In Exercises 1 through 24, find the indicated principal roots.   **EXERCISES**

1. $\sqrt{36}$ 2. $\sqrt{81}$ 3. $-\sqrt{169}$ 4. $-\sqrt{225}$

5. $\sqrt{0.25}$ 6. $\sqrt{0.01}$ 7. $\sqrt[3]{8}$ 8. $\sqrt[3]{27}$

9. $\sqrt[3]{-8}$ 10. $\sqrt[3]{-27}$ 11. $-\sqrt[3]{125}$ 12. $-\sqrt[3]{-125}$

13. $\sqrt[3]{0.125}$ 14. $\sqrt[3]{-0.001}$ 15. $\sqrt[4]{16}$ 16. $-\sqrt[4]{625}$

17. $\sqrt[5]{243}$ 18. $-\sqrt[5]{-243}$ 19. $\sqrt[6]{64}$ 20. $-\sqrt[8]{256}$

21. $\sqrt{-4}$ 22. $\sqrt{-100}$ 23. $\sqrt{-0.49}$ 24. $-\sqrt{-0.0001}$

In Exercises 25 through 28, perform the indicated operations.

25. $(5i)^2$ 26. $5i^2$ 27. $(3i)(4i)$ 28. $(-4i)^2$

In Exercises 29 and 30, identify those numbers which are rational, and those which are irrational.

29. $\sqrt{4}$, $\sqrt{2}$, $\sqrt[3]{8}$, $\sqrt[3]{27}$, $\sqrt[3]{100}$, $\sqrt[4]{0.0001}$, $\sqrt{0.16}$

30. $\sqrt{15}$, $\sqrt{50}$, $\sqrt{144}$, $\sqrt[3]{250}$, $\sqrt[5]{32}$, $\sqrt[3]{0.027}$, $\sqrt{0.64}$

In Exercises 31 through 36, solve the given problems.

31. The period T, in seconds, of a pendulum of length l, in feet, is given by the equation

$$T = \frac{\pi}{2}\sqrt{\frac{l}{2}}.$$

What is the period of a pendulum 8.00 ft long?

32. The ratio of the rates of diffusion of two gases is given by $r_1/r_2 = \sqrt{m_2}/\sqrt{m_1}$, where m_1 and m_2 are the masses of the molecules of the gases. Find the ratio r_1/r_2 if $m_1 = 25$ units and $m_2 = 81$ units.

33. A cubical water tank holds 512 cu. ft. What is the length of an edge of the tank?

34. At the end of a certain biology experiment it was observed that the number of bacteria in a certain culture equaled 1000 times the fourth root of the number originally present. If 160,000 bacteria were originally present, how many were observed at the end of the experiment?

35. The ratio between successive speeds of a six-speed gear box is $\sqrt[5]{1024/243}$, given that the maximum speed is 1024 rev/min and the minimum speed is 243 rev/min. Determine this ratio.

36. A certain problem reads: The length of a rectangular area is 3 ft more than its width. Find its dimensions if the area is 42 sq ft. The solution to this problem leads to two possible values,

$$\text{(a) } \frac{-3 + \sqrt{177}}{2} \quad \text{and} \quad \text{(b) } \frac{-3 - \sqrt{177}}{2}.$$

Which of these must be the proper value, and therefore what is the final answer?

11-4 SIMPLIFYING RADICALS

A basic property of radicals allows us to change many of them into simpler, more convenient, forms. This property is that the root of a product equals the product of the roots of its factors. That is,

$$\sqrt{ab} = \sqrt{a}\sqrt{b}. \qquad \qquad 11\text{-}3$$

To avoid difficulties with imaginary numbers, we shall assume that all letters represent positive numbers.

Example A   We know that $\sqrt{36} = 6$. If we now consider

$$\sqrt{36} = \sqrt{4 \cdot 9} = \sqrt{4}\sqrt{9} = 2 \cdot 3,$$

we see that the same result, 6, is obtained.

In Eq. (11-3), if the root of either a or b can be found exactly, we may simplify the radical in that the remaining indicated root is that of a number smaller than the number that was originally present. Consider the following example.

By writing $\sqrt{48} = \sqrt{16 \cdot 3}$, we have the following result: **Example B**

$$\sqrt{48} = \sqrt{16 \cdot 3} = \sqrt{16}\sqrt{3} = 4\sqrt{3}.$$

Thus $\sqrt{48}$ can be expressed in terms of $\sqrt{3}$. Also,

$$\sqrt{175} = \sqrt{25 \cdot 7} = \sqrt{25}\sqrt{7} = 5\sqrt{7}.$$

This method of simplifying radicals makes it possible to evaluate many additional square roots by the use of Table 1. This is most conveniently done when factors of 100 are present in a number. However, so long as the square root is expressed as the product of square roots less than 100, it can be evaluated by multiplication. The following example illustrates each type.

$$\sqrt{300} = \sqrt{3}\sqrt{100} = 10\sqrt{3} = 10(1.732) = 17.32,$$

Example C

$$\sqrt{310000} = \sqrt{31}\sqrt{10000} = 100\sqrt{31} = 100(5.568) = 556.8,$$

$$\sqrt{310} = \sqrt{31}\sqrt{10} = (5.568)(3.162) = 17.61,$$

$$\sqrt{180} = \sqrt{36}\sqrt{5} = 6\sqrt{5} = 6(2.236) = 13.42.$$

Square roots of products involving literal symbols can also be simplified by use of Eq. (11–3). The simplification is based on the fact that the square root of the square of a positive number is that number. That is,

$$\sqrt{a^2} = a. \qquad\qquad \textbf{11-4}$$

By use of Eq. (11–3) an algebraic product can be expressed as the product of square roots. Then, for any of these products for which Eq. (11–4) is applicable, the expression can be simplified. The following example gives three illustrations.

$$\sqrt{a^2 b^2 c} = \sqrt{a^2}\sqrt{b^2}\sqrt{c} = ab\sqrt{c},$$

Example D

$$\sqrt{25a^4} = \sqrt{25}\sqrt{a^4} = 5\sqrt{(a^2)^2} = 5a^2,$$

$$\sqrt{6a^2 b^6 x} = \sqrt{6}\sqrt{a^2}\sqrt{b^6}\sqrt{x} = (\sqrt{6})(a)(\sqrt{(b^3)^2})(\sqrt{x})$$

$$= (\sqrt{6})(a)(b^3)(\sqrt{x})$$

$$= ab^3\sqrt{6}\sqrt{x} = ab^3\sqrt{6x}.$$

If a radical appears in the denominator of a fraction, the evaluation of the expression usually becomes a more lengthy process. For this reason, another operation in the simplification of radicals is the *rationalization* of denominators. We perform this step by multiplying both numerator and denominator of the fraction by the proper expression so that no radicals appear in the resulting denominator. We proceed as follows:

$$\sqrt{\frac{a}{b}} = \sqrt{\frac{a \cdot b}{b \cdot b}} = \frac{\sqrt{ab}}{\sqrt{b^2}} = \frac{\sqrt{ab}}{b}.$$

11-5

The use of Eq. (11-5) is demonstrated in the following examples.

Example E

$$\sqrt{\frac{1}{3}} = \sqrt{\frac{1 \cdot 3}{3 \cdot 3}} = \frac{\sqrt{3}}{\sqrt{3^2}} = \frac{\sqrt{3}}{3},$$

$$\sqrt{\frac{12}{5}} = \sqrt{\frac{4 \cdot 3}{5}} = \sqrt{\frac{4 \cdot 3 \cdot 5}{5 \cdot 5}} = \frac{2\sqrt{3 \cdot 5}}{\sqrt{5^2}} = \frac{2\sqrt{15}}{5}.$$

Example F

$$\sqrt{\frac{a^2}{b}} = a\sqrt{\frac{1}{b}} = a\sqrt{\frac{b}{b^2}} = \frac{a\sqrt{b}}{b},$$

$$\sqrt{\frac{a^4b}{c^3}} = \sqrt{\frac{a^4b}{c^2c}} = \frac{a^2}{c}\sqrt{\frac{b}{c}} = \frac{a^2}{c}\sqrt{\frac{bc}{c^2}} = \frac{a^2\sqrt{bc}}{c^2},$$

$$\sqrt{\frac{4a^3}{7b}} = 2a\sqrt{\frac{a}{7b}} = 2a\sqrt{\frac{a \cdot 7b}{(7b)^2}} = \frac{2a\sqrt{7ab}}{7b}.$$

We have devoted our attention thus far to the simplification of expressions involving square roots, since they are of primary importance in our later work. However, we can carry out similar operations with expressions involving other roots. The following example illustrates this.

Example G

$$\sqrt[3]{16} = \sqrt[3]{8}\,\sqrt[3]{2} = 2\sqrt[3]{2},$$

$$\sqrt[4]{3a^7} = \sqrt[4]{3}\,\sqrt[4]{a^4}\,\sqrt[4]{a^3} = (\sqrt[4]{3})(a)(\sqrt[4]{a^3}) = a\sqrt[4]{3a^3},$$

$$\sqrt[5]{32x^8} = (\sqrt[5]{32})(\sqrt[5]{x^5})(\sqrt[5]{x^3}) = (2)(x)(\sqrt[5]{x^3}) = 2x\sqrt[5]{x^3}.$$

In conclusion, we shall consider a radical as being expressed in simplest form if all perfect powers have been removed, and if all fractions are rationalized.

EXERCISES   In Exercises 1 through 24, express the given radicals in simplest form.

1. $\sqrt{8}$ 2. $\sqrt{18}$ 3. $\sqrt{150}$ 4. $\sqrt{99}$

5. $\sqrt{\frac{1}{2}}$ 6. $\sqrt{\frac{2}{3}}$ 7. $\sqrt{\frac{1}{8}}$ 8. $\sqrt{\frac{12}{27}}$

9. $\sqrt{ac^2}$ 10. $\sqrt{3a^4}$ 11. $\sqrt{a^3b^2}$ 12. $\sqrt{12a^5}$

13. $\sqrt{\dfrac{a}{2}}$ **14.** $\sqrt{\dfrac{4a}{5}}$ **15.** $\sqrt{\dfrac{27a}{b}}$ **16.** $\sqrt{\dfrac{8b^3}{x}}$

17. $\sqrt{4a^2bc^3}$ **18.** $\sqrt{98a^3b}$ **19.** $\sqrt{80x^4yz^5}$ **20.** $\sqrt{240xy^7z^6}$

21. $\sqrt{\dfrac{ab^2}{12}}$ **22.** $\sqrt{\dfrac{c^3e^5}{44}}$ **23.** $\sqrt{\dfrac{2x^2y}{5a^8}}$ **24.** $\sqrt{\dfrac{13xy^5}{40a^3}}$

In Exercises 25 through 32, use Table 1 to evaluate the given square roots.

25. $\sqrt{500}$ **26.** $\sqrt{7700}$

27. $\sqrt{620}$ (to two decimal places)   **28.** $\sqrt{17000}$

29. $\sqrt{0.4}$ $(0.4 = \frac{40}{100})$ **30.** $\sqrt{8.4}$ $(8.4 = \frac{840}{100})$ (to two decimal places)

31. Evaluate $\sqrt{2}/\sqrt{3}$ without rationalizing and then by evaluating $\sqrt{6}/3$.

32. Evaluate $\sqrt{15}/\sqrt{8}$ without rationalizing and then by evaluating $\sqrt{30}/4$.

In Exercises 33 through 40, simplify the given radicals.

33. $\sqrt[3]{54}$ **34.** $\sqrt[3]{24}$ **35.** $\sqrt[3]{8a^4}$ **36.** $\sqrt[3]{6a^{10}}$

37. $\sqrt[4]{16a^9}$ **38.** $\sqrt[4]{243a^{11}}$ **39.** $\sqrt[5]{64x^7}$ **40.** $\sqrt[8]{a^9b^{16}c^5}$

In Exercises 41 through 45, solve the given problems.

41. Find the side of the square whose area is 640 in.^{2} by first simplifying the appropriate radical and then using Table 1.

42. The expression for the resonant frequency of a certain electric circuit is given by

$$f = \frac{1}{2\pi}\sqrt{\frac{1}{LC}}.$$

Express this equation in rationalized form.

43. A rectangular lot is twice as long as it is wide and has an area of 16,200 ft^2. What are its dimensions?

44. In statistics, the standard deviation of a set of numbers is that number which when subtracted from and added to the average of the set gives the values between which about two-thirds of the numbers lie. In the study of the I.Q.'s of 21 children, the average I.Q. was found to be 105 and the standard deviation was $\sqrt{\frac{4000}{21}}$. Find the values of I.Q. between which two-thirds of those of the children lie.

45. Experiment shows that the stopping distance x of a car is proportional to the square of the speed s of the car before the brakes are applied. A given car traveling at 100 ft/sec can stop in 400 ft. Set up the equation relating x and s. Then determine the speed of the car if it stops in 800 ft (assume three-significant-digit accuracy in all values).

11-5 BASIC OPERATIONS WITH RADICALS

Now that we have seen how radicals may be simplified, we can show how the basic operations of addition, subtraction, multiplication, and division are performed on them. These operations follow the basic algebraic operations, the only difference being that radicals are involved. Also, these radicals must be expressed in simplest form in order that the final result may be in simplest form.

In adding and subtracting radicals, we add and subtract *like* radicals, just as we add and subtract like terms when we add and subtract algebraic expressions. Consider the following example.

Example A
$$\sqrt{3} + 4\sqrt{5} - 3\sqrt{3} + \sqrt{5} = (\sqrt{3} - 3\sqrt{3}) + (4\sqrt{5} + \sqrt{5})$$
$$= -2\sqrt{3} + 5\sqrt{5}.$$

However, when working with radicals we must be certain that all radicals are in simplest form. We must make sure of this, since many radicals which do not appear to be similar in form actually are similar, as shown in the following example.

Example B
$\sqrt{3} + \sqrt{80} - \sqrt{27} + \sqrt{5}$ appears to have four different types of terms, none of them being similar. However, noting that

$$\sqrt{80} = \sqrt{16 \cdot 5} = 4\sqrt{5} \quad \text{and} \quad \sqrt{27} = \sqrt{9 \cdot 3} = 3\sqrt{3},$$

we have the equivalent expression $\sqrt{3} + 4\sqrt{5} - 3\sqrt{3} + \sqrt{5}$, which, of course, is the same as that which appears in Example A. Therefore the third term and the first term are similar, as are the second and fourth terms. Thus

$$\sqrt{3} + \sqrt{80} - \sqrt{27} + \sqrt{5} = \sqrt{3} + 4\sqrt{5} - 3\sqrt{3} + \sqrt{5}$$
$$= -2\sqrt{3} + 5\sqrt{5}.$$

The examples which follow further illustrate the method of addition and subtraction of radicals.

Example C
$$\sqrt{8} + \sqrt{18} - 6\sqrt{2} + 3\sqrt{32} = \sqrt{4 \cdot 2} + \sqrt{9 \cdot 2} - 6\sqrt{2} + 3\sqrt{16 \cdot 2}$$
$$= 2\sqrt{2} + 3\sqrt{2} - 6\sqrt{2} + 12\sqrt{2}$$
$$= 11\sqrt{2},$$
$$\sqrt{20} + 3\sqrt{5} - 7\sqrt{12} + 2\sqrt{45} = \sqrt{4 \cdot 5} + 3\sqrt{5} - 7\sqrt{4 \cdot 3} + 2\sqrt{9 \cdot 5}$$
$$= 2\sqrt{5} + 3\sqrt{5} - 14\sqrt{3} + 6\sqrt{5}$$
$$= 11\sqrt{5} - 14\sqrt{3}.$$

$$\sqrt{a^2b} + \sqrt{9b} - 2\sqrt{16c^2b} = a\sqrt{b} + 3\sqrt{b} - 2(4c)\sqrt{b}$$
$$= (a + 3 - 8c)\sqrt{b},$$
$$\sqrt{3a^3c^2} - \sqrt{12ab^2} + \sqrt{24ac^3} = ac\sqrt{3a} - 2b\sqrt{3a} + 2c\sqrt{6ac}$$
$$= (ac - 2b)\sqrt{3a} + 2c\sqrt{6ac}.$$

Example D

When multiplying expressions containing radicals, we proceed just as in any algebraic multiplication. When simplifying the result, we use the relation

$$\sqrt{a}\,\sqrt{b} = \sqrt{ab},$$

which is actually Eq. (11–3). The following examples illustrate the method.

$$\sqrt{2}(\sqrt{6} + 3\sqrt{5}) = \sqrt{2}\,\sqrt{6} + 3\sqrt{2}\,\sqrt{5} = \sqrt{12} + 3\sqrt{10}$$
$$= 2\sqrt{3} + 3\sqrt{10},$$
$$(\sqrt{3} - 2\sqrt{2})(3\sqrt{3} + 5\sqrt{2}) = 3\sqrt{3}\,\sqrt{3} - \sqrt{3}\,\sqrt{2} - 10\sqrt{2}\,\sqrt{2}$$
$$= 3\sqrt{9} - \sqrt{6} - 10\sqrt{4}$$
$$= 3(3) - \sqrt{6} - 10(2)$$
$$= 9 - \sqrt{6} - 20 = -11 - \sqrt{6}.$$

Example E

$$(\sqrt{a} - 3\sqrt{b})(2\sqrt{a} + \sqrt{b}) = 2\sqrt{a}\,\sqrt{a} - 5\sqrt{a}\,\sqrt{b} - 3\sqrt{b}\,\sqrt{b}$$
$$= 2\sqrt{a^2} - 5\sqrt{ab} - 3\sqrt{b^2}$$
$$= 2a - 5\sqrt{ab} - 3b,$$
$$(\sqrt{2} - 3\sqrt{x})(\sqrt{2} + \sqrt{3}) = \sqrt{2}\,\sqrt{2} + \sqrt{2}\,\sqrt{3} - 3\sqrt{x}\,\sqrt{2} - 3\sqrt{x}\,\sqrt{3}$$
$$= 2 + \sqrt{6} - 3\sqrt{2x} - 3\sqrt{3x}.$$

Example F

In the last section we showed how to rationalize an expression in which a radical appeared in the denominator. However, we restricted our attention to the simpler cases of rationalization. The following example illustrates rationalizing an expression in which the numerator is a sum of terms.

$$\frac{\sqrt{3} + 5}{\sqrt{2}} = \frac{\sqrt{2}(\sqrt{3} + 5)}{\sqrt{2}\,\sqrt{2}} = \frac{\sqrt{2}\,\sqrt{3} + 5\sqrt{2}}{\sqrt{4}} = \frac{\sqrt{6} + 5\sqrt{2}}{2}.$$

Example G

If the denominator is the sum of two terms, the fraction can be rationalized by multiplying both numerator and denominator by the difference of the same two terms. This is so because

$$(\sqrt{a} + \sqrt{b})(\sqrt{a} - \sqrt{b}) = a - b,$$

11–6

which results in an expression without radicals. The following example illustrates the method.

Example H

$$\frac{\sqrt{3}}{\sqrt{2}-\sqrt{5}} = \frac{\sqrt{3}(\sqrt{2}+\sqrt{5})}{(\sqrt{2}-\sqrt{5})(\sqrt{2}+\sqrt{5})} = \frac{\sqrt{6}+\sqrt{15}}{2-5}$$

$$= -\frac{\sqrt{6}+\sqrt{15}}{3},$$

$$\frac{\sqrt{a}}{2\sqrt{a}-3} = \frac{\sqrt{a}(2\sqrt{a}+3)}{(2\sqrt{a}-3)(2\sqrt{a}+3)} = \frac{2\sqrt{a}\sqrt{a}+3\sqrt{a}}{2\cdot 2\cdot\sqrt{a}\sqrt{a}-3\cdot 3}$$

$$= \frac{2a+3\sqrt{a}}{4a-9}.$$

EXERCISES

In Exercises 1 through 32, perform the indicated operations, expressing each answer in simplest form.

1. $\sqrt{7}-\sqrt{5}+3\sqrt{7}+2\sqrt{5}$　　**2.** $\sqrt{11}+8\sqrt{11}-\sqrt{17}+3\sqrt{11}$

3. $\sqrt{8}+\sqrt{18}+\sqrt{32}$　　**4.** $\sqrt{12}+\sqrt{27}+\sqrt{48}$

5. $\sqrt{28}-2\sqrt{63}+5\sqrt{7}-8\sqrt{20}$　　**6.** $2\sqrt{24}+\sqrt{128}+\sqrt{6}-2\sqrt{54}$

7. $2\sqrt{8}-2\sqrt{12}-\sqrt{50}+2\sqrt{75}$　　**8.** $2\sqrt{20}-\sqrt{44}+3\sqrt{11}+3\sqrt{125}$

9. $\sqrt{2a}+\sqrt{8a}+\sqrt{32a^3}$　　**10.** $\sqrt{ac}+\sqrt{4ac}+\sqrt{16a^3c}$

11. $a\sqrt{2}+\sqrt{72a^2}-\sqrt{12a}+a\sqrt{27}$

12. $\sqrt{x^2yz}-\sqrt{y^3z}-\sqrt{4y^5z^3}+2x\sqrt{y^2z}$

13. $\sqrt{3}(\sqrt{7}-3\sqrt{6})$　　**14.** $\sqrt{5}(\sqrt{20}-6\sqrt{3})$

15. $\sqrt{2}(\sqrt{8}-\sqrt{32}+5\sqrt{18})$　　**16.** $\sqrt{7}(\sqrt{14}+2\sqrt{6}-\sqrt{56})$

17. $\sqrt{a}(\sqrt{ab}+3\sqrt{ac})$　　**18.** $\sqrt{2a}(\sqrt{8}+\sqrt{6a^3})$

19. $(\sqrt{2}+\sqrt{3})(2\sqrt{2}-\sqrt{3})$　　**20.** $(\sqrt{7}-2\sqrt{5})(3\sqrt{7}+\sqrt{5})$

21. $(\sqrt{5}-3\sqrt{3})(2\sqrt{5}+\sqrt{27})$　　**22.** $(2\sqrt{11}-\sqrt{8})(3\sqrt{2}+\sqrt{22})$

23. $(\sqrt{a}-3\sqrt{c})(2\sqrt{a}+5\sqrt{c})$　　**24.** $(\sqrt{2b}+3)(\sqrt{2}-\sqrt{b})$

25. $\dfrac{\sqrt{2}}{\sqrt{3}+\sqrt{2}}$　　**26.** $\dfrac{\sqrt{3}}{\sqrt{5}+\sqrt{6}}$

27. $\dfrac{\sqrt{7}-\sqrt{3}}{2\sqrt{7}+\sqrt{3}}$　　**28.** $\dfrac{\sqrt{11}+2\sqrt{5}}{\sqrt{5}-3\sqrt{11}}$

29. $\dfrac{\sqrt{a}}{\sqrt{a}+2\sqrt{b}}$　　**30.** $\dfrac{\sqrt{x}}{2\sqrt{x}-3\sqrt{y}}$

31. $\dfrac{\sqrt{x} + 2\sqrt{y}}{2\sqrt{x} - \sqrt{y}}$ **32.** $\dfrac{\sqrt{x} + \sqrt{2}}{\sqrt{8} - 3\sqrt{x}}$

In Exercises 33 through 35, solve the given problems.

33. Three square pieces of land are along a straight road, as shown in Fig. 11–1. Find the distance x along the road in simplest radical form.

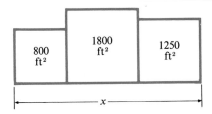

                                                              Figure 11-1

34. In the theory of waves in wires, one encounters the expression

$$\frac{\sqrt{d_1} - \sqrt{d_2}}{\sqrt{d_1} + \sqrt{d_2}}.$$

Evaluate this expression for $d_1 = 10$ and $d_2 = 3$.

35. In the theory dealing with vibratory motion, the equation

$$a^2 - 2al + k^2 = 0$$

is found. Show that $a = l + \sqrt{l^2 - k^2}$ and $a = l - \sqrt{l^2 - k^2}$ both satisfy the equation.

11–6 FRACTIONAL EXPONENTS

Thus far, the only numbers we have used for exponents have been the positive integers, the negative integers, and zero. A natural question which then arises is whether or not fractions may be used as exponents. The answer to this is that fractions can be used as exponents, and as it turns out, these fractional exponents are very convenient in certain topics of mathematics. We discuss this subject at this time because, as we shall see, an expression raised to a fractional exponent can be interpreted as a radical.

    For fractional exponents to be meaningful, they must satisfy the basic laws of exponents already established. The significance of fractional exponents is established in the following example.

Example A   If $a^{1/3}$ is to have meaning, then

$$a^{1/3}a^{1/3}a^{1/3} = a^{1/3+1/3+1/3} = a$$

and

$$(a^{1/3})^3 = a.$$

However, we have already established that

$$(\sqrt[3]{a})^3 = a.$$

This means that $a^{1/3}$ must be interpreted as $\sqrt[3]{a}$ in order that the basic laws of exponents hold.

Generalizing on the conclusion of Example A, we define $a^{1/n}$ to mean the nth principal root of a, or

$$a^{1/n} = \sqrt[n]{a}. \qquad\qquad \textbf{11-7}$$

The following example gives several illustrations of the meaning of Eq. (11–7).

Example B $$4^{1/2} = \sqrt{4} = 2, \qquad (27)^{1/3} = \sqrt[3]{27} = 3,$$
$$(-32)^{1/5} = \sqrt[5]{-32} = -2, \qquad (x^4)^{1/2} = \sqrt{x^4} = \sqrt{(x^2)^2} = x^2.$$

Normally it is not necessary, and in fact it is often cumbersome, to include the radical interpretation when evaluating expressions with fractional exponents. Thus the above results would usually be written as

$$4^{1/2} = 2, \qquad (27)^{1/3} = 3, \qquad (-32)^{1/5} = -2, \qquad \text{and} \qquad (x^4)^{1/2} = x^2.$$

When an expression of the form $a^{1/n}$ is raised to some power, say m, the basic laws of exponents should still be valid. Thus

$$(a^{1/n})^m = a^{(1/n)(m)} = a^{m/n}.$$

The meaning of $a^{m/n}$ is shown in the following example.

Example C $(a^{1/3})^2 = a^{2/3}$, which can be written as $(a^2)^{1/3}$. Thus, $(a^{1/3})^2 = (a^2)^{1/3}$, or $(\sqrt[3]{a})^2 = \sqrt[3]{a^2}$.

Generalizing on the result of Example C, we see that

$$a^{m/n} = (\sqrt[n]{a})^m = \sqrt[n]{a^m}. \qquad\qquad \textbf{11-8}$$

The meaning of $a^{m/n}$ is illustrated in the following examples.

$$8^{2/3} = (8^{1/3})^2 = 2^2 = 4,$$ **Example D**

$$(27)^{4/3} = [(27)^{1/3}]^4 = 3^4 = 81,$$

$$4^{7/2} = (4^{1/2})^7 = 2^7 = 128,$$

$$(x^4)^{3/2} = [(x^4)^{1/2}]^3 = (x^2)^3 = x^6.$$

$8^{2/3}$ written in radical form is $\sqrt[3]{8^2}$ or $(\sqrt[3]{8})^2$. Since $\sqrt[3]{8^2} = \sqrt[3]{64} = 4$ **Example E**
and $(\sqrt[3]{8})^2 = 2^2 = 4$, we see that $8^{2/3} = \sqrt[3]{8^2} = (\sqrt[3]{8})^2$. Also, $4^{7/2} = (\sqrt{4^7}) = (\sqrt{4})^7$.

The following examples illustrate the use of the basic laws of exponents
with expressions which have fractional exponents.

$$8^{-2/3} = \frac{1}{8^{2/3}} = \frac{1}{(8^{1/3})^2} = \frac{1}{2^2} = \frac{1}{4},$$ **Example F**

$$(8^{4/5})^0 = 1,$$

$$2^{1/2}2^{1/3} = 2^{1/2+1/3} = 2^{5/6},$$

$$\frac{2^{1/2}}{2^{1/3}} = 2^{1/2-1/3} = 2^{1/6},$$

$$\frac{4^{-1/2}}{2^{-5}} = \frac{2^5}{4^{1/2}} = \frac{32}{2} = 16.$$

$$x^{1/2}x^{1/4} = x^{1/2+1/4} = x^{3/4},$$ **Example G**

$$\frac{a}{a^{1/2}b^{-2}} = a^{1-1/2}b^2 = a^{1/2}b^2,$$

$$\frac{x^{-1/3}y^{2/3}}{x^{2/3}y^{-2/3}} = \frac{y^{2/3+2/3}}{x^{2/3+1/3}} = \frac{y^{4/3}}{x}.$$

In Exercises 1 through 8, change the given expressions to radical form.   **EXERCISES**

1. $3^{1/2}$ **2.** $6^{1/3}$ **3.** $x^{1/4}$ **4.** $y^{1/5}$

5. $a^{2/5}$ **6.** $b^{3/5}$ **7.** $x^{5/3}$ **8.** $y^{7/3}$

In Exercises 9 through 32, evaluate the given expressions.

9. $9^{1/2}$ **10.** $(36)^{1/2}$ **11.** $(64)^{1/3}$ **12.** $(125)^{1/3}$

13. $(16)^{1/4}$ **14.** $(243)^{1/5}$ **15.** $(-8)^{1/3}$ **16.** $(-64)^{1/3}$

17. $8^{4/3}$ **18.** $(27)^{2/3}$ **19.** $9^{3/2}$ **20.** $(16)^{3/4}$

21. $(-8)^{2/3}$ **22.** $(-27)^{5/3}$ **23.** $(16)^{-1/4}$ **24.** $(32)^{-2/5}$

25. $-(-32)^{-1/5}$ **26.** $-(64)^{-2/3}$ **27.** $(4^{1/2})(27^{2/3})$ **28.** $2^{-1/2} \cdot 2^{3/2}$

29. $\dfrac{(64)^{1/2}}{(64)^{1/3}}$ **30.** $(4^{-2})(27^{-1/3})$

31. $\dfrac{(25)^{-3/2}}{(81)^{3/4}}$ **32.** $(125)^{-2/3} + 4(25)^{-1/2}$

In Exercises 33 through 40, use the laws of exponents to simplify the given expressions. Express all answers with positive exponents.

33. $a \cdot a^{1/2}$ **34.** $\dfrac{b}{b^{1/3}}$ **35.** $\dfrac{ab}{a^{1/4}}$ **36.** $\dfrac{xyz^2}{z^{-3/2}}$

37. $\dfrac{x(x^{1/3})^4}{x^{2/5}}$ **38.** $\dfrac{xy^{1/2}}{(y^{2/3})^{-2}}$ **39.** $\dfrac{x^{-1/2}x^2}{x^{2/3}}$ **40.** $\dfrac{xy^{-1/2}z}{z^{-2/3}x^{-1/2}}$

In Exercises 41 through 47, solve the given problems.

41. Use fractional exponents to express the side x of a square in terms of the area A of the square.

42. An expression which arises in Einstein's theory of relativity is $\sqrt{(c^2 - v^2)/c^2}$. Express this with the use of fractional exponents and then simplify.

43. When the volume of a gas changes very rapidly, an approximate relation is that the pressure p varies inversely as the 3/2 power of the volume. Given that p is 3 atm when $V = 100$ in^3, find p when $V = 25$ in^3.

44. Considering only the volume of gasoline vapor and air mixture in the cylinder, the efficiency of an internal combustion engine is approximately

$$E = 100 \left(1 - \frac{1}{R^{2/5}}\right),$$

where E is in percent and R is the compression ratio of the engine. Rewrite this equation in radical form.

45. In the determination of the magnetic field within a coil of wire, the expression

$$kNia^2(a^2 + b^2)^{-3/2}$$

is used. Rewrite this expression in radical form.

46. The expression for the plate resistance of an electronic vacuum tube may be expressed as

$$r_p = \frac{2K^{-2/3}I^{-1/3}}{3D}.$$

Write this expression without negative exponents.

47. Kepler's third law of planetary motion may be stated as follows: *The mean radius (about the sun) of any planet is proportional to the 2/3 power of the period of that planet.* Using the facts that the earth has a mean radius of about 93,000,000 mi, and that its period is 1 yr, calculate the mean radius of Saturn, assuming that its period is 27 yr (actually it is about 29.5 yr but the answer obtained is only about 6% in error).

In Exercises 1 through 32, evaluate the given expressions.

1. 5^{-1} **2.** 3^{-4} **3.** $\dfrac{1}{2^{-3}}$ **4.** $\dfrac{1}{5^{-1}}$

5. $3^0 6^{-1}$ **6.** $\dfrac{9^0}{4^{-3}}$ **7.** $\sqrt{169}$ **8.** $-\sqrt{900}$

9. $\sqrt[3]{216}$ **10.** $-\sqrt[3]{-125}$ **11.** $-\sqrt{256}$ **12.** $\sqrt{0.0081}$

13. $\sqrt{\dfrac{1}{9}}$ **14.** $\sqrt{\dfrac{4}{25}}$ **15.** $-\sqrt{\dfrac{9}{121}}$ **16.** $-\sqrt{\dfrac{144}{169}}$

17. $(100)^{1/2}$ **18.** $(625)^{1/2}$ **19.** $(1000)^{1/3}$ **20.** $(8000)^{1/3}$

21. $(49)^{3/2}$ **22.** $(243)^{3/5}$ **23.** $(121)^{3/2}$ **24.** $(8)^{7/3}$

25. $\dfrac{(16)^{3/4}}{(27)^{2/3}}$ **26.** $\dfrac{(25)^{3/2}}{5^{-1}}$ **27.** $\dfrac{(-216)^{2/3}}{3^{-2}}$ **28.** $\dfrac{(81)^{-3/4}}{(32)^{2/5}}$

29. $\sqrt{-81}$ **30.** $\sqrt{-169}$ **31.** $-\sqrt{-0.64}$ **32.** $-\sqrt{-0.01}$

In Exercises 33 through 40, write the given numbers in scientific notation.

33. 490   **34.** 703000   **35.** 6.87   **36.** 0.115

37. 0.0000808   **38.** 7750600   **39.** 86.95   **40.** 1011

In Exercises 41 through 48, use Table 1 to evaluate the given square roots.

41. $\sqrt{6900}$ **42.** $\sqrt{1300}$ **43.** $\sqrt{240}$ **44.** $\sqrt{108}$

45. $\sqrt{0.47}$ **46.** $\sqrt{0.6}$ **47.** $\sqrt{0.06}$ **48.** $\sqrt{0.0031}$

In Exercises 49 through 60, write the given expressions in simplest form, expressing all results with positive exponents.

49. $3a^{-2}b$ **50.** $\dfrac{2rs^{-1}}{t^{-5}}$ **51.** $\dfrac{2x^3 y^{-1}}{3x^{-2}y^2}$ **52.** $\dfrac{(2a)^0(b^{-1}c)}{4a^2bc^{-3}}$

53. $\dfrac{(-a)^{-2}xy^0}{(-x)^{-1}y^{-3}}$ **54.** $\dfrac{3^{-1}(ab^{-1})^{-2}}{(ab^0)^{-1}}$ **55.** $a^{1/4}a^{1/3}$ **56.** $x^{1/5}x^{2/3}$

57. $\dfrac{a^{2/3}}{a^{-1/2}}$ **58.** $\dfrac{b^{-1}}{b^{-1/2}}$ **59.** $\dfrac{(st^{1/2})^{2/3}}{t^{-2}}$ **60.** $\dfrac{(16c^2)^{3/4}}{ac^{-1/5}}$

In Exercises 61 through 80, express the given radicals in simplest form.

61. $\sqrt{40}$ **62.** $\sqrt{90}$ **63.** $\sqrt{128}$ **64.** $\sqrt{54}$

65. $\sqrt{\frac{1}{5}}$ **66.** $\sqrt{\frac{6}{11}}$ **67.** $\sqrt{\frac{4}{7}}$ **68.** $\sqrt{\frac{36}{37}}$

69. $\sqrt{4a^2}$ **70.** $\sqrt{28a}$ **71.** $\sqrt{125b^2c}$ **72.** $\sqrt{90b^3}$

73. $\sqrt{\dfrac{6}{a}}$ **74.** $\sqrt{\dfrac{3}{a^2}}$ **75.** $\sqrt{\dfrac{28}{3a}}$ **76.** $\sqrt{\dfrac{400000}{ab}}$

77. $\sqrt[3]{16a^3}$ **78.** $\sqrt[3]{81x^2y^4}$ **79.** $\sqrt[5]{64a^8}$ **80.** $\sqrt[7]{64a^8}$

In Exercises 81 through 98, perform the indicated operations and simplify.

81. $3\sqrt{7} - 2\sqrt{6} + \sqrt{28}$ **82.** $5\sqrt{3} - \sqrt{27} - \sqrt{15}$

83. $2\sqrt{40} - 3\sqrt{90} + \sqrt{70}$ **84.** $\sqrt{12} - 3\sqrt{27} + 2\sqrt{80}$

85. $\sqrt{2a^2} + 3\sqrt{8} - \sqrt{32a^2}$ **86.** $\sqrt{20a} + 4\sqrt{5a^3} - 3\sqrt{45a}$

87. $\sqrt{2}(\sqrt{6} - 2\sqrt{24})$ **88.** $\sqrt{3}(3\sqrt{6} + \sqrt{54})$

89. $\sqrt{a}(\sqrt{ab} - 3\sqrt{5b})$ **90.** $\sqrt{ab}(\sqrt{b} - 3\sqrt{a})$

91. $(\sqrt{6} - \sqrt{5})(2\sqrt{6} - 3\sqrt{5})$ **92.** $(3\sqrt{7} + 4\sqrt{2})(\sqrt{7} - 3\sqrt{2})$

93. $(\sqrt{a} - 3\sqrt{b})(2\sqrt{a} + \sqrt{b})$ **94.** $(\sqrt{ab} - \sqrt{c})(2\sqrt{ab} + \sqrt{c})$

95. $\dfrac{\sqrt{2}}{\sqrt{5} - \sqrt{2}}$ **96.** $\dfrac{3}{\sqrt{7} - 2\sqrt{3}}$

97. $\dfrac{\sqrt{2} - 1}{2\sqrt{2} + 3}$ **98.** $\dfrac{\sqrt{11} - \sqrt{5}}{2\sqrt{11} + \sqrt{5}}$

In Exercises 99 through 114, solve the given problems.

99. The center of gravity of a half-ring is found by using the expression

$$(r^2 + 4R^2)(2\pi R)^{-1},$$

where r is the radius of the cross section and R is the radius of the ring. Write this expression without negative exponents.

100. Some computers can read information at a rate of more than 75,000 characters per second. Write this number in scientific notation.

101. An oil film on water is about 0.0000002 in. thick. Write this number in scientific notation.

102. The charge on an electron is 1.6×10^{-19} coul. Write this number in ordinary notation.

103. Light travels 3.1×10^{16} ft in one year. Write this number in ordinary notation.

104. Some gamma rays have wavelengths of 5×10^{-11} cm. Write this number in ordinary notation.

105. The density of steam is about 6×10^{-4} g/cm^3. Write this in ordinary notation.

106. A ten-gram ball dropped from a height of ten meters reaches the ground with a kinetic energy of 9.8×10^6 ergs. Write this in ordinary notation.

107. The voltage across a resistor is found by using the formula $V = IR$, where V is the voltage, I is the current, and R is the resistance. Find V given that $I = 5.6 \times 10^{-3}$ amp and $R = 6.9 \times 10^2$ ohm.

108. In order to compute the volume V of a helium-filled balloon which can support a weight w, one uses the formula

$$V = \frac{w}{d_a - d_h}.$$

Here d_a is the density of air and d_h is the density of helium. Find V, given that $w = 650$ kg, $d_a = 1.29 \times 10^{-3}$ kg/m^3, and $d_h = 0.18 \times 10^{-3}$ kg/m^3.

109. The speed of sound through a medium is given by $v = \sqrt{E/d}$, where E and d are constants depending on the medium. Rationalize this expression.

110. An expression encountered in the study of the flow of fluids in pipes is

$$\frac{0.38}{N^{1/5}}.$$

Evaluate this expression, given that $N = 3.2 \times 10^6$.

111. A manufacturer found the standard deviation (see Exercise 44 of Section 11–4) of the diameters of a certain machine part to be $\sqrt{2100/486}$ thousandths of an inch. Evaluate this standard deviation.

112. The velocity of sound in air, in meters/second, is proportional to the square root of $(273 + T)/273$, where T is the centigrade temperature. Given that $v = 331$ m/sec when $T = 0°C$, find the equation relating the velocity of sound and temperature in rationalized form.

113. The density of an object equals its weight divided by its volume. A certain metal has a density of 1331 lb/cu ft. What is the edge of a cube of this metal which weighs 8.00 lb?

114. The absolute temperature of the filament of a light bulb equals approximately 1000 times the fourth root of the wattage. Find the centigrade temperature (273° less than the absolute temperature) of the filament of a 25-watt bulb.

12 Quadratic Equations

12–1 QUADRATIC EQUATIONS

In Chapter 6 we introduced the basic methods of solving simple equations. Since then additional algebraic operations have been discussed. We are now in a position to solve another important type of equation, the *quadratic equation.*

Given that a, b, and c are constants, the equation

$$ax^2 + bx + c = 0 \qquad\qquad \text{12–1}$$

is called *the general quadratic equation in x.* It is the purpose of this section to identify quadratic equations and to discuss what is meant by the solution of the quadratic equation. The two sections which follow will discuss basic methods of solving such equations.

The equation $2x^2 + 3x + 7 = 0$ is in the form of Eq. (12–1). There-   **Example A**
fore it is a quadratic equation, where $a = 2$, $b = 3$, and $c = 7$.

The equation $4x^2 - 7x + 9 = 0$ is also in the form of Eq. (12–1), despite the presence of the minus sign, since we may identify $a = 4$, $b = -7$, and $c = 9$.

The equation $x^3 - 9x + 8 = 0$ is *not* of the form of Eq. (12–1) due to the presence of the x^3.

Since it is the term in x^2 which distinguishes the quadratic equation from other types of equations, if $a = 0$ the equation is not considered to be quadratic. However, either b, or c, or both may be zero, and the equation is quadratic.

The equation $4x - 9 = 0$ is not a quadratic equation. It would fit the   **Example B**
form of Eq. (12–1) only if $a = 0$, and such an equation is not quadratic.

The equation $3x^2 - 19 = 0$ is a quadratic equation, where $a = 3$, $b = 0$, and $c = -19$.

The equation $x^2 - 8x = 0$ is a quadratic equation, where $a = 1$, $b = -8$, and $c = 0$.

If basic operations can be performed on an equation so that it may be written in the form of Eq. (12–1), it is then a quadratic equation. Once this form is found, the values of a, b, and c may be determined. Consider the illustrations of the following example.

Example C   The equation $3x^2 - 6 = 7x$ is not of the form of Eq. (12–1), but may easily be put in this form by subtracting $7x$ from each side of the equation. Performing this operation, we have

$$3x^2 - 7x - 6 = 0,$$

which means $a = 3$, $b = -7$, and $c = -6$.

The equation $2x^2 = (x - 8)^2$ is not in the form of Eq. (12–1). In order to determine whether or not it may be put in this form, we must square the right-hand side as indicated. By then collecting terms on the left, we can establish the form of the equation. This leads to

$$2x^2 = x^2 - 16x + 64,$$

or

$$x^2 + 16x - 64 = 0.$$

This last equation is of the form of Eq. (12–1), where $a = 1$, $b = 16$, and $c = -64$.

The equation $3x^2 = (3x - 1)(x + 2)$ becomes

$$3x^2 = 3x^2 + 5x - 2 \qquad \text{or} \qquad -5x + 2 = 0.$$

We see that this last form is not the same as Eq. (12–1), and therefore the equation is not quadratic.

From Chapter 6 we recall that a solution of an equation is a value of the unknown which, when substituted into the equation, makes the two sides of the equation equal. Therefore, if a value of x is substituted into Eq. (12–1), the left-hand side must result in zero if that value of x is a solution. As we shall see in the next section, the solution of a quadratic equation is generally a pair of numbers, although occasionally only one number satisfies the equation. In any case there cannot be more than two numbers which satisfy a quadratic equation. The following example illustrates checking possible values of x as solutions of a quadratic equation.

Example D   Determine which, if any, of the values $x = 1$, $x = -3$, $x = \frac{1}{2}$, $x = 2$ are solutions of the equation $2x^2 + 5x - 3 = 0$.

Testing $x = 1$, we have

$$2(1)^2 + 5(1) - 3 = 2 + 5 - 3 = 4.$$

Since the resulting value is not 0, the value $x = 1$ is not a solution.

Testing $x = -3$, we have

$$2(-3)^2 + 5(-3) - 3 = 2(9) - 15 - 3 = 18 - 15 - 3 = 0.$$

Since the value is zero, the value $x = -3$ is a solution.

Testing $x = \frac{1}{2}$, we have

$$2(\tfrac{1}{2})^2 + 5(\tfrac{1}{2}) - 3 = 2(\tfrac{1}{4}) + \tfrac{5}{2} - 3 = \tfrac{1}{2} + \tfrac{5}{2} - 3 = 3 - 3 = 0.$$

Since the value is zero, the value $x = \frac{1}{2}$ is also a solution. Since we have now found two such values, we know that the solutions to this equation are $x = -3$ and $x = \frac{1}{2}$. Any other value of x will prove not to be a solution.

Testing $x = 2$, we have

$$2(2)^2 + 5(2) - 3 = 2(4) + 10 - 3 = 15,$$

which means that $x = 2$ is not a solution.

Our primary concern will be with quadratic equations which have real roots. However, it is possible that the solution of a quadratic equation can contain numbers with $i = \sqrt{-1}$. It is also possible that the real solutions of a quadratic equation are equal, and therefore only one value satisfies the equation.

The equation $x^2 + 4 = 0$ has the solutions of $2i$ and $-2i$. This can be verified by substitution.   **Example E**

$$(2i)^2 + 4 = 4i^2 + 4 = 4(-1) + 4 = -4 + 4 = 0,$$
$$(-2i)^2 + 4 = (-2)^2 i^2 + 4 = 4(-1) + 4 = -4 + 4 = 0.$$

The equation $x^2 + 4x + 4 = 0$ has the solution $x = -2$ only. The two solutions here are equal. The reason for this will be seen in the following section.

In Exercises 1 through 10, determine whether or not the given equations are   **EXERCISES** quadratic by performing algebraic operations which could put each in the form of Eq. (12–1). If the resulting form is quadratic, identify a, b, and c.

1. $x^2 - 7x = 4$ **2.** $3x^2 = 5 - 9x$

3. $x^2 = (x - 1)^2$ **4.** $2x^2 - x = x(x + 8)$

5. $(x + 2)^2 = 0$ **6.** $x(x^2 - 1) = x^3 + x^2$

7. $x^2 = x(1 - 6x)$ **8.** $x(x^2 + 2x - 1) = 0$

9. $x^2(1 - x) = 4$ **10.** $x(x^3 + 6) - 1 = x^2(x^2 + 1)$

In Exercises 11 through 20, if the equation is not of the form of Eq. (12–1), put it in the proper form. Then test the given values to determine which, if any, are solutions of the equation.

11. $x^2 - x - 2 = 0$, $x = 1, x = -1, x = 2$

12. $x^2 + 4x + 3 = 0$, $x = -1, x = 2, x = 1, x = -3$

13. $2x^2 - 3x + 1 = 0$, $x = -1, x = 0, x = \frac{1}{2}, x = 1$

14. $y^2 = 3y + 10$, $y = 2, y = -1, y = 5$

15. $(3x - 4)(x - 2) = 0$, $x = -2, x = 1, x = 3$

16. $3t^2 + t + 2 = 2(t + 2)$, $t = -\frac{2}{3}, t = -1, t = 1$

17. $s^2 = 4(s - 1)$, $s = -2, s = 1, s = 2$

18. $x(x + 4) = 2x$, $x = -3, x = -2, x = 0, x = 1$

19. $n^2 + 6n - 3 = 6(n + 1)$, $n = -3, n = -1, n = 3$

20. $x^2 + 16 = 0$, $x = -4, x = 2, x = 4$

In Exercises 21 through 25, solve the given problems.

21. A certain number is 42 less than its square. Show that the equation for this statement is quadratic.

22. A rectangle has a width w and a length which is 4.0 in. more than the width. Given that the area is 45 in^2, show that the resulting equation involving the width is quadratic.

23. Under certain circumstances the distance s that an object is above the ground is given by $s = 96t - 16t^2$, where t is the time in seconds. Given that $s = 144$ ft, find the resulting quadratic equation. Show that $t = 3.00$ sec is a solution of the equation.

24. In order to find the current in a certain alternating-current electric circuit, it is necessary to solve the equation

$$m^2 + 10m + 2500 = 0.$$

Show that $-5 + 15i\sqrt{11}$ and $-5 - 15i\sqrt{11}$ are the solutions of this equation.

25. Show that the following problem leads to an equation which is quadratic: A jet, by increasing its speed by 200 mi/hr, could cover 6000 mi in 1 hr less. What is the speed of the jet?

12–2 SOLUTION BY FACTORING

If a quadratic equation is in the form of Eq. (12–1), and the left-hand side is factorable, the solution is rather easily obtained. Once the factors are determined, each is set equal to zero, and the solution reduces to solving two simple equations of the type discussed in Chapter 6. The reason for this is that the product of the factors is zero if at least one of the factors is zero.

Solve the equation $x^2 - x - 2 = 0$.   **Example A**

We first write the left-hand side in factored form. This gives

$$(x - 2)(x + 1) = 0.$$

Next we set each factor equal to zero, and solve the resulting equations. Therefore we have

$$x - 2 = 0, \qquad x + 1 = 0,$$
$$x = 2; \qquad x = -1.$$

Hence the solutions are $x = 2$ and $x = -1$. Checking each of these values, we have

$$2^2 - 2 - 2 = 4 - 2 - 2 = 0$$

and

$$(-1)^2 - (-1) - 2 = 1 + 1 - 2 = 0.$$

Checking the solutions is always a good idea.

In Example A, if $x - 2 = 0$, the left-hand side may be written $0 \cdot (x + 1)$, and this product is zero, regardless of the value of $x + 1$. Therefore we see that setting this factor equal to zero should give us a solution to the original equation. The same is true if $x + 1 = 0$. We must keep in mind, however, that the equation must be written in the form of Eq. (12–1) before we factor the left-hand side. This is necessary since we must have zero on the right. If any number other than zero appears on the right, this method is not applicable.

Solve the equation $x^2 - 10x = -21$.   **Example B**

Many students would be tempted to factor the left-hand side into $x(x - 10)$ and then set $x = -21$ and $x - 10 = -21$. The "solutions" obtained, $x = -21$, and $x = -11$, are not correct, as can be verified by substitution.

The correct procedure is to first write the equation as

$$x^2 - 10x + 21 = 0,$$

which factors into $(x - 7)(x - 3) = 0$. In this manner, we obtain the correct solutions $x = 7$ and $x = 3$.

Example C Solve the equation $6x^2 = 5 - 7x$.

Following the procedure described above, we have

$$6x^2 + 7x - 5 = 0,$$
$$(2x - 1)(3x + 5) = 0,$$
$$2x - 1 = 0, \qquad 3x + 5 = 0,$$
$$2x = 1, \qquad 3x = -5,$$
$$x = \tfrac{1}{2}; \qquad x = -\tfrac{5}{3}.$$

In order to be certain that no improper algebraic steps have been taken, it is best to check each solution in the original equation, even though it is not in the form of Eq. (12–1). Thus, we check and obtain

$$6(\tfrac{1}{2})^2 \overset{?}{=} 5 - 7(\tfrac{1}{2}), \qquad 6(-\tfrac{5}{3})^2 \overset{?}{=} 5 - 7(-\tfrac{5}{3}),$$
$$6(\tfrac{1}{4}) \overset{?}{=} 5 - \tfrac{7}{2}, \qquad 6(\tfrac{25}{9}) \overset{?}{=} 5 + \tfrac{35}{3},$$
$$\tfrac{3}{2} = \tfrac{3}{2}; \qquad \tfrac{50}{3} = \tfrac{50}{3}.$$

Since the values on each side are equal, the solutions check.

In the last section we mentioned that the two solutions, *roots* of the equation, can be equal. This is true when the two factors are the same. The following example illustrates this type of quadratic equation.

Example D Solve the equation $4x^2 - 12x + 9 = 0$.

Factoring this equation, we obtain

$$(2x - 3)(2x - 3) = 0.$$

Setting each factor equal to zero gives

$$2x - 3 = 0,$$
$$x = \tfrac{3}{2}.$$

Since both factors are the same, the equation has a *double root* of $\tfrac{3}{2}$. Checking verifies the solution.

Many students tend to improperly solve a quadratic equation in which $c = 0$. The following example illustrates this type and the error often made in its solution.

Example E

Solve the equation $x^2 - 6x = 0$.

Noting that the two terms of this equation contain x, the student makes the error of dividing through by x. This results in the equation $x - 6 = 0$, and the solution $x = 6$. However, the solution $x = 0$ was lost by the division by x.

Instead of dividing through by x, we should factor the equation into

$$x(x - 6) = 0.$$

By setting each factor equal to zero, we obtain

$$x = 0, \qquad x - 6 = 0, \qquad x = 6.$$

Therefore the two solutions are $x = 0$ and $x = 6$. Checking verifies these roots.

A number of different kinds of verbally stated problems may lead to quadratic equations. The following example illustrates setting up and solving such a problem.

Example F

The width of a certain box is 3 ft, and the height is 3 ft less than the length. If the volume of the box is 84 cu. ft, find the length and height.

One good choice of unknowns is to let $h = $ the height of the box. Then, noting the second part of the first sentence of the statement of the problem, we have

$$h + 3 = \text{the length of the box.}$$

(It would also be possible to let $l = $ the length of the box and $l - 3$ equal its height.) Now using the fact that the volume is 84 cu. ft, we have

$$3(h)(h + 3) = 84,$$
$$3h^2 + 9h = 84,$$
$$h^2 + 3h = 28,$$
$$h^2 + 3h - 28 = 0,$$
$$(h + 7)(h - 4) = 0,$$
$$h + 7 = 0, \qquad h - 4 = 0,$$
$$h = -7; \qquad h = 4.$$

Since a negative value for the height has no practical significance, the height is 4 ft. This means that the length is 7 ft. Checking, we find that a box with dimensions 3 ft, 4 ft, and 7 ft has a volume of $(3)(4)(7) = 84 \text{ ft}^3$.

EXERCISES   In Exercises 1 through 24, solve the given quadratic equations by factoring.

1. $x^2 - 4 = 0$ **2.** $4x^2 - 9 = 0$ **3.** $x^2 + x - 2 = 0$

4. $x^2 - 5x + 6 = 0$ **5.** $2x^2 + 3x = 2$ **6.** $3y^2 = 8 - 10y$

7. $s^2 = 6s + 7$ **8.** $6x^2 - 7x - 20 = 0$ **9.** $6n^2 - n = 2$

10. $v^2 = 9v + 10$ **11.** $5x^2 + 4 = 21x$ **12.** $9p^2 + 20 = -27p$

13. $2x^2 = 9 + 7x$ **14.** $6x^2 + 7x = 10$ **15.** $x^2 + 4x + 4 = 0$

16. $x^2 + 9 = 6x$ **17.** $x^2 - 5x = 0$ **18.** $9x^2 + 30x + 25 = 0$

19. $t^2 = 3t$ **20.** $3r^2 = 21r$ **21.** $8m + 3 = 3m^2$

22. $3 - x = 4x^2$ **23.** $x^2 - 4a^2 = 0$ (a is constant)

24. $2x^2 - 8ax + 8a^2 = 0$

In Exercises 25 through 32, solve any resulting quadratic equations by factoring.

25. Under certain conditions, the motion of an object suspended by a helical spring requires the solution of the equation

$$D^2 + 8D + 12 = 0.$$

Solve for D.

26. Under specified conditions, the deflection of a beam requires the solution of the equation

$$4Lx - x^2 - 4L^2 = 0,$$

where x is the distance from one end and $2L$ is the length of the beam. Solve for x in terms of L.

27. Three times a positive number subtracted from the square of the number results in 4. Find the number.

28. Compute the approximate boiling point of water on the top of Mt. Baker in Washington (altitude is about 10,800 ft). See Exercise 57 of Section 9–5.

29. The perimeter of a rectangular field is 100 ft and the area is 600 ft². Find the dimensions of the field.

30. The distance an object falls due to gravity is given by $s = 16t^2$, where s is the distance in feet and t is the time in seconds. How long does it take an object to fall 36.0 ft?

31. The floor of a certain room is covered with 324 square tiles. If the side of each tile were 1 in. longer, it would take only 256 tiles to cover the floor. Find the length of a side of each tile.

32. Find the velocity of the jet in Problem 25 of Section 12–1.

12–3 SOLUTION BY FORMULA

Many quadratic equations cannot be solved by factoring. It is, however, possible to derive a formula by which any quadratic equation may be solved. The method of deriving this formula requires that we write the equation in a different form in the intermediate steps. The following example follows the basic line of reasoning we shall use to derive the formula.

Solve the equation $x^2 + 4x - 21 = 0$.   **Example A**

This equation can easily be solved by factoring. However, there is an alternative *method* in which we are interested here.

The terms $x^2 + 4x$ are two of the terms we may obtain by expanding $(x + 2)^2$. In fact, if 4 is added to $x^2 + 4x$, we have $(x + 2)^2$ exactly. Therefore let us write the given equation as

$$x^2 + 4x \qquad = 21,$$
$$x^2 + 4x + 4 = 21 + 4.$$

This means that another form of the equation is

$$(x + 2)^2 = 25.$$

If we now take square roots of each side, we have

$$x + 2 = +5 \qquad \text{or} \qquad x + 2 = -5.$$

Solving each of these equations gives us the solutions $x = 3$ and $x = -7$, which can be verified by checking.

The key to this solution is that the left-hand side is a perfect square, which allows us to solve simple equations after we find the square root.

The method used to find the solution in Example A is called *completing the square*. The basic idea of this method is to create the perfect square of a simple algebraic expression on the left, allowing the right to have any numerical value. Since $(x + a)^2 = x^2 + 2ax + a^2$, we see that the square of one-half the coefficient of x added to $x^2 + 2ax$ gives such a perfect square. We shall now use this method to derive the general formula for solving quadratic equations.

First we start with the general quadratic equation

$$ax^2 + bx + c = 0. \qquad \text{12-1}$$

Next we divide through by a, obtaining

$$x^2 + \frac{b}{a}x + \frac{c}{a} = 0.$$

Let us subtract c/a from each side, which gives

$$x^2 + \frac{b}{a}x = -\frac{c}{a}.$$

Now we take one-half of b/a, which is $b/2a$, square it, obtaining $b^2/4a^2$, and add this to each side of the equation. Therefore we have

$$x^2 + \frac{b}{a}x + \frac{b^2}{4a^2} = \frac{b^2}{4a^2} - \frac{c}{a}.$$

The left-hand side is now the perfect square of $(x + b/2a)$. Indicating this and combining fractions on the right, we have

$$\left(x + \frac{b}{2a}\right)^2 = \frac{b^2 - 4ac}{4a^2}.$$

Taking the square root of each side, we have

$$x + \frac{b}{2a} = \frac{\sqrt{b^2 - 4ac}}{2a} \quad \text{and} \quad x + \frac{b}{2a} = \frac{-\sqrt{b^2 - 4ac}}{2a}.$$

Subtracting $b/2a$ from each side, combining fractions, and writing the result as one basic equation, we have

$$x = \frac{-b \pm \sqrt{b^2 - 4ac}}{2a}, \qquad \text{12-2}$$

which is known as the *quadratic formula*. If an equation is in the form of Eq (12–1), then direct substitution of the appropriate quantities into Eq. (12–2) gives the solutions. Remember, there are two solutions indicated in Eq. (12–2), one each for the + sign and − sign of the ± sign. The following examples illustrate the use of Eq. (12–2).

Solve the equation $x^2 - 5x + 6 = 0$ by the quadratic formula.   **Example B**

Since the equation is in the proper form, we recognize that $a = 1, b = -5$, and $c = 6$. Therefore

$$x = \frac{-(-5) \pm \sqrt{(-5)^2 - 4(1)(6)}}{2(1)} = \frac{5 \pm \sqrt{25 - 24}}{2} = \frac{5 \pm 1}{2}.$$

Therefore

$$x = \frac{5 + 1}{2} = 3 \quad \text{and} \quad x = \frac{5 - 1}{2} = 2.$$

These roots could have been found by factoring, but we see that the same results are obtained by using the formula. The roots are easily checked in the original equation.

Solve $2x^2 + 7x = 3$ by the quadratic formula.   **Example C**

Before the formula can be used, the equation must be put in the form of Eq. (12–1). This gives

$$2x^2 + 7x - 3 = 0,$$

and therefore $a = 2, b = 7$, and $c = -3$. The solutions are

$$x = \frac{-7 \pm \sqrt{49 - 4(2)(-3)}}{2(2)} = \frac{-7 \pm \sqrt{49 + 24}}{4} = \frac{-7 \pm \sqrt{73}}{4}.$$

This form of the result is generally acceptable. However, if decimal approximations are required, then using $\sqrt{73} = 8.544$, we have

$$x = \frac{-7 + 8.544}{4} = 0.386 \quad \text{and} \quad x = \frac{-7 - 8.544}{4} = -3.886.$$

Solve the equation $3x^2 = 2x - 5$ by the quadratic formula.   **Example D**

Putting the equation in the proper form as $3x^2 - 2x + 5 = 0$, we have $a = 3, b = -2$, and $c = 5$. Therefore

$$x = \frac{-(-2) \pm \sqrt{(-2)^2 - 4(3)(5)}}{2(3)} = \frac{2 \pm \sqrt{4 - 60}}{6}$$

$$= \frac{2 \pm \sqrt{-56}}{6} = \frac{2 \pm 2\sqrt{-14}}{6} = \frac{1 \pm \sqrt{-14}}{3}.$$

Since $\sqrt{-14} = i\sqrt{14}$, we see that the result contains imaginary numbers.

Example E   A uniform strip is mowed around the four sides of a field 80 ft by 100 ft. A rectangular section of 6000 ft² remains unmowed. Find the width of the strip.

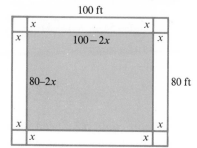

Figure 12–1

A figure will help us visualize the situation. In Fig. 12–1 we have let $x =$ the width of the strip. We see that the area which remains unmowed is given by

$$(80 - 2x)(100 - 2x) = 6000.$$

Simplifying, we have

$$8000 - 200x - 160x + 4x^2 = 6000,$$
$$4x^2 - 360x + 2000 = 0,$$
$$x^2 - 90x + 500 = 0.$$

Solving this last equation by the quadratic formula, we have

$$x = \frac{90 \pm \sqrt{8100 - 2000}}{2}$$
$$= \frac{90 \pm \sqrt{6100}}{2} = \frac{90 \pm 10\sqrt{61}}{2} = 45 \pm 5\sqrt{61}.$$

Since $\sqrt{61} = 7.810$, it follows that $5\sqrt{61} = 39.05$. Thus, $x = 5.95$ and $x = 84.05$. However, the strip mowed would be wider than the field if $x = 84.05$, which means that this answer cannot be true. If the strip is 5.95 ft, the unmowed portion of the field is 88.1 ft by 68.1 ft, and this area is 6000 ft². This means that the strip is about 5.95 ft wide.

EXERCISES   Solve the quadratic equations of Exercises 1 through 24 by using the quadratic formula.

1. $x^2 - x - 6 = 0$ 2. $x^2 + 2x - 15 = 0$

3. $2x^2 + x - 1 = 0$ **4.** $3y^2 - 5y + 2 = 0$

5. $x^2 + 5x + 3 = 0$ **6.** $x^2 - 3x - 1 = 0$

7. $4t^2 = 8t - 3$ **8.** $3x^2 = x + 10$

9. $4x^2 - 9 = 0$ **10.** $3p^2 = 48$

11. $4x^2 - 12x = 7$ **12.** $2x^2 + 7x + 2 = 0$

13. $x^2 + x = -2$ **14.** $r^2 - 2r + 5 = 0$

15. $4x^2 = 8 - 2x$ **16.** $3u^2 = 18 - 6u$

17. $x^2 - 8x = 0$ **18.** $3q^2 = 10q$

19. $2t^2 - 3t = -8$ **20.** $4x^2 = 9x - 6$

21. $10l + 8 = 3l^2$ **22.** $7 - 15x = -2x^2$

23. $6a^2x^2 + 11ax + 3 = 0$ (a is constant)

24. $2x^2 + (a + 2)x + a = 0$

Solve the quadratic equations of Exercises 25 through 30 by the method of completing the square. In Exercise 30 use p, q, and r as constants.

25. $x^2 + 2x - 3 = 0$ **26.** $x^2 + 6x - 7 = 0$

27. $x^2 - 4x + 3 = 0$ **28.** $x^2 = 8x - 5$

29. $2x^2 + 3x + 1 = 0$ **30.** $px^2 + qx + r = 0$

In Exercises 31 through 37, solve by means of the quadratic formula any quadratic equations which may arise.

31. Find two consecutive positive integers whose product is 132.

32. The side of one square exceeds the side of another square by 3 ft. The total area of the two squares is 65 ft^2. Find the side of each square.

33. Under certain conditions, the distance s that an object is above the ground is given by $s = 100t - 16t^2$, where t is the time in seconds. After what amount of time is the object 80.0 ft above the ground?

34. Under specified conditions, the power developed in an element of an electric circuit is

$$P = EI - RI^2,$$

where P is the power, E is a specified voltage, and R is a specified resistance. Assuming that P, E, and R are constants, solve for I.

35. How wide a strip around the outside of a field 400 yd by 600 yd must a farmer mow in order to mow half the area?

36. In order to find the current in an alternating electric current circuit containing an inductance L, a resistance R, and a capacitor C, it is necessary to solve the equation

$$LCm^2 + RCm + 1 = 0$$

for m. Solve this equation.

37. An object is sold for \$10, which includes a profit of as many percent as the number of dollars of original cost. Find the original cost.

12–4 REVIEW EXERCISES

In Exercises 1 through 12, solve the given quadratic equations by factoring.

1. $x^2 + 7x + 6 = 0$ **2.** $x^2 + 11x - 12 = 0$

3. $2x^2 - 7x + 5 = 0$ **4.** $4x^2 = 8x - 3$

5. $6n^2 = 35n + 6$ **6.** $9s^2 - 5s = 0$

7. $16x^2 - 24x + 9 = 0$ **8.** $4p^2 + 49 = 28p$

9. $18x^2 + 7x = 0$ **10.** $9r^2 - 55r + 6 = 0$

11. $t^2 + t = 110$ **12.** $2x^2 + 39x = 20$

In Exercises 13 through 18, solve the given quadratic equations by (a) factoring and (b) the quadratic formula.

13. $x^2 + 4 = 5x$ **14.** $2x^2 + 3 = 5x$

15. $6m^2 + 5 = 11m$ **16.** $7x^2 + 24x = 16$

17. $3x^2 - 6x + 3 = 0$ **18.** $5x^2 + 40x = 0$

In Exercises 19 through 30, solve the given quadratic equations by using the quadratic formula.

19. $x^2 + x + 1 = 0$ **20.** $x^2 + x - 1 = 0$

21. $2x^2 - 5x + 1 = 0$ **22.** $3r^2 + 4r - 2 = 0$

23. $y^2 - 6y = 6$ **24.** $5t^2 = 5t + 3$

25. $2x^2 + 4x + 3 = 0$ **26.** $3u^2 - u = -9$

27. $x^2 + 4 = 0$ **28.** $4y^2 = -25$

29. $4x^2 = 36$ **30.** $5p^2 = 35p$

In Exercises 31 through 33, solve the given quadratic equations by completing the square.

31. $x^2 + 2x + 2 = 0$ **32.** $x^2 - 4x = 8$ **33.** $2x^2 - 5x = 3$

Many equations containing algebraic fractions may be solved as quadratic equations. By first clearing fractions (see Section 10–5), we can derive the quadratic form. We must be careful, however, to exclude any values which may indicate division by zero. Exercises 34 through 36 illustrate this type of equation ($\neq$ means "does not equal").

34. $\dfrac{1}{x} + x = 4 \quad (x \neq 0)$ **35.** $\dfrac{1}{x} - \dfrac{2}{x-1} = 2 \quad (x \neq 0,\ x \neq 1)$

36. $\dfrac{1}{2}(x+2) - \dfrac{3}{x} = \dfrac{3}{2} \quad (x \neq 0)$

Solve the quadratic equations which result in Exercises 37 through 49 by any appropriate method.

37. Two positive numbers differ by 6. Their product is 91. Find the numbers.

38. Two consecutive positive integers have a product of 240. Find these integers.

39. The length of a rectangle is 1 in. more than the width. If 3 in. are added to the length and 1 in. to the width, the new area is twice the original area. Find the dimensions of the original rectangle.

40. If the radius of a circle is doubled, its area increases by 192π ft^2. Find the radius of the circle.

41. Under particular frictional conditions, the motion of an object on a spring requires the solution of the equation

$$D^2 + 2rD + k^2 = 0,$$

where r and k are constants of the system. Solve for D.

42. Under specified conditions, the partial pressure of a certain gas (in atmospheres) is found by solving the equation

$$P^2 - 3P + 1 = 0.$$

Solve for P such that $P < 1$ atm.

43. A projectile is fired vertically into the air. The distance (in ft) above the ground, in terms of the time in seconds, is given by the formula $s = 3200t - 16t^2$. How long will it take to hit the ground?

44. In a certain electric circuit there is a resistance R of 2 ohms and a voltage E of 60 volts. The equation between current i (in amps), E, and R is $i^2R + iE = 8000$. What current ($i > 0$) flows in the circuit?

45. A man who is designing a machine part finds that if he changes a square part to a rectangular part by increasing one dimension of the square by 2 mm, the area becomes 50 mm^2. Determine the side of the square part.

46. A metal cube expands when heated. If the volume changes by 6.00 mm^3 and each edge is 0.20 mm longer after the cube is heated, what was the original length of the edge of the cube?

47. A general formula for the distance s traveled by an object, given an initial velocity v and acceleration a in time t, is

$$s = vt + \tfrac{1}{2}at^2.$$

Solve for t.

48. An object is sold for \$24, which includes a profit of twice as many percent as the number of dollars of original cost. Find the original cost.

49. After flying 1200 mi, a pilot determines that he can make the return trip in one hour less if he increases his average speed by 100 mi/hr. What was his original average speed?

Logarithms 13

13-1 INTRODUCTION; POWERS OF TEN

The basic operations of arithmetic provide a basis for numerical calculations. Algebra is developed by generalizing on these operations. However, we may encounter a calculation which is either long and tedious,
or difficult, or both. In many cases the slide rule may be used to perform
the calculation, but the slide rule does have limitations as to the calculations which it can perform and also as to the accuracy of results, since
most results are limited to three-place accuracy at best. In this chapter
we shall develop a basic method by which such calculations may be
performed, and to an accuracy greater than that possible on the slide
rule. This method employs what are known as *logarithms*. Those who
continue their study of mathematics will find that logarithms are used
extensively for purposes other than calculations. This means that their
importance will continue despite the increased use of electronic computers
for many calculations.

Example A   If $100 is invested at 4% interest compounded quarterly, it will grow in
10 years to an amount whose value is given by the expression $100(1.01)^{40}$.
This calculation would be long and tedious if we employed successive
multiplications.

When one is finding the efficiency of an internal combustion engine,
it is necessary to find the $\frac{2}{5}$ power of the compression ratio. Some slide
rules can handle this type of calculation, although with the limitation
of three-place accuracy.

From Example A we can see that it would be most helpful if we had
a method of computation which would simplify the raising of a number
to a power and the extraction of any root (not just square roots). Logarithms, as we shall see, provide a method for these purposes as well as for
multiplication and division.

Before we can learn to use logarithms, we must first investigate some
preliminary matters involving powers of 10. From our previous work
with powers we know that

$$10^0 = 1 \quad \text{and} \quad 10^1 = 10.$$

We now consider the question: Can 10 be raised to some power so that
the result is a number between 1 and 10? Recalling our work with
fractional exponents, we can see that it is possible, as shown in the
following example.

Since $\sqrt{10} = 3.162$, and $\sqrt{10} = 10^{1/2}$, we know that   Example B

$$10^{1/2} = 3.162.$$

From Table 1, we see that $\sqrt[3]{10} = 2.154$. Therefore, since $\sqrt[3]{10} = 10^{1/3}$,

$$10^{1/3} = 2.154.$$

By finding other roots of 10, and by using the laws of exponents, one can find numerous other fractional powers of 10 which give a result between 1 and 10. To illustrate this, consider the following example.

The fourth root of 10 is 1.778. Therefore $\sqrt[4]{10} = 1.778$, which means that   Example C

$$10^{1/4} = 1.778.$$

Now, since

$$(10^{1/2})(10^{1/4}) = 10^{1/2+1/4} = 10^{3/4},$$

we have

$$(3.162)(1.778) = 10^{3/4} \qquad \text{or} \qquad 10^{3/4} = 5.623.$$

Let us now tabulate some of the results which we have found. Also, instead of writing the exponents as fractions, we shall write the exponents in their equivalent decimal form. For example, instead of writing $10^{1/4}$, we shall write $10^{0.2500}$. This will prove to be convenient as we go on. Therefore, we have

$$10^{0.0000} = 1.000$$
$$10^{0.2500} = 1.778$$
$$10^{0.3333} = 2.154$$
$$10^{0.5000} = 3.162$$
$$10^{0.7500} = 5.623$$
$$10^{1.0000} = 10.000$$

Through advanced mathematics it can be proved in general that, *given a positive number N, it is possible to find an exponent x such that*

$$10^x = N. \qquad\qquad \textbf{13-1}$$

For example,

$$10^{0.3010} = 2.000$$
$$10^{0.4771} = 3.000$$
$$10^{0.8451} = 7.000.$$

By knowing the necessary values of x for N between 1 and 10, we can use the laws of exponents to find values of N in other ranges. This is illustrated in the following examples.

Example D

$$20 = (2)(10) = (10^{0.3010})(10^{1.0000}) = 10^{1.3010}.$$
$$3000 = (3)(1000) = (10^{0.4771})(10^{3.0000}) = 10^{3.4771}.$$
$$\frac{1}{7} = \frac{1}{10^{0.8451}} = 10^{-0.8451} \quad \text{or} \quad 0.1429 = 10^{-0.8451}.$$

Example E

$$10^{4.5000} = 10^{4.0000+0.5000} = (10^{4.0000})(10^{0.5000})$$
$$= (10{,}000)(3.162) = 31{,}620.$$
$$10^{2.2500} = 10^{2.000+0.2500} = (10^{2.0000})(10^{0.2500})$$
$$= (100)(1.778) = 177.8.$$
$$10^{-1.3010} = \frac{1}{10^{1.3010}} = \frac{1}{20} \quad \text{(see Example D)} = 0.0500$$

Thus we see that we can find an exponent x that will make 10^x equal to any positive number. In the next section we shall assign the name *logarithms* to these exponents and study their properties. In this section we noted the use of *decimal* powers of 10 and showed that they followed the laws of exponents as we had previously developed them.

EXERCISES   In Exercises 1 through 6, rewrite the given expressions so that the powers of 10 are written in decimal, not fractional, form.

1. $10^{1/5} = 1.585$ **2.** $10^{2/3} = 4.642$ **3.** $10^{2/7} = 1.931$

4. $10^{5/8} = 4.217$ **5.** $10^{9/10} = 7.943$ **6.** $10^{11/20} = 3.548$

In Exercises 7 through 10, rewrite the given expressions so that decimal powers of 10 are substituted for the given roots of 10.

7. $\sqrt[6]{10} = 1.468$ **8.** $\sqrt[7]{10} = 1.390$

9. $\sqrt[5]{10^2} = 2.512$ **10.** $\sqrt[8]{10^7} = 7.499$

In Exercises 11 through 14, find the decimal equivalent of the indicated power of 10 by the method indicated.

11. $10^{0.7781}$;   since $10^{0.7781} = 10^{0.3010+0.4771} = (10^{0.3010})(10^{0.4771}) = $ (2.000)(3.000),

the result is found by this indicated multiplication.

12. $10^{0.5510}$; since $10^{0.5510} = 10^{0.3010+0.2500} = (10^{0.3010})(10^{0.2500}) = (2.000)(1.778)$,

the result is found by this indicated multiplication.

13. $10^{0.6020}$; since $10^{0.6020} = (10^{0.3010})^2 = (2.000)^2$,

the result is found by evaluating the indicated power.

14. $10^{2.5353}$; since $10^{2.5353} = (10^{0.8451})^3 = (7.000)^3$

the result is found by evaluating the indicated power.

In Exercises 15 through 18, express each number as a decimal power of 10 (see Example D). Only the decimal powers established in this section are used.

15. 2000　　　　　**16.** 700　　　　　**17.** 31.62　　　　　**18.** 0.5000 $(= \frac{1}{2})$

In Exercises 19 through 22, express each power of 10 as a number in ordinary notation (see Example E). Only the decimal powers established in this section are used.

19. $10^{3.2500}$　　　**20.** $10^{1.4771}$　　　**21.** $10^{4.3333}$　　　**22.** $10^{-2.8451}$

In Exercises 23 through 26, solve the given problems.

23. In the study of light, a basic law gives the amount transmitted through a medium. This amount is expressed as a power of 10. The percentage of light transmitted in a particular experiment is $100(10^{-0.3010})$. What percentage is this?

24. Given that $(1.01)^{40} = 10^{0.1720}$, use Exercises 1 and 7 to estimate the value of the $100 investment of Example A.

25. The area of a square equals $10^{1.2500}$ ft^2. What is the approximate length of the side of the square? [*Hint:* A square root of a number is found by multiplying the power by $\frac{1}{2}$.]

26. The length of a certain rectangle is $10^{1.1452}$ ft and its width is $10^{0.3319}$ ft. What is its area? Express your result in ordinary notation.

13–2 THE LOGARITHM OF A NUMBER

In the previous section we found that it is possible to express any positive number as a power of 10. In the following sections we shall show how these powers of 10 can be used to perform certain calculations quite rapidly. In these calculations we shall be using numbers which have no more than three significant digits (except for Section 13–5, in which we shall use numbers with four significant digits).

The powers of 10 which we considered in Section 13–1 are themselves the logarithms which are so useful to calculations. In general, the exponent x in Eq. (13–1) is called the *logarithm to the base 10* of the number N. This can also be written as

$$\log N = x. \qquad\qquad \textbf{13–2}$$

The forms of Eqs. (13–1) and (13–2) are different, but the two equations are identical in meaning.

In the Appendix there is a table of four-place logarithms (the logarithms are written with four significant digits) for numbers with three significant digits from 1.00 to 9.99. From our discussion of Section 13–1, we know that these are decimals ranging from 0.0000 to 0.9996. We also know that these logarithms are powers to which 10 must be raised in order to equal the given number N. The method of finding the logarithm of a number from 1.00 to 9.99 from this table is illustrated in the following example.

Example A To find the logarithm of 8.36 we first look under N to find 83 (the first two significant digits). To the right of 83 and under 6 (the third significant digit) we find the digits 9222. Therefore,

$$\log 8.36 = 0.9222.$$

This means that $10^{0.9222} = 8.36$.

To find the logarithm of 4.08 we look to the right of 40 and under 8 and find the digits 6107. Thus

$$\log 4.08 = 0.6107,$$

which means that $10^{0.6107} = 4.08$.

Now the question arises as to how one may find the logarithm of a positive number not between 1.00 and 9.99. Let us first consider numbers greater than 10.

By writing a number in scientific notation we can use the basic laws of exponents along with the meaning of the logarithm to find the logarithms of such numbers. Consider the following example.

Example B To find the logarithm of 5340, we first write

$$5340 = 5.34 \times 10^3.$$

We find the logarithm of 5.34 to be 0.7275, which means that $5.34 = 10^{0.7275}$. Thus

$$5340 = 5.34 \times 10^3 = (10^{0.7275})(10^{3.0000}) = 10^{3.7275}.$$

Since 3.7275 is the required power to which 10 must be raised to equal 5340, we have

$$\log 5340 = 3.7275.$$

Generalizing on this example, if we express a positive number N in scientific notation as

$$N = M \times 10^C, \qquad \text{13-3}$$

we note that the logarithm of N is given by the equation

$$\log N = C + \log M. \qquad \text{13-4}$$

In Eq. (13-4) C is known as the *characteristic* of the logarithm of N, and $\log M$ is the *mantissa* of the logarithm of N. We see that the characteristic is the integral power of 10 of the number in scientific notation, and the mantissa is the logarithm of the number between 1 and 10 of this form.

69,200 = 6.92×10^4. Therefore,   Example C

$$\log 69{,}200 = 4 + \log 6.92 = 4 + 0.8401 = 4.8401.$$

20.6 = 2.06×10^1. Therefore,

$$\log 20.6 = 1 + \log 2.06 = 1 + 0.3139 = 1.3139.$$

When we wish to find the logarithm of a positive number less than 1 we follow the same method. The only apparent difference is that the characteristic is negative. Consider the following example.

0.0272 = 2.72×10^{-2}. Therefore,   Example D

$$\log 0.0272 = -2 + \log 2.72 = -2 + 0.4346.$$

We shall find that for some purposes this form of the logarithm is somewhat inconvenient. Thus we shall express the characteristic as $8 - 10$. In fact, we shall follow the procedure of expressing all negative characteristics in a similar manner: subtracting 10 from a positive number.

Thus

$$\log 0.0272 = -2 + 0.4346 = 8 - 10 + 0.4346 = 8 + 0.4346 - 10$$
$$= 8.4346 - 10.$$

(Note that the form $-2 + 0.4346$ *cannot* be written as -2.4346, for this would indicate that the entire number is negative. Only the 2 is negative, but the 0.4346 is positive.)

If we look closely at the above examples, we see that we can find the characteristic of the logarithm of a number by the following method: Move the decimal point so that it follows the first significant digit of the number. The value of the characteristic equals the number of places the decimal point is moved. The characteristic is positive if it is moved to the left; it is negative if it is moved to the right; it is zero if it is not moved.

Example E

Number	Form in scientific notation	Indicated movement of decimal point	Characteristic	Mantissa	Logarithm
12	1.2×10	1 . 2	+1	0.0792	1.0792
30,400	3.04×10^4	3 . 0 4 0 0	+4	0.4829	4.4829
0.123	1.23×10^{-1}	0 . 1 2 3	−1	0.0899	9.0899 − 10
0.00065	6.5×10^{-4}	0 . 0 0 0 6 5	−4	0.8129	6.8129 − 10
7.68	7.68×10^0	7 . 6 8	0	0.8854	0.8854

Logarithms may be found to three significant digits on the L-scale of a slide rule. Just as tables give only the mantissa, the reading from the L-scale also only gives the mantissa. To find the logarithm of a number using the L-scale, set the hairline over the number whose logarithm is required on the D-scale and read the mantissa on the L-scale.

Example F   The setting for finding the mantissa of the logarithm of 68400 is shown in Fig. 13–1. The reading on the L-scale is seen to be .835. Since the characteristic is 4, the logarithm of 68400 is 4.835.

In this section we have demonstrated how one finds the logarithm of a positive number. It might be pointed out that more errors occur in the proper determination of the characteristic than in any other step.

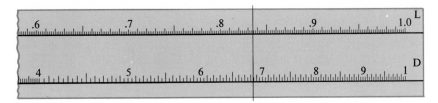

Figure 13-1

The meaning of a logarithm has also been shown. In our discussion we have used powers of 10, and 10 is the base of *common logarithms*. Other bases are used, but generally for specific purposes other than calculations.

In Exercises 1 through 12, determine the characteristic of the logarithm of each of the given numbers. Write any negative characteristics in the −10 notation.   **EXERCISES**

1. 27.5   2. 356   3. 4090   4. 6.92

5. 0.106   6. 0.000752   7. 89.2   8. 63300000

9. 0.0395   10. 0.00000632   11. 0.0649   12. 0.998

In Exercises 13 through 32, determine the logarithm of each of the given numbers by using the 4-place table in the Appendix.

13. 6.93   14. 3.17   15. 5.02   16. 6.10

17. 5800   18. 79,000   19. 105   20. 900000

21. 29   22. 85.7   23. 879   24. 707,000,000

25. 0.0642   26. 0.00163   27. 0.303   28. 0.990

29. 0.000863   30. 0.0101   31. 0.00000884   32. 0.0909

In Exercises 33 through 40, find the logarithms of each of the given numbers by using the L-scale on a slide rule.

33. 9.52   34. 5.21   35. 2030   36. 448

37. 0.0108   38. 0.396   39. 0.000614   40. 0.00203

In Exercises 41 through 46, answer the given questions.

41. A certain radio station broadcasts at a frequency of 1340000 cycles per second. What is the characteristic of the logarithm of this number?

42. The weight of the Milky Way has been estimated to be about 6×10^{41} lb. What is the characteristic of the logarithm of this number?

43. The Grand Coulee Dam contains about 10,600,000 yd^3 of concrete. What is the logarithm of this number?

44. A research chemist noted that the magnification of his microscope was 20,000 to 1. What is the logarithm of the magnification?

45. A bank charges 6.5% on loans that it makes. What is the logarithm of this number?

46. The coefficient of thermal expansion for aluminum is 2.2 × 10^{-5} per °C. What is the logarithm of this number?

13-3 MULTIPLICATION AND DIVISION BY LOGARITHMS

We are now in a position to perform computations by means of logarithms. In this section we shall develop the methods by which logarithms may be used to perform multiplication and division. In the next section we shall discuss methods for finding powers and roots of numbers. The following example develops the essential reasoning for the use of logarithms in multiplication.

Example A   Find the product of 2.15 and 3.84.

First we find the logarithms of the two given numbers. Also, we use the fact that the logarithm of each is that power to which 10 must be raised to equal the given number. Thus

$$\log 2.15 = 0.3324 \quad \text{and} \quad \log 3.84 = 0.5843,$$

which means that

$$10^{0.3324} = 2.15 \quad \text{and} \quad 10^{0.5843} = 3.84.$$

Expressing the product of 2.15 and 3.84, we have

$$(2.15)(3.84) = (10^{0.3324})(10^{0.5843}) = 10^{0.3324+0.5843} = 10^{0.9167}.$$

If we now find the number which equals $10^{0.9167}$, we shall have the desired product. This is the same as finding the number whose logarithm is 0.9167. Looking in the body of the table of logarithms, we find that the number closest to 9167 is 9165, which we shall use to determine our answer. Since 0.9165 is the logarithm of 8.25, we have

$$(2.15)(3.84) = 8.25.$$

Following the method of the above example, we shall now generalize the method for multiplication. To find the product of two numbers P and Q, which may be expressed as 10^x and 10^y, respectively, we have

$$PQ = (10^x)(10^y) = 10^{x+y},$$

where

$$x = \log P, \qquad y = \log Q, \qquad \text{and} \qquad x + y = \log PQ,$$

or

$$\log PQ = \log P + \log Q. \qquad\qquad \text{13-5}$$

Thus we see that

the logarithm of the product of two numbers is equal to the sum of the logarithms of the numbers.

In finding the product we must determine the number whose logarithm has been found by addition. This number, found from a known logarithm, is called an *antilogarithm*. Therefore we have the following procedure for multiplication by use of logarithms.

1. Determine the logarithms of the numbers to be multiplied.
2. Find the sum of these logarithms.
3. The required product is the antilogarithm of this sum.

The following examples illustrate the method.

Find the product of 1.30 and 120 by use of logarithms.   Example B

$$\log PQ = \log P + \log Q,$$
$$\log 1.30 = 0.1139$$
$$\log 120 \ = 2.0792$$
$$\overline{ 2.1931}$$

From the table, we find that a mantissa of 0.1931 is the logarithm of 1.56. Since the characteristic of the logarithm is 2, we have

$$PQ = 1.56 \times 10^2 = 156.$$

Find the product of 0.00472 and 60.8 by logarithms.   Example C

$$\log 0.00472 = 7.6739 - 10$$
$$\log 60.8 \quad\ = 1.7839$$
$$\overline{ 9.4578 - 10}$$

From the table, we find that the mantissa nearest to 0.4578 is 0.4579. Using this value, we have the logarithm of 2.87. Since the characteristic is $9 - 10 = -1$, the antilogarithm of $9.4578 - 10$ is 0.287. Thus

$$(0.00472)(60.8) = 0.287.$$

Example D   Find the product of 0.196 and 0.0422, using logarithms.

$$\begin{array}{rl} \log 0.196 = & 9.2923 - 10 \\ \log 0.0422 = & \underline{8.6253 - 10} \\ & 17.9176 - 20 \end{array}$$

Here, $17 - 20 = -3$ is the characteristic. The mantissa nearest to 0.9176 is 0.9175, which is the logarithm of 8.27. Therefore

$$(0.196)(0.0422) = 8.27 \times 10^{-3} = 0.00827.$$

Following precisely the same line of reasoning as that used to develop the method for multiplication, we now show how logarithms may be used in division. To find the quotient P/Q, where $P = 10^x$ and $Q = 10^y$, we have

$$\frac{P}{Q} = \frac{10^x}{10^y} = 10^{x-y},$$

where

$$x = \log P,$$
$$y = \log Q,$$

and

$$x - y = \log\left(\frac{P}{Q}\right).$$

Therefore

$$\log\left(\frac{P}{Q}\right) = \log P - \log Q. \qquad \text{13-6}$$

This means that

the logarithm of the quotient of two numbers is equal to the logarithm of the numerator minus the logarithm of the denominator.

Therefore, to divide one number by another using logarithms, we subtract the logarithm of the denominator from the logarithm of the numerator, and then find the antilogarithm of the result. The following examples illustrate the method.

Find the quotient $629/27.0$ by using logarithms.   Example E

$$\log\left(\frac{P}{Q}\right) = \log P - \log Q,$$

$$\log 629 = 2.7987$$
$$\log 27.0 = \underline{1.4314}$$
$$1.3673$$

From the table, we find that the mantissa nearest to 0.3673 is 0.3674, which is the logarithm of 2.33. The characteristic is 1. Therefore

$$\frac{629}{27.0} = 2.33 \times 10 = 23.3.$$

Find the quotient $39.2/0.0512$ by using logarithms.   Example F

To avoid any possible confusion in the subtraction and the results, we shall set up the logarithms so that the result of subtracting the parts of the logarithms containing the mantissa will be positive. To do this for this problem, we express the characteristic of 39.2 as $11 - 10$. Therefore we have the following steps:

$$\log 39.2 \quad = 11.5933 - 10$$
$$\log 0.0512 = \underline{\;\;8.7093 - 10}$$
$$2.8840$$

From the table, we find that the mantissa nearest to 0.8840 is 0.8842, which is the logarithm of 7.66. The characteristic is 2. (Note that in the subtraction of the logarithms the -10's subtracted out.) Therefore

$$\frac{39.2}{0.0512} = 7.66 \times 10^2 = 766.$$

Find the quotient $0.00402/0.938$ by using logarithms.   Example G

To have the part of the result containing the mantissa positive, we shall express the characteristic of the logarithm of 0.00402 as $17 - 20$. Thus

$$\log 0.00402 = 17.6042 - 20$$
$$\log 0.938 \quad = \underline{\;\;9.9722 - 10}$$
$$7.6320 - 10$$

From the table, we find that the mantissa nearest to 0.6320 is 0.6325, which is the logarithm of 4.29. The characteristic is $7 - 10 = -3$.

This means that

$$\frac{0.00402}{0.938} = 4.29 \times 10^{-3} = 0.00429.$$

When evaluating a fraction in which several multiplications are indicated, we follow this procedure:

1. Find the logarithm of each number.
2. Find the sum of the logarithms of the numbers in the numerator.
3. Find the sum of the logarithms of the numbers in the denominator.
4. Subtract the result of Step 3 from that of Step 2.
5. The desired result is the antilogarithm of the difference found in Step 4.

The following example illustrates the method.

Example H   By using logarithms, evaluate

$$\frac{(45.7)(0.0827)(6800)}{(3.07)(567)}.$$

log 45.7	=	1.6599	log 3.07	=	0.4871
log 0.0827	=	8.9175 − 10	log 567	=	2.7536
log 6800	=	3.8325			3.2407
		14.4099 − 10			
		3.2407			
		11.1692 − 10			

From the table, we see that the mantissa nearest to 0.1692 is 0.1703, which is the logarithm of 1.48. The characteristic is $11 - 10 = 1$. Thus the result is

$$1.48 \times 10 = 14.8.$$

EXERCISES   In each of the following exercises, perform the indicated calculations by means of logarithms.

1. (5.20)(1.83)
2. (31.9)(4.92)
3. (0.831)(92.1)
4. (0.0726)(452)
5. (6000)(3.18)
6. (0.00709)(0.847)
7. (78,000)(1.47)
8. (8080)(0.0715)
9. $\dfrac{8.12}{3.07}$
10. $\dfrac{84,600}{45.2}$
11. $\dfrac{0.841}{0.617}$
12. $\dfrac{0.00721}{8.15}$

13. $\dfrac{1.83}{92.5}$

14. $\dfrac{58.5}{9060}$

15. $\dfrac{0.0984}{0.0076}$

16. $\dfrac{156{,}000}{79{,}400}$

17. $\dfrac{(45.1)(6.12)}{73.8}$

18. $\dfrac{(8.01)(7230)}{647}$

19. $\dfrac{729}{(5.04)(1.97)}$

20. $\dfrac{3.14}{(0.184)(61.3)}$

21. $\dfrac{(5.03)(89.1)}{(46.1)(2.36)}$

22. $\dfrac{(0.0187)(816)}{(51.5)(0.0845)}$

23. $\dfrac{(65)(43.1)(0.0111)}{(0.473)(83.8)}$

24. $\dfrac{(45)(47)(82)(645)}{(1.6)(472)(0.836)}$

25. What is the circumference of a circle whose diameter is 49.2 ft? Let $\pi = 3.14$.

26. A bank pays 4.75% annual interest on deposits. How much is the annual interest on a deposit of $3580 in this bank?

27. Balsa wood has a density of 8.25 lb/ft^3. Lead has a density of 705 lb/ft^3. How many cubic feet of balsa wood have the same weight as one cubic foot of lead?

28. If sea water is 3.25% salt, how many pounds of sea water must be evaporated to obtain 675 lb of salt?

29. The voltage V across an electric resistor R in which a current I is flowing is given by $V = IR$. Find V, given that $I = 3.75 \times 10^{-2}$ amp and $R = 56.8$ ohms.

30. The cutting speed of a milling machine is the product of the circumference of the cutter and the number of revolutions per minute that it makes. Find the cutting speed of a milling cutter which is 5.25 in. in diameter, given that it makes 35.0 rev/min.

31. In a particular year, a farmer had 535 acres of land in wheat. He harvested 14,300 bushels. What was his average production per acre?

32. The coefficient of performance of a refrigerator is defined as the heat removed divided by the work done. Find the coefficient of performance for a refrigerator if 575 BTU (British thermal units) of heat are removed while 125 BTU of work is being done.

33. A tank 6.25 ft long, 3.75 ft wide, and 2.38 ft high is filled in 1.33 hr. What is the rate of flow (in cubic feet per hour) through the pipe which filled the tank?

34. The general gas law of chemistry and physics, $PV = RT$, gives the relation among the pressure, volume, and temperature of a body of gas (R is a constant equal to about 0.0821 units). If the pressure of a certain gas is 3.67 atm and its temperature is 373° (degrees absolute), what is its volume (in liters)?

13–4 POWERS AND ROOTS OBTAINED BY LOGARITHMS

In this section we shall show how logarithms can be used to find powers and roots of numbers. The reasoning underlying the development of the method is the same as that employed in the last section.

To find a power of a number P, which may be expressed as 10^x, we have

$$P = 10^x, \qquad P^n = (10^x)^n = 10^{nx},$$

where $x = \log P$ and $nx = \log P^n$. This means that

$$\log P^n = n \log P. \qquad\qquad \textbf{13-7}$$

Therefore

the logarithm of the nth power of a number is equal to n times the logarithm of the number.

The exponent may be integral or fractional. Therefore, if we wish to find the root of a number, we interpret n as a fractional exponent. The following examples illustrate the use of Eq. (13–7) for finding powers and roots of numbers.

Example A   Evaluate $(2.05)^3$ by logarithms.

$$\log P^n = n \log P,$$
$$\log 2.05 = 0.3118,$$
$$3(\log 2.05) = 3(0.3118) = 0.9354.$$

In the table, we see that the mantissa nearest to 0.9354 is 0.9355, which is the logarithm of 8.62. Therefore

$$(2.05)^3 = 8.62.$$

Example B   Evaluate $(6840)^5$ by logarithms.

$$\log 6840 = 3.8351, \qquad 5(\log 6840) = 5(3.8351) = 19.1755.$$

In the table, the mantissa nearest to 0.1755 is 0.1761, which is the logarithm of 1.50. The characteristic is 19. Therefore

$$(6840)^5 = 1.50 \times 10^{19}.$$

This is the most convenient form of the answer. If we write it in ordinary notation, we have 15,000,000,000,000,000,000.

Evaluate $(0.0743)^4$ by logarithms.   Example C

$$\log 0.0743 = 8.8710 - 10$$
$$4(\log 0.0743) = 4(8.8710 - 10) = 35.4840 - 40.$$

In the table, the mantissa nearest to 0.4840 is 0.4843, which is the logarithm of 3.05. The characteristic is $35 - 40 = -5$. Therefore

$$(0.0743)^4 = 3.05 \times 10^{-5} = 0.0000305.$$

Evaluate $\sqrt{86.7}$ by logarithms.

$$\sqrt{86.7} = (86.7)^{1/2}, \qquad \log 86.7 = 1.9380,$$
$$\tfrac{1}{2}(\log 86.7) = \tfrac{1}{2}(1.9380) = 0.9690.$$

In the table, the mantissa nearest to 0.9690 is 0.9689, which is the logarithm of 9.31. Therefore
$$\sqrt{86.7} = 9.31.$$

Evaluate $\sqrt[5]{7340}$ by logarithms.

$$\sqrt[5]{7340} = (7340)^{1/5}, \qquad \log 7340 = 3.8657,$$
$$\tfrac{1}{5}(\log 7340) = \tfrac{1}{5}(3.8657) = 0.7731 \quad \text{(rounded off).}$$

In the table we find that 0.7731 is the logarithm of 5.93. Thus
$$\sqrt[5]{7340} = 5.93.$$

Evaluate $\sqrt[3]{0.916}$ by logarithms.

$$\sqrt[3]{0.916} = (0.916)^{1/3}, \qquad \log 0.916 = 9.9619 - 10.$$

In order to have 10 subtracted from the term containing the mantissa *after the division*, we write the characteristic as $29 - 30$. Therefore

$$\log 0.916 = 29.9619 - 30,$$
$$\tfrac{1}{3}(\log 0.916) = \tfrac{1}{3}(29.9619 - 30) = 9.9873 - 10.$$

In the table, the mantissa nearest to 0.9873 is 0.9872, which is the logarithm of 9.71. The characteristic is $9 - 10 = -1$. Therefore

$$\sqrt[3]{0.916} = 9.71 \times 10^{-1} = 0.971.$$

Example G   Evaluate $(569)^{0.7}$ by logarithms.

$$\log 569 = 2.7551,$$
$$(0.7)(\log 569) = (0.7)(2.7551) = 1.9286 \quad \text{(rounded off)}.$$

In the table, the mantissa nearest to 0.9286 is 0.9284, which is the logarithm of 8.48. The characteristic is 1. Therefore $(569)^{0.7} = 8.48 \times 10 = 84.8$.

Example H   Evaluate $(65.1)\sqrt{804}/6.82$ by logarithms.

In evaluating this expression, we follow the same procedure as in Example H of the previous section. The only apparent difference is that in evaluating the logarithm for the numerator we add the logarithm of 65.1 to one-half the logarithm of 804. The solution is shown below.

$$\begin{aligned} \log 65.1 &= 1.8136 \qquad \log 804 = 2.9053 \\ \tfrac{1}{2}(\log 804) &= \underline{1.4527} \\ &\quad\ 3.2663 \\ \log 6.82 &= \underline{0.8338} \qquad\qquad \text{(subtract)} \\ &\quad\ 2.4325 \end{aligned}$$

In the table, the mantissa nearest to 0.4325 is 0.4330, which is the logarithm of 2.71. The characteristic is 2. Therefore the result is

$$2.71 \times 10^2 = 271.$$

Students often do not see the advantages of logarithms when performing simple multiplications and divisions, and therefore fail to see the advantages logarithms provide. For very simple calculations, logarithms are not significantly faster than basic arithmetical methods. However, for extended calculations, such as that of Example H of the last section, or for finding powers and roots, such as in each of the examples of this section, logarithmic calculations are much more rapid. Also, there are no basic arithmetic means for finding many roots, such as that of Example E of this section. We have therefore increased the types of calculations we are able to perform.

EXERCISES   In each of the following exercises, perform the indicated calculations by means of logarithms.

  1. $(6.45)^2$ **2.** $(34.1)^3$ **3.** $(1.45)^{10}$ **4.** $(21,900)^2$

5. $(0.531)^2$ **6.** $(0.0874)^4$ **7.** $(9.08)^7$ **8.** $(0.00806)^5$

9. $\sqrt{26.8}$ **10.** $\sqrt{268}$ **11.** $\sqrt[3]{56.9}$ **12.** $\sqrt[3]{1950}$

13. $\sqrt[4]{31.9}$ **14.** $\sqrt[5]{250}$ **15.** $\sqrt{0.592}$ **16.** $\sqrt[3]{0.0828}$

17. $(9.84)^{0.3}$ **18.** $(482)^{0.6}$ **19.** $(2.56)^{2.1}$ **20.** $(89.5)^{1.3}$

21. $(\sqrt{56.9})(\sqrt[3]{18.8})$ **22.** $\dfrac{\sqrt[4]{8540}}{12.4}$

23. $\dfrac{(73.8)(\sqrt{0.854})}{0.308}$ **24.** $\dfrac{(0.544)^{0.3}(\sqrt{12900})}{(17.8)^3(0.0441)}$

25. What is the side of a square whose area is 308 ft^2?

26. The velocity of sound in air is given by $v = \sqrt{1.410p/d}$, where p is the pressure and d is the density. Given that $p = 1.01 \times 10^6$ units and $d = 1.29 \times 10^{-3}$ units, find v (in cm/sec).

27. Referring to Example A of Section 13–1, calculate the value of the $100 investment after 10 years.

28. The radius of a weather balloon is 12.2 ft. Calculate the volume of the gas it contains. (The volume of a sphere of radius r is $\frac{4}{3}\pi r^3$.)

29. The maximum range R of a rocket fired with a velocity v is given by

$$R = \frac{v^2}{g},$$

where g is the acceleration due to gravity. Find the maximum range of a rocket if

$$v = 9850 \text{ ft/sec} \qquad \text{and} \qquad g = 32.2 \text{ ft/sec}^2.$$

30. Under certain conditions the efficiency (in percent) of an internal combustion engine is found by evaluating

$$100\left(1 - \frac{1}{R^{0.4}}\right),$$

where R is the compression ratio. Compute the efficiency of an engine with a compression ratio of 6.55.

31. The ratio between successive speeds of a six-speed gear box is $\sqrt[5]{625/178}$ if the maximum speed is 625 rev/min and the minimum speed is 178 rev/min. Determine this ratio.

32. When a fluid flows through a pipe, frictional effects cause a loss of pressure. A numerical factor used in the determination of pressure losses, under certain conditions, equals $0.316/\sqrt[4]{5000}$. Calculate this factor.

13–5 INTERPOLATION

In the calculations of preceding sections we have been using the mantissa in the table which is closest to the obtained value. It is, however, possible to use the obtained value and at the same time achieve greater accuracy. We shall now show how we may use the four-place table of logarithms with numbers having four significant digits.

The method of using mantissas which lie between those listed is known as linear *interpolation*. The basic assumption of this method is that differences between mantissas are in the same proportion as the difference between the associated numbers. The assumption is not strictly correct, although it is an excellent approximation. The following example develops the method and its reasoning.

Example A
Find the logarithm of 3.267.

The logarithm of 3.267 lies between log 3.260 and log 3.270. Since 3.267 lies at $\frac{7}{10}$ of the way from 3.260 to 3.270, we assume that log 3.267 lies $\frac{7}{10}$ of the way from log 3.260 to log 3.270. The value of log 3.267 can be found by the use of the following diagram.

$$10 \left[7 \begin{bmatrix} \log 3.260 = 0.5132 \\ \log 3.267 = \vdots \end{bmatrix} x \\ \log 3.270 = 0.5145 \right] 13$$

First, we note that 13 is the *tabular difference* (the actual position of the decimal point is not of importance here) between the values of the logarithms. Next, we set up the *proportion* (a statement of equality between two ratios)

$$7/10 = x/13,$$

which gives the value of $x = 9.1$. Since the mantissa of the required logarithm may have only four significant digits, we round off the value of x to $x = 9$. This is then added to the logarithm of 3.260 to yield

$$\log 3.267 = 0.5141.$$

Example B
Find the logarithm of 67.28.

The solution is indicated in the following diagram.

$$10 \left[8 \begin{bmatrix} \log 67.20 = 1.8274 \\ \log 67.28 = \vdots \end{bmatrix} x \\ \log 67.30 = 1.8280 \right] 6$$

Setting up the proportion, we have

$$\frac{8}{10} = \frac{x}{6},$$

which gives $x = 4.8$. Rounding off, we have $x = 5$, and this means

$$\log 67.28 = 1.8279.$$

When calculations are performed by means of logarithms, it is necessary to interpolate in order to find the values of antilogarithms. The procedure is the same as that previously shown, as the following examples illustrate.

Find the number whose logarithm is 0.4554.   **Example C**

The nearest mantissas in the table are 0.4548 and 0.4564. This leads to the following diagram.

$$10 \begin{bmatrix} x \begin{bmatrix} \log 2.850 = 0.4548 \\ \log \ldots \ = 0.4554 \end{bmatrix} 6 \\ \log 2.860 = 0.4564 \end{bmatrix} 16$$

We now have the proportion

$$\frac{x}{10} = \frac{6}{16},$$

which leads to $x = 3.75$. Rounding this off to the nearest integer, we have $x = 4$. Thus

$$\log 2.854 = 0.4554,$$

and the required result is 2.854.

Find the number whose logarithm is 3.9303.   **Example D**

From the table we set up the following diagram.

$$10 \begin{bmatrix} x \begin{bmatrix} \log 8510 = 3.9299 \\ \log \ldots \ = 3.9303 \end{bmatrix} 4 \\ \log 8520 = 3.9304 \end{bmatrix} 5$$

We now set up the proportion

$$\frac{x}{10} = \frac{4}{5},$$

which leads to $x = 8$. Therefore $\log 8518 = 3.9303$, and the required result is 8518.

The following examples illustrate calculations in which interpolation is used for determining logarithms and antilogarithms.

Example E   Evaluate (6.481)(376.7) by means of logarithms.

$$\log 6.481 = 0.8117$$
$$\log 376.7 = 2.5760$$
$$\overline{3.3877}$$

The antilogarithm of 3.3877 is 2442, which means that

$$(6.481)(376.7) = 2442.$$

Example F   Evaluate $\sqrt{21840}/(3.146)^3$ by means of logarithms.

$$\log 21840 = 4.3393, \qquad \tfrac{1}{2}(\log 21840) = 2.1697$$
$$\log 3.146 = 0.4977, \qquad 3(\log 3.146) = \underline{1.4931} \qquad \text{(subtract)}$$
$$0.6766$$

The antilogarithm of 0.6766 is 4.749, which is the desired result.

EXERCISES   In Exercises 1 through 8, find the logarithm of each of the given numbers.

1. 6.942   2. 8514   3. 0.3167   4. 0.001053

5. 49.11   6. 100.5   7. 3.142×10^3 8. 7.081×10^{-4}

In Exercises 9 through 16, find the antilogarithm of each of the given logarithms.

9. 0.6407   10. 0.9209   11. 1.9412   12. 3.2475

13. 2.4585   14. $9.8706 - 10$ 15. $5.4567 - 10$ 16. $19.1049 - 20$

In Exercises 17 through 32, perform the indicated calculations by means of logarithms:

17. (67.08)(0.4921)   18. $\dfrac{16.72}{6.893}$

19. $(51.82)^3$ 20. $\sqrt{93.12}$

21. $(75.18)\sqrt{3805}$ 22. $\dfrac{\sqrt[3]{0.9105}}{45.19}$

23. $\dfrac{(0.6112)(0.1052)^4}{\sqrt{0.08737}}$ 24. $\dfrac{\sqrt{23.75}\,\sqrt[5]{56.18}}{\sqrt[4]{456.6}\,\sqrt[3]{1.764}}$

25. A certain alloy is 53.85% iron. How many pounds of iron are there in 212.4 lb of this alloy?

26. A farmer sold 1225 bu of apples for $3866. How much did he receive per bushel?

27. Find the side of a cube whose volume is 893.4 in^3.

28. If an amount of $1845 is deposited in a bank which pays 4.5% interest, compounded annually, the value of this deposit in 8 yr is 1845(1.045)^8. Calculate this value.

29. The surface area of a sphere is given by $A = 4\pi r^2$, where r is the radius of the sphere. Calculate the surface area of the earth, assuming that $r = 3959$ mi and $\pi = 3.142$.

30. If a pendulum is to beat seconds, the formula for its length is $L = g/\pi^2$. Find the length, in feet, of a pendulum which is to beat seconds, if $g = 32.16$ units and $\pi = 3.142$.

31. The effective value of the current I in an alternating current circuit is given by

$$I = \frac{I_m}{\sqrt{2}},$$

where I_m is the maximum value of the current. Determine I, given that $I_m = 2.542$ amp.

32. The error in determining the length of a cable hanging between two supports is given by

$$E_l = \frac{4y^4}{5x^3},$$

where x is half the distance between the supports and y is the distance the cable sags. Find E_l, given that $y = 1.325$ ft and $x = 36.32$ ft. Note the size of this value compared with the length of the cable of 72.71 ft.

13-6 REVIEW EXERCISES

In the following exercises, perform all indicated calculations by means of logarithms. If the letter i appears after the number of the exercise, interpolation is required.

1. (4.15)(8.39)

2. (459)(1.83)

3. (0.941)(7.11)

4. (0.0312)(14,900)

5. (0.0181)(0.00721)

6. (16,200)(531)

7i. (84.12)(6.947)

8i. (0.01361)(9.103)

9. $\dfrac{7.14}{2.63}$

10. $\dfrac{98500}{670}$

11. $\dfrac{67.1}{4.11}$

12. $\dfrac{0.985}{2.31}$

13. $\dfrac{7.14}{9310}$ **14.** $\dfrac{0.0862}{0.174}$ **15i.** $\dfrac{89.15}{9.176}$

16i. $\dfrac{15010}{0.9007}$ **17.** $(10.8)^3$ **18.** $(1.08)^{10}$

19. $(76.1)^4$ **20.** $(0.405)^5$ **21i.** $(6.184)^4$

22i. $(1.034)^{0.3}$ **23.** $\sqrt{23.1}$ **24.** $\sqrt{84.9}$

25. $\sqrt[3]{1.17}$ **26.** $\sqrt[3]{789}$ **27i.** $\sqrt{1308}$

28i. $\sqrt[3]{0.9006}$ **29.** $(61.2)(\sqrt{128})$ **30.** $\dfrac{\sqrt{86000}}{45.8}$

31. $\dfrac{(0.721)(98.4)}{\sqrt[3]{8.17}}$ **32.** $\dfrac{(6.10)(\sqrt[5]{38.1})}{(8.01)^3}$ **33i.** $\dfrac{(67.11)(9.004)}{(8.114)^{0.3}}$

34. The number of bacteria in a certain culture after t hr is given by

$$N = (1000)10^{0.0451t}.$$

How many are present after 3 hr?

35. The intensity level of a sound is defined by the equation

$$B = 10 \log \frac{I}{I_0}$$

where I is the intensity of the sound and I_0 is a reference intensity which is taken as 10^{-16} watt/cm². B is expressed in decibels. Suppose that a riveter creates noise with the intensity of 10^{-6} watt/cm². What is the intensity level of the noise?

36. Find the area of a rectangular vegetable garden whose length is 154 ft and whose width is 93.7 ft.

37. A person with an income of \$18,500 in a given year found that he paid about 31.7% of his income in taxes. How much in taxes did he pay?

38. Milk is about 87.3% water. How many pounds of water are there in 125 lb of milk?

39. A car averages 15.8 mi/gal of gasoline. At a particular stop it took 13.6 gal of gasoline to fill the tank. Assuming that this is the volume used since it was last filled, how far had the car traveled between gasoline stops?

40. Light travels at the rate of 186,000 mi/sec. The earth is about 92,900,000 mi from the sun. How long does it take the light from the sun to reach the earth?

41. The radiator of a certain car contains 6.25 qt of alcohol and 9.45 qt of water. What percent of the mixture is alcohol?

42. A man drove 556 mi in 11 hr and 12 min. What was his average speed?

43. If an object is falling due to gravity, its velocity v in terms of the distance h fallen is given by $v = \sqrt{64.4\, h}$. What is the velocity, in feet per second, of an object which has fallen 655 ft?

44. The velocity v of a rocket is given by the formula

$$v = 2.30\, u \log \frac{m_0}{m},$$

where u is the exhaust velocity, m_0 is the initial mass of the rocket, and m is the final mass of the rocket. Calculate v, given that $u = 2.05$ km/sec, $m_0 = 1250$ tons and $m = 6.35$ tons.

45. If an electric capacitor C is discharging through a resistor R, the current I at any time t is given by

$$I = I_0 e^{-t/RC},$$

where I_0 is the initial current and $e = 2.72$. Calculate the current after 0.02 sec, given that $R = 100$ ohm, $C = 10^{-4}$ farad, and $I_0 = 0.0528$ amp.

46i. A formula for the area of a triangle with sides a, b, and c is

$$A = \sqrt{s(s - a)(s - b)(s - c)},$$

where s is half the perimeter. Calculate the area of a triangle with sides 45.78 ft, 56.81 ft, and 32.17 ft.

47i. The maximum bending moment of a beam supported at both ends is given by the formula $M = wl^2/8$, where w is the weight per unit length and l is the distance between supports. Find M for a beam that is 30.25 ft long, is supported at each end, and weighs 96.38 lb.

48i. Calculate the square root of 893.4 by means of logarithms and by the method of Section 1–9. Compare the methods.

49. Calculate $(456)(1.88)(5.19)(0.994)$ by means of logarithms and by direct multiplication. Compare the methods.

14   Graphs

In the earlier chapters we established the basic operations of algebra and discussed the solution of certain types of equations. Furthermore, we introduced various basic formulas from geometry and other fields. In these formulas and equations one quantity can be expressed in terms of one or more other quantities by the use of the basic operations. It therefore can be seen that the various quantities of a formula have a specific interrelation as denoted by the formula.

If a scientific experiment were to be performed to determine whether or not a relationship exists between the distance an object falls and the time of its fall, observation of the results should indicate (approximately at least) that $s = 16t^2$, where s is the distance (in feet) and t is the time (in seconds) of fall. The experiment would thus show that the distance and the time were related.

The percentage of chromium in iron-base alloys affects the rate of corrosion of the alloy. In general, as the percentage of chromium in the alloy increases, the rate of corrosion decreases. Thus it is possible to set up an approximate equation or a chart to show the relation of the chromium percentage and corrosion rate.

Considerations such as these lead us to the important mathematical concept of a *function*. In general,

if two variables are so related that for each value of the first variable a single value of the second variable can be determined, the second variable is a function of the first variable.

We shall restrict our attention to functions that are defined by formulas, equations, and graphical representations.

An important idea connected with functions is that of *dependence*. From the above paragraphs we see that the distance an object falls *depends* on the time, and the corrosion rate *depends* on the chromium percentage. For this reason, in the definition of a function, the first variable is called the *independent variable*, and the second is called the *dependent variable*.

The formula for the area of a circle in terms of its radius is $A = \pi r^2$.   **Example A**
Here A is a function of r. The variable r is the independent variable, and A is the dependent variable. We can see that the words "dependent" and "independent" are appropriately chosen. As the formula is written,

we choose a value of r, and once this is done, the value of A depends on that choice. Therefore, in this example, we say that the area of a circle is a function of the radius of the circle.

Example B   The stretching force of a steel spring is directly proportional to the elongation of the spring. This can be stated in an equation as $F = kx$. Here x is the independent variable and F is the dependent variable.

It may be well to ask: What is the advantage of introducing the word function, since the formulas we have been dealing with seem sufficient? In mathematics the word "function" specifically refers to the operation which is performed on the independent variable to find the dependent variable. Consider the following example.

Example C   The distance s (in feet) which an object falls in t sec is given by $s = 16t^2$. The electric power developed in a 16-ohm resistor by a current of i amp is given by $P = 16i^2$. Here s is a function of t and P is a function of i. However, the function is the same. That is, in order to evaluate the dependent variable, we square the independent variable and multiply this result by 16. Even though the letters are different, the *operation* is the same.

For convenience of notation and to emphasize the importance of the operational meaning of a function, the phrase "function of x" is written $f(x)$. (This is a special notation, and does *not* mean f times x.) Therefore, to state that "y is a function of x" we write $y = f(x)$.

Example D   For the equation $y = x^2 - 5$, we say that $y = f(x)$, where $f(x) = x^2 - 5$. Thus $y = x^2 - 5$ and $f(x) = x^2 - 5$ are different ways of writing the same function.

A particularly important use of the functional notation $f(x)$ is to designate the value of a function for a specified value of the independent variable. Thus "the value of the function $f(x)$ when $x = a$" is expressed as $f(a)$.

Example E   If $f(x) = 5 - 2x$, $f(0)$ is the value of the function for $x = 0$. Thus

$$f(0) = 5 - 2(0) = 5.$$

To find $f(-1)$, we have

$$f(-1) = 5 - 2(-1) = 5 + 2 = 7.$$

Thus $f(0) = 5$ and $f(-1) = 7$. We note that to find the value of the function for the number specified on the left, we substitute this number into the function on the right. Also, if we state that $y = f(x)$, then $y = 5$ for $x = 0$ and $y = 7$ for $x = -1$.

It is possible for us to establish many functions from verbal statements. Such functions may be based on geometric formulas or a proper interpretation of a given statement.

Express the area of a circle as a function of its circumference.   **Example F**

The area of a circle is usually expressed as a function of its radius in the formula $A = \pi r^2$. However, we wish to express A as a function of the circumference c. We do know that $c = 2\pi r$, which means that $r = c/2\pi$. Substituting this into the formula for A, we have

$$A = \pi r^2 = \pi \left(\frac{c}{2\pi}\right)^2 = \pi \left(\frac{c^2}{4\pi^2}\right) = \frac{\pi c^2}{4\pi^2} = \frac{c^2}{4\pi}.$$

Therefore we have expressed the area as a function of the circumference, where $f(c) = c^2/4\pi$.

One last comment regarding functions is in order at this time. Not all functions are valid for all values of the independent variable, nor are all values of the dependent variable always possible. The following example illustrates this point.

In Example A, there is no real meaning for negative values of the radius   **Example G**
or the area. Thus we would restrict values of r and A to 0 and greater. That is, $r \geq 0$ and $A \geq 0$.

If we restrict our attention to real numbers, $f(x) = \sqrt{x - 1}$ is valid only for values of x greater than or equal to 1. That is, $x \geq 1$. Also, since the positive square root is indicated, the values of the function are 0 or greater.

If $f(x) = 1/x$, all values of x are possible except $x = 0$, for $x = 0$ would necessitate division by zero.

In Exercises 1 through 4, identify the dependent and the independent variable of each of the given functions.

1. $y = 3x^4$ **2.** $s = -16t^2$

3. $p = c/V$ (c is a constant)   **4.** $v = a(1.05)^t$ (a is a constant)

In Exercises 5 through 8, state the basic operation of the function which is to be performed on the independent variable (see Example C).

5. $f(x) = 3x$ **6.** $f(y) = y + 3$

7. $f(r) = 2 - r^2$ **8.** $f(s) = s + s^2$

In Exercises 9 through 12, indicate the function expressed by each of the given equations by replacing the dependent variable by the $f(x)$ type of notation (see Example D).

9. $y = 5 - x$ **10.** $F = 6q^2$

11. $v = t^2 - 3t$ **12.** $s = 10^{-5r}$

In Exercises 13 through 28, find the indicated values of the given functions.

13. $f(x) = x$; $f(0)$, $f(1)$ **14.** $f(x) = x + 2$; $f(1)$, $f(-2)$

15. $f(t) = 2t - 1$; $f(4)$, $f(-2)$ **16.** $f(r) = 2 - r$; $f(3)$, $f(-3)$

17. $f(x) = 3x^2 - 2$; $f(0)$, $f(\frac{1}{2})$ **18.** $f(z) = z^2 - z$; $f(2)$; $f(-2)$

19. $f(x) = 3 - x^2$; $f(2)$, $f(-0.3)$ **20.** $f(x) = 2x - 3x^2$; $f(-1)$, $f(-3)$

21. $f(s) = s^3$; $f(-1)$, $f(2)$ **22.** $f(p) = p^3 + 2p - 1$; $f(a)$

23. $f(t) = 3t - t^3$; $f(1)$, $f(-2)$ **24.** $f(x) = x^3 - x^4$; $f(3)$, $f(-3)$

25. $f(x) = x - 2x^2$; $f(a^2)$, $f\left(\dfrac{1}{a}\right)$ **26.** $f(v) = v + \dfrac{1}{v}$; $f(\frac{1}{5})$, $f(5)$

27. $f(q) = \dfrac{q}{q - 3}$; $f(-3)$, $f(3)$ **28.** $f(x) = 4^x$; $f(-2)$, $f(\frac{1}{2})$

In Exercises 29 through 38, find the indicated functions.

29. Express the circumference of a circle as a function of its radius.

30. Express the volume of a cube as a function of an edge.

31. Express the area of a square as a function of its perimeter.

32. Express the simple interest I on \$100 at an interest rate of 5% per year as a function of the number of years t.

33. Express the distance s in miles traveled in 3 hr as a function of the velocity v in miles per hour.

34. Express a taxi fare F as a function of the distance d traveled, given that the charge is 45¢ for the first $\frac{1}{5}$ mi and 10¢ for each $\frac{1}{5}$ mi thereafter.

35. One electronic data-processing card-sorter can sort 1500 more cards per minute than a second sorter. Express the rate R_1 of the first sorter as a function of the rate R_2 of the second sorter.

36. The corn production of one field is 5000 bushels less than twice the production of a second field. Express the production p_1 of the first field as a function of the production p_2 of the second field.

37. The voltage V across an electric resistor varies directly as the current i in the resistor. Given that the voltage is 10 volts when the current is 2 amp, express the current as a function of the voltage.

38. The stopping distance d of a car varies directly as the square of its speed s. Express d as a function of s, given that $d = 120$ ft when $s = 40$ mi/hr.

14–2 TYPES OF GRAPHS

One of the most valuable ways of representing data and functions is by means of graphical methods. Graphs present a way of "seeing" the relationship which may exist for sets of data or between sets of numbers. A graph usually allows one to obtain a quick and meaningful understanding of a relationship, and for this reason graphs are used extensively in science and technology.

We shall discuss two important types of graphs: those representing statistical sets of data and those representing functional relations. In this section, we shall discuss graphs used for statistical data, and in the remaining sections of the chapter we shall develop the basic graphical representation of functions.

Of the numerous graphical methods used for representing data, we shall discuss three: the circle graph, the bar graph, and the broken-line graph. The first of these, the circle graph, is particularly useful for showing the relationship of a whole category to the various parts of the category. This is done by determining the percentage that each part is of the whole. Since there are 360° in a circle, each percentage multiplied by 360° will give the number of degrees of the circle to be used for each part. Consider the following example.

In a particular year the liquid petroleum products produced in the United States were as follows: 1,700,000,000 barrels of motor fuel, 1,400,000,000 barrels of fuel oil, 300,000,000 barrels of jet fuel, 200,000,000 barrels of liquid petroleum gases, and 400,000,000 barrels of other products. Now, 1,700,000,000 is 42.5% of the total production of 4,000,000,000 barrels,

Example A

Table 14.1

Product	% of production	Angle
Motor fuel	42.5	153°
Fuel oil	35	126°
Jet fuel	7.5	27°
Liquid gases	5	18°
Others	10	36°

and 42.5% of 360° is 153°. Therefore the part of the circle used to represent motor-fuel production will have an angle of 153°. In this way we may set up Table 14–1, which in turn is used for the graph in Fig. 14–1.

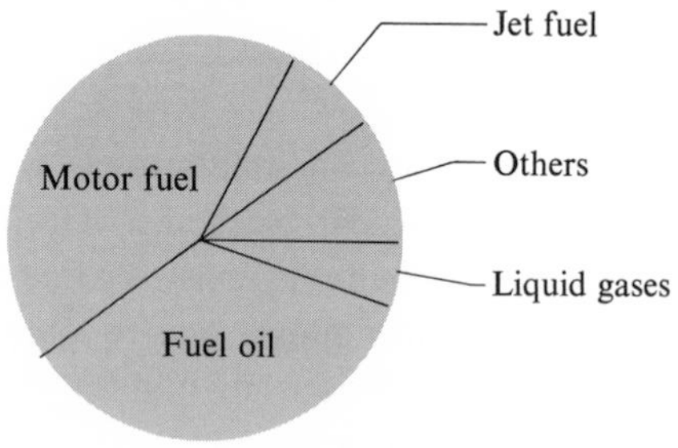

Figure 14–1

A type of graph valuable for showing the relative magnitude of discrete data is the bar graph. In constructing a bar graph, one chooses a scale suitable for the data and then determines the length of each bar. The bars are then constructed either horizontally or vertically and clearly labeled. The following is an example of a bar graph.

Example B   Among the more important canals in the world are the Panama Canal (51 mi), the Suez Canal (103 mi), the Kiel Canal (61 mi), and the King Albert Canal (80 mi). Draw a bar graph of these data.

For the graph to be good, the scale should be as large as is reasonable. In this case we shall choose a scale of $\frac{1}{4}$ in. for 10 mi. With this scale, we obtain Table 14–2 for the approximate lengths of the bars to be used to represent the lengths of the canals (see Fig. 14–2).

Table 14.2

Canal	Length, mi	Length of bar, in.
Panama	51	1.3
Suez	103	2.6
Kiel	61	1.5
Albert	80	2.0

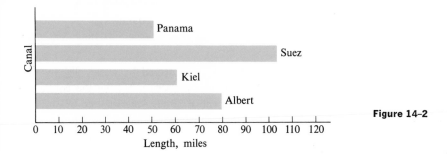

Figure 14–2

The last type of graph we shall consider in this section is the broken-line graph. One constructs graphs of this kind by connecting a series of points by straight-line segments. It is used primarily to show how one variable changes as another variable (the equivalent of the independent variable of a function) changes continuously. Appropriate scales should be chosen for each of the variables and properly labeled. Usually, the scale of the independent variable is placed horizontally, and that of the other variable (the dependent variable) is placed vertically. The points are then located and joined.

The temperature recorded for a certain city from noon to midnight   Example C
is shown in the table below. The broken-line graph of these data is shown in Fig. 14–3.

Temperature, °F	15	18	20	26	25	23	20	17	12	13	10	8	6
Time		12	1	2	3	4	5	6	7	8	9	10	11	12

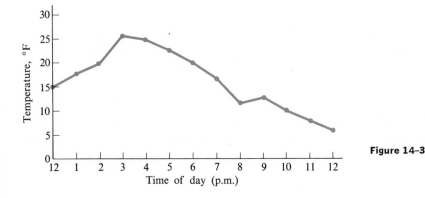

Figure 14–3

In Exercises 1 through 6, make a circle graph to show the given data.

  1. The approximate world wheat production by countries is as follows: USSR 21%, United States 17%, Canada 6%, France 5%, India 5%, and other countries 46%.

  2. Of the surface area of the earth, 71% is covered by water, 9% by the continent of Asia, 6% by the continent of Africa, 5% by the continent of North America, 3% by the continent of South America, and 6% by the remaining land areas, including the continents of Europe, Antarctica, and Australia.

  3. A certain type of brass is made with 85% copper, 5% zinc, 5% tin, and 5% lead.

  4. The number of electric motors shipped to a company during a given year had the following horsepower ratings: 2 hp, 120; 2.5 hp, 75; 3 hp, 155; 3.25 hp, 25; 3.5 hp, 180; 4 hp, 110.

  5. Of accidental deaths in the United States in a typical year, about 40,000 are due to motor vehicle accidents, 30,000 are due to home accidents, 15,000 are due to work accidents, and 15,000 are due to other types of accidents.

  6. In a certain company, 22 employees earn less than $2.50/hr, 32 earn between $2.50/hr and $3.00/hr, 18 earn between $3.00/hr and $3.50/hr, and 8 earn more than $3.50/hr.

In Exercises 7 through 12, make a bar graph to represent the given data.

  7. The number of calories per one-cup servings of various beverages are: apple juice (125), orange juice (110), ginger ale (80), milk (165), cocoa (230).

  8. The steel production of a particular plant for the years 1963–1968 is given in the following table:

  1963, 105,000 tons   1966, 115,000 tons
  1964, 135,000 tons   1967, 140,000 tons
  1965, 145,000 tons   1968, 160,000 tons

  9. The sales (in millions of dollars) of a corporation during a given year were found to be: from heavy machinery (58), light machinery (30), chemicals (14), special tools (10), and other sources (15).

  10. In testing a set of electric resistors it was found that (to the nearest ohm) 5 had a resistance of 5 ohms, 8 a resistance of 6 ohms, 17 a resistance of 7 ohms, 4 a resistance of 8 ohms, and 2 a resistance of 9 ohms.

  11. The enrollment in each of the technologies in a certain technical institute for a given year were as follows: electrical, 360; mechanical, 170;

drafting, 220; construction, 190; chemical, 40; business, 620; data processing, 110.

12. Lengths of some of the important bridges in the United States are as follows: Golden Gate, 4200 ft; Mackinac Straits, 3800 ft; George Washington, 3500 ft; Narrows (Washington), 2800 ft; Delaware Memorial, 2150 ft; Greater New Orleans, 1575 ft.

In Exercises 13 through 18, construct a broken-line graph to represent the given data.

13. A thermocouple is a special type of voltage source for an electric circuit. The voltage is a function of the temperature. An experiment on a particular thermocouple gave the following results.

Voltage, volts	0	2.9	5.9	9.0	12.3	15.8
Temperature, °C	0	10	20	30	40	50

14. The value of a $100 deposit earning 5% interest compounded annually is given in the following table.

Value, $	100	105	110	116	122	128	134	141
t, yr	0	1	2	3	4	5	6	7

15. The amount of material necessary to make a cylindrical gallon container varies with the diameter, as shown in the following table.

Diameter, in.	Sq in. of material
3	322
4	256
5	224
6	211
7	209
8	216
9	230

16. In an experiment in which pressure and volume of air were measured, the following results were obtained.

Volume, in^3	200	180	160	140	120	100
Pressure, atm	2.0	2.2	2.6	3.0	3.6	4.5

17. The amount x that a cam lifts a valve varies with the angle θ (the Greek theta) through which the cam is rotated. For a particular cam the values

of x and θ are as follows:

θ, degrees	0	30	60	90	120	150	180	210	240
x, in.	0.00	0.08	0.26	0.38	0.32	0.20	0.12	0.09	0.00

18. The number of isotopes of some of the heavier elements (the atomic number of each element is the first number given) are: 82 (lead) 16, 84 (polonium) 19, 86 (radon) 12, 88 (radium) 11, 90 (thorium) 12, 92 (uranium) 14, 94 (plutonium) 11.

In Exercises 19 through 21, obtain the appropriate graphs.

19. From the financial section of a recent newspaper, find and clip out a graph which is of a type (at least approximately) discussed in this section.

20. From a newspaper or magazine (from other than the financial section), find and clip out a graph which is of a type discussed in this section.

21. Toss two dice 100 times, recording at each toss the sum that appears. Draw an appropriate graph of each sum and the total number of times it appears.

14-3 THE RECTANGULAR COORDINATE SYSTEM

In this section we shall develop the basic system by which we shall be able to represent the graph of a function. Just as the graphical methods shown in the previous section help us to visualize the relation in statistical data, the graph of a function is often very useful as a means of depicting the basic characteristics of the function.

In Chapter 4 we showed how numbers can be represented on a line. Since a function represents two related sets of numbers, it is necessary to use such a number line for each of these sets. This is most conveniently done if the lines intersect at right angles, in the same manner as on a broken-line graph.

Therefore one line is placed horizontally and labeled the *x-axis*. It is labeled just as the number line in Chapter 4 was labeled, with a point chosen as 0—zero, the *origin*. The positive values are to the right and the negative values to the left. It is customary to use the numbers on the *x*-axis for the values of the independent variable.

Through the origin, and perpendicular to the *x*-axis, another line is placed and labeled the *y-axis*. The origin is also 0 for values on the *y*-axis, with positive values above and negative values below. The *y*-axis is customarily used for values of the dependent variable.

The x-axis and the y-axis as described above constitute what is known as the *rectangular coordinate system.* The four parts into which the plane is divided by the axes are known as *quadrants,* and are numbered as shown in Fig. 14–4.

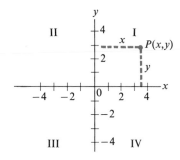

Figure 14–4

Any point P in the plane of the rectangular coordinate system is designated by the pair of numbers (x, y), always written in this order. Here x is the value of the independent variable, and y is the corresponding value of the dependent variable. It can be seen that the x-value (called the *abscissa*) is the perpendicular distance of P from the y-axis, and the y-value (called the *ordinate*) is the perpendicular distance of P from the x-axis. The values of x and y are called the *coordinates* of the point P.

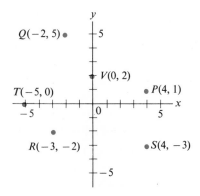

Figure 14–5

The positions of points $P(4, 1)$, $Q(-2, 5)$, $R(-3, -2)$, $S(4, -3)$, $T(-5, 0)$, and $V(0, 2)$ are shown in Fig. 14–5. Note that this representation of points allows *only one point for any pair of values* (x, y).

Example A

Example B   If we let the points $A(5, 2)$, $B(1, 2)$, $C(-3, -4)$, and $D(6, -4)$ be the vertices of a quadrilateral, and connect them in order, we see that the resulting geometric figure is a trapezoid. The upper base is seen to be parallel to the x-axis, since the y-coordinates are the same. This is also true of the lower base. Since they are both parallel to the x-axis, they are parallel to each other (see Fig. 14–6).

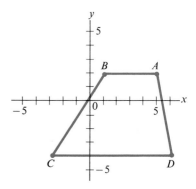

Figure 14–6

Example C   What is the sign of the ratio of the abscissa to the ordinate of a point in the second quadrant?

Since any point in the second quadrant is above the x-axis, the y-value (ordinate) is positive. Also, since any point in the second quadrant is to the left of the y-axis, the x-value (abscissa) is negative. The ratio of a negative number to a positive number is negative, which is the required answer.

Example D   In what quadrant does a point (a, b) lie if $a < 0$ and $b < 0$?

A point for which the abscissa is negative (which is the meaning of $a < 0$) must be in either the second or third quadrant. A point for which the ordinate is negative is in either the third or fourth quadrant. Therefore the required answer is the third quadrant.

EXERCISES   In Exercises 1 through 4, determine (at least approximately) the coordinates of the points specified in Fig.14–7.

    1. A, B **2.** C, D **3.** E, F **4.** G, H

In Exercises 5 through 8, plot (at least approximately) the given points.

    5. $A(0, 3)$, $B(3, 0)$ **6.** $A(-3, -6)$, $B(2, -4)$

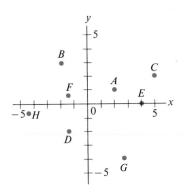

Figure 14-7

7. $A(-1, 4)$, $B(\frac{1}{2}, 5)$ **8.** $A(-\frac{2}{3}, \frac{2}{3})$, $B(0, -4)$

In Exercises 9 through 12, draw the geometric figures, the coordinates of whose vertices are given (do not cross lines).

9. Triangle: $A(0, 3)$, $B(5, -1)$, $C(2, 3)$

10. Quadrilateral: $A(-1, -2)$, $B(0, -3)$, $C(1, 3)$, $D(-2, 4)$

11. Rectangle: $A(-2, -2)$, $B(5, -2)$, $C(5, 4)$, $D(-2, 4)$

12. Rhombus: $A(-1, -2)$, $B(2, 2)$, $C(7, 2)$, $D(4, -2)$

In Exercises 13 through 24, answer the given questions.

13. What is the abscissa of each point on the y-axis?

14. What is the ordinate of each point on the x-axis?

15. In which quadrants is the ratio of the abscissa to the ordinate positive?

16. In which quadrants is the ratio of the abscissa to the ordinate negative?

17. In what quadrant does a point (a, b) lie if $a > 0$ and $b < 0$?

18. In what quadrant does a point (a, b) lie if $a < 0$ and $b > 0$?

19. What are the coordinates of the vertices of a square with side of 2.5 in., whose center is at the origin and whose sides are parallel to the axes?

20. Describe the type of triangle whose vertices are at $(0, 3)$, $(0, 0)$, and $(-2, 0)$.

21. Describe the type of triangle whose vertices are at $(-2, 0)$, $(2, 0)$, and $(0, 3)$.

22. Three vertices of a rectangle are $(1, -3)$, $(7, -3)$, and $(7, 2)$. What are the coordinates of the fourth vertex?

23. The vertices of the base of an isosceles triangle are $(-2, -3)$, and $(8, -3)$. What is the abscissa of the third vertex?

24. Describe the location of all points whose abscissas equal the ordinates.

14-4 THE GRAPH OF A FUNCTION

Having introduced the rectangular coordinate system in the last section, we are now in a position to find the graph of a function. In this way we shall be able to get a "picture" of the function, and this picture allows us to see the behavior of the function. In this section we shall restrict our attention to functions whose graphs are *straight lines* and functions whose graphs are what are known as *parabolas*.

The graph of a function consists of all points whose coordinates (x, y) satisfy the functional relationship $y = f(x)$. By choosing a specific value for x, we can then find the corresponding value for y by evaluating $f(x)$. In this manner we obtain the coordinates of one point. Repeating this process, we obtain as many points as necessary to plot the graph of the function. Usually we need to find only enough points to get a good approximation to the graph by joining these points by a smooth curve (as opposed to a broken-line graph).

We shall first consider the graph of a *linear function*, which is a function of the form

$$f(x) = ax + b, \qquad\qquad 14\text{-}1$$

where a and b are constants. It is called *linear*, since the graph of such a function is always a straight line. The following example illustrates the basic technique used.

Example A   Graph the function $3x + 2$.

Since $f(x) = 3x + 2$, by letting $y = f(x)$ we may write $y = 3x + 2$. Now by substituting numerical values for x, we can find the corresponding values for y. If $x = 0$, then

$$y = f(0) = 3(0) + 2 = 2.$$

Therefore the point $(0, 2)$ is on the graph of $3x + 2$. If $x = 1$, then

$$y = f(1) = 3(1) + 2 = 5.$$

This means that the point $(1, 5)$ is on the graph of $3x + 2$. This information will be most helpful when it appears in tabular form. We strongly recommend that in preparing the table, you list the values of x in ascending order. In this way the points indicated can be joined in order. After the table has been set up, the indicated points are plotted on a rectangular coordinate system and then joined. The table for this function is given below. The graph is shown in Fig. 14–8. Note that the line is extended beyond the points found in the table. This indicates that we know it continues in each direction.

x	-3	-2	-1	0	1	2
y	-7	-4	-1	2	5	8

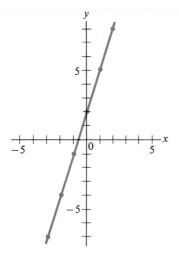

Figure 14–8

The knowledge that a function of the form $ax + b$ is a straight line can be used to definite advantage. By finding two points, we can draw the line. Two points which are easily determined are those where the curve crosses each of the axes. These points are known as the *intercepts* of the line. The reason these are easily found is that one of the coordinates is zero. By setting $x = 0$ and $y = 0$, in turn, and determining the corresponding value of the other, respectively, we obtain the coordinates of the intercepts. A third point should be found as a check.

Graph the function $-2x - 5$.   **Example B**

By setting $y = -2x - 5$ and then letting $x = 0$, we obtain $y = -5$. This means that the graph passes through the point $(0, -5)$. Now, setting $y = 0$, we have $x = -\frac{5}{2}$. This means the graph passes through the point $(-\frac{5}{2}, 0)$. As a check, we let $x = 1$ and find $y = -7$, meaning that the line passes through $(1, -7)$. The table is given at the top of the next page, and the graph is shown in Fig. 14–9.

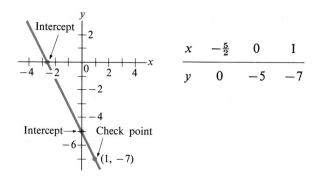

x	$-\frac{5}{2}$	0	1
y	0	-5	-7

Figure 14-9

If a line passes through the origin, it has only this one intercept (0, 0). In this case it is necessary to find at least one point other than the intercept in order to plot the graph. However, the origin and two other points (one as a check) are always easily found. Exercises 1, 2, and 4 at the end of this section illustrate this type of straight line.

We now turn our attention to the graph of the quadratic function

$$f(x) = ax^2 + bx + c, \qquad \text{14-2}$$

where a, b, and c are constants. The graph of this function is a parabola, which is illustrated in the examples which follow. Note that the right-hand side of Eq. (14-2) is the same expression as that appearing in the quadratic equations of Chapter 12.

Example C   Graph the function $y = x^2/2$.

The method of plotting this type of function is precisely the same as that explained in Example A. We choose values of x, and then obtain the values of y. We thus determine the coordinates of a set of representative points on the graph and tabulate these. In finding the y-values we must be careful in handling negative values of x. Remember that the square of a negative number is a positive number. With these ideas in mind, we obtain the following table for $y = x^2/2$.

x	-3	-2	-1	0	1	2	3
y	$\frac{9}{2}$	2	$\frac{1}{2}$	0	$\frac{1}{2}$	2	$\frac{9}{2}$

Note that the points are connected in Fig. 14-10 with a smooth curve, not straight-line segments.

Figure 14–10 shows the basic shape of a parabola, which is the graph of a quadratic function. However, the parabola may be shifted right or left, and up or down, or it may open down. The following examples illustrate the graphs of other quadratic functions.

Graph the function $y = 2x^2 - 4x - 7$.   **Example D**

Again we set up a table and find the y-values by assuming certain values for x. The question arises: Exactly how many values of x should be chosen?

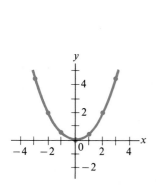

Figure 14–10

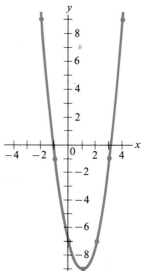

Figure 14–11

There is no explicit answer. However, we should determine enough points so that we can easily connect the points and indicate the true basic shape of the curve. Also, for this function, we must again be careful in handling the negative values of x. For example, if $x = -2$, then

$$y = 2(-2)^2 - 4(-2) - 7 = 2(4) + 8 - 7 = 9.$$

The table for this function is given below, and the graph is shown in Fig. 14–11.

x	-2	-1	0	1	2	3	4
y	9	-1	-7	-9	-7	-1	9

Example E   Graph the function $y = 4 + 2x - x^2$.

We set up the table as shown and graph the function in Fig. 14–12. Once again, special care must be used in finding y-values for negative values of x. For example, if $x = -2$, we have

$$y = 4 + 2(-2) - (-2)^2 = 4 - 4 - (4) = -4.$$

x	-3	-2	-1	0	1	2	3	4	5
y	-11	-4	1	4	5	4	1	-4	-11

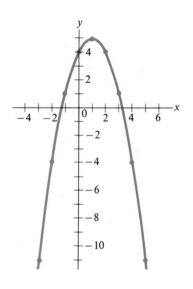

Figure 14–12

EXERCISES   In Exercises 1 through 24, graph the given functions.

1. $y = x$ 2. $y = -x$ 3. $y = 3x - 5$

4. $y = 4x$ 5. $y = 9 - 4x$ 6. $y = 2x + 14$

7. $y = \dfrac{x}{4} + 3$ 8. $y = \dfrac{x}{2} + \dfrac{1}{3}$ 9. $y = \dfrac{2x}{3} - \dfrac{2}{5}$

10. $y = \dfrac{2 - x}{3}$ 11. $y = \dfrac{3 - 2x}{4}$ 12. $y = \dfrac{4 + 3x}{2}$

13. $y = x^2$ 14. $y = -x^2$ 15. $y = x^2 - 4$

16. $y = 4 - x^2$ 17. $y = 2x - x^2$ 18. $y = x^2 - 2x$

19. $y = \dfrac{x^2}{3}$ **20.** $y = \dfrac{x^2}{4}$ **21.** $y = 1 - \dfrac{x^2}{2}$

22. $y = 2 + \dfrac{x^2}{3}$ **23.** $y = 2x^2 - 3x + 2$ **24.** $y = 3 - x - x^2$

In Exercises 25 through 34, graph the functions by plotting the dependent variable along the y-axis and the independent variable along the x-axis. In the applied problems, be certain to determine whether or not negative values of the variables and the scales on each axis are meaningful.

25. A spring is stretched x in. by a force F; the equation relating x and F is $F = kx$, where k is a constant. A force of 10 lb stretches a given spring 2 in. Plot the graph for F and x.

26. The *mechanical advantage* of an inclined plane is the ratio of the length of the plane to its height. This can be expressed in a formula as $M = L/h$. Suppose that the height of a given plane is 6 ft. Plot the graph of the mechanical advantage and length.

27. The electric resistance of wire resistors varies with the temperature according to the relation $R_2 = R_1 + R_1\alpha(T_2 - T_1)$, where R_2 is the resistance at temperature T_2, R_1 is the resistance at temperature T_1, and α (the Greek alpha) is a constant depending on the type of wire. Plot the graph of R_2 and T_2 for a copper wire resistor ($\alpha = 0.004$ per °C), given that $R_1 = 20$ ohms and $T_1 = 10$°C.

28. A board 20 ft long is cut into two pieces. Express the length y of one piece as a function of the length x of the other piece. Plot the graph.

29. A man lives 50 mi from an airport. Given that a jet averages 600 mi/hr while it is in the air, express the total distance d traveled by the man in going from his home to the city of his destination as a function of the hours t that the plane is in the air. Plot the graph.

30. The shape of the surface of a fluid in a rotating container is parabolic. The equation of the parabola is

$$y = \frac{\omega^2}{2g}x^2,$$

where ω (the Greek omega) is the angular velocity of the container and g is the acceleration due to gravity. Plot the shape of the surface of a liquid [the origin is at the lowest (middle) point of the surface], given that $\omega = 10$ per sec and $g = 32$ ft/sec^2. Assume that the container is 4 ft in diameter.

31. Under certain conditions, the relation between the weight W per unit area of an oxide forming on metal and the time t of oxidation is $t = kW^2$, where k is a constant depending on the metal. Plot the graph for W and t for a metal where $k = 0.025$ hr-cm^2/mg, t is measured in hours, and W in mg/cm^2.

32. Express the total surface area of a cube as a function of an edge and plot the graph.

33. The distance h (in feet) above the surface of the earth of an object as a function of the time (in seconds) is given by $h = 60t - 16t^2$ if the object is given an initial upward velocity of 60 ft/sec. Plot the graph.

34. The *specific weight* of an object is its weight per unit length. The specific weight w of a bridge at a distance of x ft from the center of the bridge is $w = 150 + 0.5x^2$. Plot the graph of w and x, given that the bridge is 100 ft long and w is measured in pounds per foot.

14-5 GRAPHS OF OTHER FUNCTIONS

In the last section we discussed the method of plotting the graph of a function. However, we limited our discussion to two important types of functions. In this section we shall introduce the graphs of several other types of functions.

The basic procedure for plotting the graphs of functions is that presented in the last section. That is, we select specific values of x and find the corresponding values of y in order to find particular points which lie on the graph of the function. Following are four examples of plotting the graphs of functions which are not linear or quadratic.

Example A   Graph the function $y = 2^x$.

In order to plot the graph of this function it is necessary to handle properly powers of 2, including both positive and negative exponents. For example, if $x = 3$, we have $y = 2^3 = 8$. If $x = -2$, we have

$$y = 2^{-2} = \frac{1}{2^2} = \tfrac{1}{4}.$$

The table below gives the values from which the points are plotted in Fig. 14-13.

x	-2	-1	0	1	2	3
y	$\tfrac{1}{4}$	$\tfrac{1}{2}$	1	2	4	8

This is the graph of an *exponential function*.

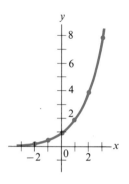

Figure 14–13   **Figure 14–14**

Graph the function $y = 2 + 1/x$.   **Example B**

In finding the points for this graph we must be careful not to set $x = 0$, for this would necessitate division by zero. However, in order to get an accurate graph, we must choose values of x near zero. Therefore you will find fractional values of x in the table below. For example, if $x = \frac{1}{2}$, then

$$y = 2 + 1/\tfrac{1}{2} = 2 + 2 = 4.$$

This graph is known as a *hyperbola*. See Fig. 14–14.

x	-3	-2	-1	$-\frac{1}{2}$	$-\frac{1}{4}$	$\frac{1}{4}$	$\frac{1}{2}$	1	2	3
y	$\frac{5}{3}$	$\frac{3}{2}$	1	0	-2	6	4	3	$\frac{5}{2}$	$\frac{7}{3}$

Graph the function $y = x^3 - 3x$.   **Example C**

Proper use of signed numbers and their powers is essential in finding the values of y for values of x, particularly negative values. For example, if $x = -2$, then

$$y = (-2)^3 - 3(-2) = -8 + 6 = -2.$$

The following table gives the points used to plot the graph in Fig. 14–15.

x	-3	-2	-1	0	1	2	3
y	-18	-2	2	0	-2	2	18

This curve is known as a *cubic* curve. Note that the scale is different for each of x and y. This is done when the range of values used differs considerably.

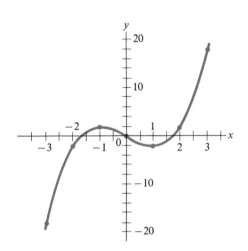

Figure 14-15

Example D   Graph the function $y = \sqrt{x + 1}$.

In finding the y-values of this graph, we must be careful to use only values of x which will give us real values for y. This means that the value under the radical sign must be zero or greater. For example, if $x = -5$, we would have $y = \sqrt{-4}$, which is an imaginary number. Therefore, x cannot be -5. In fact, we cannot have any value of x which is less than -1. Thus we find the following points for the graph:

x	-1	0	1	2	3	4	6	8
y	0	1	1.4	1.7	2	2.2	2.6	3

The graph is plotted in Fig. 14-16. This graph is *half of a parabola*.

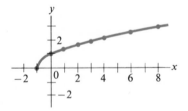

Figure 14-16

EXERCISES   In Exercises 1 through 20, graph the given functions.

1. $y = 3^x$

2. $y = 2^{2x}$

3. $y = (\tfrac{1}{3})^x$

4. $y = 2^{-x}$

5. $y = \dfrac{1}{x}$

6. $y = 1 + \dfrac{2}{x}$

7. $y = 2 - \dfrac{1}{x}$

8. $y = \dfrac{3}{x} - 4$

9. $y = \sqrt{x}$ **10.** $y = \sqrt{4 - x}$ **11.** $y = \dfrac{1}{x^2}$ **12.** $y = \dfrac{1}{x^2 + 1}$

13. $y = x^3$ **14.** $y = -\frac{1}{2}x^3$

15. $y = 2x^3 - 10$ **16.** $y = 6x - x^3$

17. $y = \frac{1}{4}x^4$ **18.** $y = x^4 - 2x^2$

19. $y = \sqrt{x^2 + 1}$ **20.** $y = \sqrt{25 - x^2}$

In Exercises 21 through 28, graph the functions by plotting the dependent variable along the y-axis and the independent variable along the x-axis. In the applied problems, be certain to determine whether or not negative values of the variables and the scales on each axis are meaningful.

21. The number of bacteria in a certain culture increases by 50% each hour. The number N of bacteria present after t hr is $N = 1000(\frac{3}{2})^t$, given that 1000 were originally present. Graph the function.

22. Under the condition of constant temperature, it was found that the pressure p (in atmospheres) and the volume V (in cubic inches) in an experiment on air were related by $p = 10/V$. Plot the graph.

23. The electric current I in a circuit with a voltage of 50 volts, a constant resistor of 10 ohms, and a variable resistor R is given by the equation

$$I = \frac{50}{10 + R}.$$

Plot the graph of I and R.

24. An object is p in. from a lens of a focal length of 5 in. The distance from the lens to the image is given by $q = 5p/(p - 5)$. Plot the graph.

25. The gravitational force of attraction between two objects is inversely proportional to the square of the distance between their centers. Assuming the constant of proportionality to be 8 units, plot the graph.

26. Under certain conditions the deflection d of a beam at a distance of x ft from one end is $d = 0.05(30x^2 - x^3)$, where d is measured in inches and x in feet. Plot the graph of d and x, given that the beam is 10 ft long.

27. One hundred dollars invested at 5% interest compounded annually has the value $V = 100(1.05)^t$ after t yr. Plot the graph. [*Hint:* Use logarithms.]

28. The amount N of a radioactive material present after t sec is found by using the formula $N = N_0 e^{-kt}$, where N_0 is the amount originally present, $e = 2.7$, and k is a constant depending on the material. Given that 200 g of a certain isotope of uranium, for which $k = 0.01$ per sec, were originally present, establish the function relating N and t and plot the graph. Use logarithms for the calculations and use 20-sec intervals for t.

14-6 GRAPHICAL INTERPRETATIONS

In the previous sections of this chapter we have showed how the graph of a function is constructed. Another important aspect of working with graphs is being able to read information from a previously constructed graph. In this section we shall demonstrate how this is done and also how equations can be solved by the use of graphs.

The procedure for reading values from a graph is essentially the reverse of plotting the coordinates of points. The following examples illustrate the method.

Example A   From the graph shown in Fig. 14–17, determine the value of y for $x = 3.5$.

We first locate 3.5 on the x-axis and then construct a line (dashed line in the figure) perpendicular to the x-axis until it crosses the curve. From this point on the curve, we draw another line perpendicular to the y-axis until it crosses the y-axis. The value at which this line crosses is the required answer. Therefore $y = 1.4$ (approximated from the graph) for $x = 3.5$. In the same way we can see that $y = -1.3$ for $x = 0.8$.

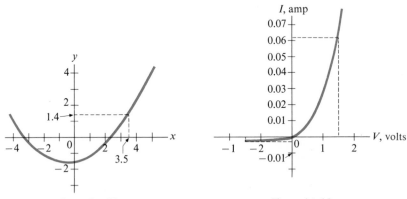

Figure 14–17   Figure 14–18

Example B   The current as a function of the voltage for a typical type of transistor is shown in Fig. 14–18. We can see that for a voltage of -1.5 volts (voltage can be considered as having direction) that the current is -0.003 amp. For a voltage of 1.5 volts the current is about 0.062 amp.

Example C   From the graph of $y = 8x - x^2$ determine the values of y for $x = -1.6$ and $x = 2.3$.

Since we are required to find y-values for x-values between $x = -2$
and $x = 3$, we shall plot only this part of the graph. The table is as
follows.

x	-2	-1	0	1	2	3
y	-20	-9	0	7	12	15

The graph is shown in Fig. 14–19, and we can see that $y = -15$ for
$x = -1.6$ and $y = 13$ for $x = 2.3$.

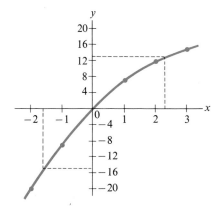

Figure 14–19

It is possible to find approximate solutions to equations by using
graphs. To solve the equation $f(x) = 0$, we set $y = f(x)$, graph this
function, and then determine from the graph those values of x for which
$y = 0$. This occurs where the graph crosses the x-axis. This method is
particularly useful when algebraic methods cannot be applied to the
equation. The following examples illustrate the method.

Solve the equation $x^2 - 4x + 2 = 0$ graphically.   **Example D**

In solving this equation, we wish to find those values of x which make
the left side zero. By setting $y = x^2 - 4x + 2$ and finding those values
of x for which y is zero, we have found the solutions to the equation.
Therefore we graph

$$y = x^2 - 4x + 2,$$

for which the table is

x	-1	0	1	2	3	4	5
y	7	2	-1	-2	-1	2	7

From the graph in Fig. 14–20, we see that the graph crosses the x-axis at $x = 0.6$ and $x = 3.4$. Use of the quadratic equation verifies these values, which, of course, are the required solutions.

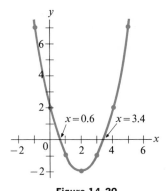

Figure 14–20   Figure 14–21

Example E   Solve the equation $2^x - 3 = 0$ graphically.

First we set $y = 2^x - 3$ and graph this function by finding the following table:

x	-1	0	1	2	3
y	-2.5	-2	-1	1	5

From the graph in Fig. 14–21, we see that the required solution is $x = 1.6$. For this equation we do not have an algebraic method which gives the solution.

EXERCISES   In Exercises 1 through 4, find the values of y for the indicated values of x from the given figure.

   1. Find y for $x = -1$ and $x = 2$ from Fig. 14–22(a).

   2. Find y for $x = 1.5$ and $x = 4.7$ from Fig. 14–22(b).

   3. Find y for $x = -2.3$ and $x = 1.8$ from Fig. 14–22(c).

   4. Find y for $x = -15$ and $x = 37$ from Fig. 14–22(d).

In Exercises 5 through 12, graph the given functions and then determine the values of y for the indicated values of x from the graph.

   5. $y = 3x + 2$; $x = 1.5$, $x = 3.2$

   6. $y = -x + 3$; $x = -1.5$, $x = 1.2$

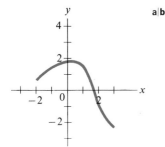
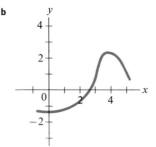

a|b

c|d

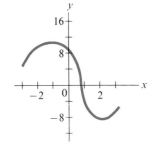
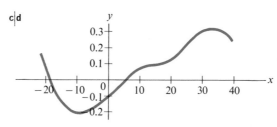

Figure 14–22

7. $y = 8 - 3x$; $x = -0.4$, $x = 2.1$

8. $y = 2 - x^2$; $x = -1.8$, $x = 1.8$

9. $y = 2x^2 - 5x + 1$; $x = -1.1$, $x = 2.7$

10. $y = 6x - x^3$; $x = -0.7$, $x = 2.3$

11. $y = \dfrac{3}{x - 3}$; $x = 1.6$, $x = 3.6$

12. $y = \sqrt{2x + 4}$; $x = 0.8$, $x = 3.1$

In Exercises 13 through 20, solve the given equations graphically.

13. $7x - 5 = 0$　　　　　　　　　**14.** $3x + 13 = 0$

15. $2x^2 - x - 4 = 0$　　　　　　**16.** $x^2 + 3x - 5 = 0$

17. $x^3 - 5 = 0$　　　　　　　　　**18.** $2x^3 - 5x + 4 = 0$

19. $\sqrt{2x + 9} - x = 0$　　　　　**20.** $3^x - 5 = 0$

In Exercises 21 through 24, determine the required values.

21. Figure 14–23 shows the graph of the charge on a capacitor and the time. Determine the charge on the capacitor at $t = 0.005$ sec and $t = 0.050$ sec.

22. Figure 14–24 shows the graph of the displacement of a valve and the time. Determine the valve displacement at $t = 0.25$ sec and $t = 0.60$ sec.

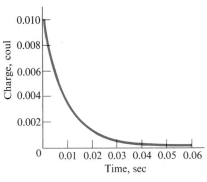

Figure 14-23

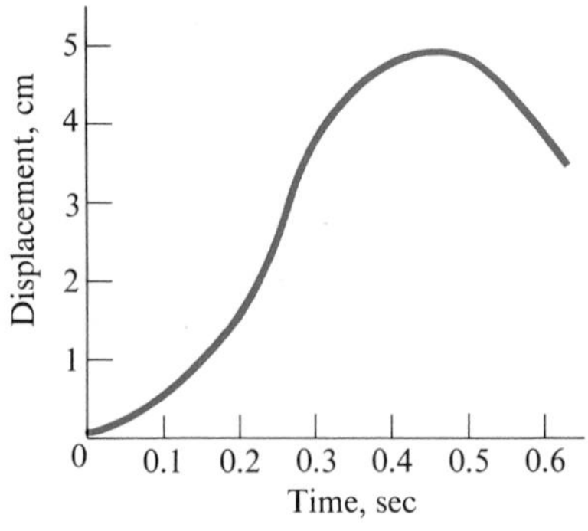

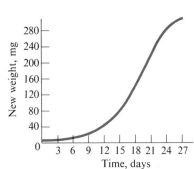

Figure 14-24

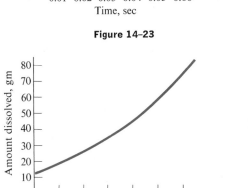

Figure 14-25

Figure 14-26

23. Figure 14–25 shows the graph of the number of grams of a certain compound which will dissolve in 100 g of water and the temperature of the water. Determine the number of grams which dissolve at 33°C and 58°C.

24. Figure 14–26 shows the graph of milligrams (mg) of new weight on a certain plant and the time in days. How much new weight is on the plant after 12 days? After 22 days?

In Exercises 25 through 28, determine the required values graphically.

25. The velocity of sound, in meters per second, for a given temperature, in °C, is given by the formula $v = 331 + 0.61T$. Determine the velocity of sound for $T = 15$°C, 25°C, 37°C, and 48°C.

26. The displacement of a particular beam as a function of the distance from a fixed end is $d = 0.2(x^2 - 10x)$, where d is measured in inches and x in feet. Find the displacement for $x = 2.8$ ft, 4.7 ft, 5.3 ft, and 8.7 ft.

27. Given that the power in an electric circuit is constant at 0.02 watt, the resistance in the circuit as a function of the current is given by $R = 0.02/I^2$. Find the resistance (in ohms) for $I = 0.005$ amp, 0.016 amp, 0.037 amp, and 0.042 amp.

28. The velocity of the flow of a liquid from a container is given by the equation $v = \sqrt{64h}$, where h is the distance of the opening in the container below the surface of the liquid. Determine the velocity of flow (in feet/second), for opening that is 3.2 ft, 5.8 ft, 6.3 ft, and 7.9 ft below the surface.

In Exercises 29 through 31, solve the given equations graphically.

29. Under certain conditions the force F on an object is found from the equation $0.8F - 22 = 0$. Solve for F.

30. The distance d that an object is above the surface of the earth as a function of time is given by $d = 85 + 60t - 16t^2$. When will it hit the ground? [*Hint:* What does d equal when the object is on the ground?]

31. In order to find the radius (in inches) of a one-quart container which requires the least amount of material to make, one must solve the equation

$$2\pi r - \frac{57.8}{r^2} = 0.$$

Solve for r, and thereby determine the required radius.

14–7 REVIEW EXERCISES

In Exercises 1 through 8, find the indicated values of the given functions.

1. $f(x) = -x;\quad f(-1), f(-\frac{1}{2})$
2. $f(x) = 1 - 3x;\quad f(-2), f(\frac{1}{3})$
3. $f(y) = 3y - 5;\quad f(-5), f(-2)$
4. $f(x) = 2x^2 - 1;\quad f(\sqrt{2}), f(-\frac{1}{2})$
5. $f(t) = -t^2;\quad f(3), f(-4)$
6. $f(z) = z^2 - 2z - 3;\quad f(-3), f(0.2)$
7. $f(r) = -r^3;\quad f(0), f\left(\frac{r}{2}\right)$
8. $f(x) = 7 - x - 4x^2;\quad f(-1), f(-v)$

In Exercises 9 through 12, plot the given points, connect them to form a geometric figure, and identify the figure.

9. $(0, 4), (-1, 2), (3, -2)$　　　　　10. $(-1, 0), (0, 1), (1, 2)$
11. $(2, 4), (3, 6), (-1, 2), (0, 0)$　　　12. $(4, 1), (0, -1), (2, 2), (1, -1)$

In Exercises 13 through 28, graph the given functions.

13. $y = 4x - 4$ **14.** $y = 4 - 4x$

15. $y = 3 - \frac{1}{2}x$ **16.** $y = 4x - \frac{2}{3}$

17. $y = \dfrac{5x - 1}{4}$ **18.** $y = \frac{1}{5}x + \frac{1}{2}$

19. $y = 3x^2 - 4$ **20.** $y = 3 - 2x^2$

21. $y = \dfrac{x^2 - 2}{4}$ **22.** $y = 1 - 3x - x^2$

23. $y = (\frac{1}{4})^{2x}$ **24.** $y = 2x^2 - x^3$

25. $y = 4 - \dfrac{1}{x}$ **26.** $y = \dfrac{1}{x - 1}$

27. $y = 2\sqrt{x} - 3$ **28.** $y = \dfrac{1}{\sqrt{x}}$

In Exercises 29 through 34, solve the given equations graphically.

29. $7x - 9 = 0$ **30.** $6x + 11 = 0$

31. $3x^2 - x - 2 = 0$ **32.** $5 - 7x - x^2 = 0$

33. $x^3 - x^2 + 2x - 1 = 0$ **34.** $x^4 - 2x^2 - x + 2 = 0$

In Exercises 35 through 40, construct the required graphs.

35. The atmosphere is a mixture of about 78% nitrogen, 21% oxygen, and 1% other gases. Make a circle graph to represent these data.

36. A certain weather station recorded the rainfall by season, with the following results: spring, 18 in.; summer, 8 in.; fall, 12 in.; winter, 14 in. Make a circle graph to represent these data.

37. Of the mountains in the world which are higher than 15,000 ft, there are 42 in Asia, 7 in Europe, 14 in North America, 28 in South America, and 7 elsewhere. Use a bar graph to represent these data.

38. A study of a certain musical sound yielded the following data for the frequency (a measure of the pitch) and the amplitude (a measure of loudness).

Frequency, cycles/sec	220	440	660	880	1100
Amplitude, units	10	2	3	1	0.5

Use a bar graph to represent these data.

39. The increase in length of a certain metal rod was measured as a function of the temperature, with the following results.

Increase in length	0.5	2.2	4.7	8.2	12
Increase in temperature, °C	50	100	150	200	250

Use a broken-line graph to represent these data.

40. In an experiment it was found that the time required for milk to curdle depends on the temperature at which it is kept, as follows:

Temperature milk kept, °F	40	50	60	70	80	90
Time to reach curdling point, hr	82	72	45	37	32	29

Make a broken-line graph to represent these data.

In Exercises 41 through 44, set up the required functions.

41. A right triangle has one leg of 6 in. and the other of x in. Express the area as a function of x.

42. The rate H at which heat is developed in a filament of an electric light bulb is proportional to the square of the electric current I. A current of 0.5 amp produces heat at the rate of 60 watts. Express H as a function of I.

43. The vertical side of the rectangle of a Norman window (a semicircle surmounted on a rectangle) is 2 ft. Express the area of the window as a function of the radius of the circular part.

44. A number of white mice were subjected to various doses of radioactivity. The time T each lived afterward was inversely proportional to the square of the intensity I of the dose. Assuming that, on the average, a mouse lived 10 hr after having received a dose of 4 units, express T as a function of I.

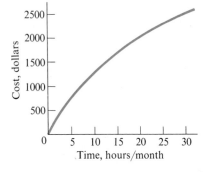

Figure 14–27

In Exercises 45 through 48, find the required values graphically.

45. One can determine the cost of using a computer owned by a certain company by the graph in Fig. 14–27. How much does it cost to use the computer for 5 hr? for 16 hr? for 28 hr in a given month?

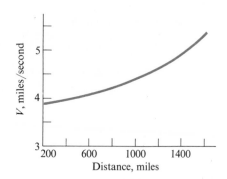

Figure 14-28

46. The velocity of an artificial satellite is a function of its distance from the surface of the earth. The graph of the velocity and distance for a particular satellite is shown in Fig. 14-28. The distance from the earth to the satellite varies from 200 mi to 1600 mi. What is the velocity of the satellite when it is 400 mi; 750 mi; 1400 mi from the earth?

47. The length of a cable hanging between two equal supports which are 100 ft apart is given by

$$L = 100(1 + 0.0003y^2)$$

where y is the sag (vertical distance from top of support to bottom of cable) in the cable. Determine the length of a cable for which the sag is 5 ft; 10 ft; 20 ft.

48. Under certain conditions, the distance from a source of light where the illumination is the least is found by solving the equation

$$x^3 + 8(x - 100)^3 = 0.$$

Find the required distance (in feet).

In Exercises 49 through 52, find the required functions and graphs.

49. A temperature in degrees fahrenheit (F) equals 32 more than $\frac{9}{5}$ the number of degrees celsius (C). Express F as a function of C and plot the graph. From the graph determine the temperature at which F = C.

50. The path of a projectile is approximately parabolic. Given that y is the vertical distance from the ground to the projectile and x is the horizontal distance traveled, the equation $y = x - 0.0004x^2$ is the equation of the path of a given projectile, where distances are measured in feet. Plot the graph, using units of 50 ft for x, and determine how far the projectile travels (assume level ground).

51. A rectangular tract of land is to have a perimeter of 800 ft. Express the area as a function of its width and plot the graph.

52. Under certain circumstances, the frequency of a generator in an electric circuit is a function of the capacitance in the circuit. This can be expressed by the equation

$$f = \frac{1}{2\pi\sqrt{C}} \cdot$$

Plot the graph of f and C, given that C varies from 10^{-5} farad to 10^{-4} farad, and f is measured in cycles/second.

15 Simultaneous Linear Equations

15–1 GRAPHICAL SOLUTION OF SIMULTANEOUS EQUATIONS

Numerous applied problems in mathematics, including those from science and technology, give rise to two separate equations involving the same two unknowns. The equations that result are referred to as *simultaneous equations*. When forces on a structure are analyzed, simultaneous equations often result. In electricity, when one is determining electric currents, simultaneous equations are used. Also many types of stated problems from many fields lead to simultaneous equations. The following example illustrates two cases.

One alloy is 70% lead and 30% zinc and another alloy is 40% lead and 60% zinc. In order to determine how many pounds of each of these alloys are needed to make 100 lb of another alloy which is to be 50% lead and 50% zinc, one could use the equations

Example A

$$x + y = 100, \qquad 0.7x + 0.4y = 50.$$

Here x and y are the weights of the two alloys.

Two planes leave the same airport at the same time and fly in opposite directions. One plane travels 200 mi/hr faster than the other, and at the end of 4 hr they are 4400 mi apart. The speeds of the planes can be found by solving the simultaneous equations

$$v_1 - v_2 = 200,$$
$$4v_1 + 4v_2 = 4400.$$

Here v_1 and v_2 are the speeds of the planes.

We shall now take up the problem of solving for the unknowns when we have two simultaneous equations with two unknowns. In all, three methods will be discussed in this chapter. In this section we shall show how the solution may be found graphically. The sections which follow will discuss two basic algebraic methods of solution.

In Chapter 14 we graphed several kinds of functions, among them the linear function. We saw that the graph of $y = ax + b$ is always a straight line. However, there are a limitless number of points on the line. If a second line were to cross a given line, there would be only one point common to the two lines. The coordinates of this point, and only this point, would satisfy the equations of both lines.

Example B   For the lines $y = 3x - 3$ and $2x + 3y = 6$, we find that the intercepts of the first line are $(0, -3)$ and $(1, 0)$, and those of the second line
are $(3, 0)$ and $(0, 2)$. These points allow us to graph each of the lines as
shown in Fig. 15–1. The actual coordinates of the point of intersection
are $(\frac{15}{11}, \frac{12}{11})$. This result can be shown to be correct, since these coordinates
satisfy the equation of each line. For the first line, we have

$$\tfrac{12}{11} = 3(\tfrac{15}{11}) - 3 = \tfrac{45}{11} - \tfrac{33}{11} = \tfrac{12}{11},$$

and for the second line, we have

$$2(\tfrac{15}{11}) + 3(\tfrac{12}{11}) = \tfrac{30}{11} + \tfrac{36}{11} = \tfrac{66}{11} = 6.$$

Even though we cannot obtain this accuracy for the coordinates of the
point of intersection from the graph, we can see that the point of intersection is about $(1.4, 1.1)$, and this is the type of solution we shall attempt
to obtain in this section.

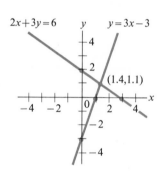

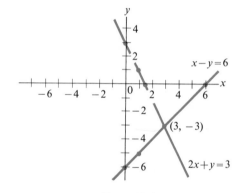

Figure 15–1   **Figure 15–2**

Therefore, in order to solve a pair of simultaneous linear equations,
we shall graph the equations and determine the point of intersection.
The x-coordinate of this point is the desired value of x, and the y-co-
ordinate of this point is the desired value of y. Together they are the
solution to the system of two equations in two unknowns. Since the
coordinates of no other point satisfy both equations, the unique solution
has been determined.

Example C   Solve graphically the system of equations

$$x - y = 6, \qquad 2x + y = 3.$$

We determine the intercepts and one check point for each of the equations. Then we graph each equation as shown in Fig. 15–2.

$x - y = 6$			$2x + y = 3$	
x	y		x	y
0	-6		0	3
6	0		$\frac{3}{2}$	0
1	-5		1	1

From the graph we see that the lines cross at about $(3, -3)$. Therefore the solution to this set of equations is $x = 3$, $y = -3$. (Actually this solution is exact, although this cannot be shown without substitution of the values into the given equations.)

Solve graphically the system of equations   **Example D**

$$-2x + 3y = 8, \qquad 3x + 4y = -6.$$

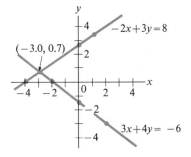

Figure 15-3

First we determine the intercepts and one check point for each equation. The lines are then graphed as shown in Fig. 15–3.

$-2x + 3y = 8$			$3x + 4y = -6$	
x	y		x	y
0	$\frac{8}{3}$		0	$-\frac{3}{2}$
-4	0		-2	0
1	$\frac{10}{3}$		2	-3

From the graph we can estimate the coordinates of the point of intersection to be $(-3.0, 0.7)$. [Actually they are $(-\frac{50}{17}, \frac{12}{17})$.] Thus the required solution is $x = -3.0$ and $y = 0.7$.

There are special circumstances in which two lines do not intersect at just one point. This is the case (1) if the lines are parallel and do not intersect at all, or (2) if the lines are coincident, all the points of one being the same as all the points of the other. When the lines are parallel, the system is called *inconsistent,* and when they are coincident the system is called *dependent.* The following examples illustrate these cases.

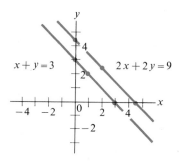

Figure 15-4

Example E   Solve graphically the system of equations

$$x + y = 3, \qquad 2x + 2y = 9.$$

We set up the following tables to indicate the intercepts and check point for each line. The lines are then graphed as in Fig. 15-4.

$x + y = 3$		$2x + 2y = 9$	
x	y	x	y
0	3	0	$\frac{9}{2}$
3	0	$\frac{9}{2}$	0
1	2	2	$\frac{5}{2}$

We observe that within the limits of accuracy of the graphing, the lines appear to be parallel. (They are, in fact, parallel. This is always the case when one equation of the system can be multiplied through by a constant so that the coefficients of the variables are the same, respectively, as those in the other equation. In this case, if the first equation is multiplied by 2, we have $2x + 2y = 6$, which is the same as the second equation except for the constant.) Since the lines are parallel, there is no solution.

Example F   Solve graphically the system of equations

$$x + 2y = 6, \qquad 3x + 6y = 18.$$

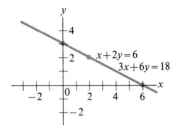

Figure 15–5

We set up the following tables to indicate the intercepts and check point for each line. The lines are then graphed as in Fig. 15–5.

$x + 2y = 6$			$3x + 6y = 18$	
x	y		x	y
0	3		0	3
6	0		6	0
2	2		2	2

We note that both intercepts are the same. Therefore the two lines are coincident. Hence every point on the lines is a solution, in that the coordinates satisfy both equations. This, in turn, means that there is an infinite number of solutions. However, since no unique solution may be determined, we call the system dependent.

In the following exercises, solve the given systems of equations graphically.   EXERCISES
Where possible, estimate the coordinates of the point of intersection to the nearest 0.1 of a unit. If variables other than x and y are used, plot the first along the x-axis and the second along the y-axis.

1. $x + y = 4$
  $x - y = 4$

2. $x - y = 2$
  $2x + y = 6$

3. $y - x = 2$
  $2y + x = 8$

4. $2x + y = 4$
  $3x + 2y = 6$

5. $r - x = 7$
  $2r + x = 5$

6. $m + n = 6$
  $3m + n = 2$

7. $x + 3y = 8$
  $x - y = 0$

8. $x + y = 1$
  $2x - 8y = 1$

9. $2y + x = 8$
  $4y + 2x = 16$

10. $2k + m = 4$
  $4k + 2m = 6$

11. $x + 4y = 4$
  $-2x + 2y = 7$

12. $3x - 2y = 4$
  $-9x - 4y = 13$

13. $a + 2b = -3$
  $3a - 5b = -3$

14. $2u - 3v = 8$
  $u + 4v = 6$

15. $s + t = 7$
  $3s + 3t = 5$

16. $2x - 5y = 10$ **17.** $3p - q = 6$ **18.** $2x - 4y = 7$
      $-6x + 15y = -30$ $2p + 2q = 7$ $3x + 2y = 3$

19. $0.5x - 1.6y = 3.2$ **20.** $\frac{1}{3}x - 2y = 8$
     $1.2x + 3.3y = 6.6$ $3x - \frac{1}{5}y = 2$

21. A board 72 in. long is cut into two pieces so that one piece is 10 in. longer than the other. The lengths x and y of the two pieces can be found by solving the equations

$$x + y = 72, \qquad x - y = 10.$$

22. The perimeter of a rectangular area is 28 mi, and the length is 4 mi longer than the width. The dimensions l and w can be found by solving the equations

$$2l + 2w = 28, \qquad l - w = 4.$$

23. A man rows downstream 10 mi in 2 hr and upstream 8 mi in 4 hr. The rate at which he rows in still water r_1 and the rate of the current of the stream r_2 can be found by solving the equations

$$2r_1 + 2r_2 = 10, \qquad 4r_1 - 4r_2 = 8.$$

24. An electrician and his helper received a total of $50 for working 5 hr on one job. They received a total of $56 when the electrician worked 4 hr and his helper 8 hr on another job. Their hourly rates e and h can be found by solving the equations

$$5e + 5h = 50, \qquad 4e + 8h = 56.$$

25. A current of 2 amp passes through a resistor R_1 and a current of 3 amp passes through a resistor R_2; the total voltage across the resistors is 8 volts. Then the current in the first resistor is changed to 4 amp and that in the second resistor is changed to 1 amp; the total voltage is 11 volts. The resistances (in ohms) can be found by solving the equations

$$2R_1 + 3R_2 = 8, \qquad 4R_1 + R_2 = 11.$$

26. If two ropes with tensions T_1 and T_2 support a 20-lb sign, the tensions can be found by solving the equations

$$0.7T_1 - 0.6T_2 = 0, \qquad 0.7T_1 + 0.8T_2 = 20.$$

15-2 SOLUTION BY ALGEBRAIC SUBSTITUTION

We have just seen how a system of two linear equations can be solved graphically. This technique is good for obtaining a "picture" of the solution of two equations. One of the difficulties of graphical solutions is that the solutions are in general approximate. If exact solutions are required, we must turn to algebraic methods. In this section we shall present a basic algebraic method of solution, and we shall discuss another one in Section 15–3.

The method of this section is called algebraic *substitution*. Using this method, we first solve one of the equations for one of the two unknowns and then substitute the result into the other equation for the unknown. We thus obtain a simple equation in one unknown. The following examples illustrate the method.

Solve, by substitution, the system of equations   **Example A**

$$2x + y = 4, \qquad 3x - y = 1.$$

The first step is to solve one of the equations for one of the unknowns. About the only consideration on which the choice of equation and unknown is based is the ease of manipulation. For example, in this system it is slightly easier to solve for y than for x, for fractions can be avoided. Inspection also shows that one algebraic step is all that is required to solve the first equation for y. Therefore the first equation would be a good choice. It should be emphasized, however, that either equation can be solved for either unknown, and the final result will be the same. Thus, solving the first equation for y, we have $y = 4 - 2x$. This is now substituted into the second equation, giving

$$3x - (4 - 2x) = 1.$$

We now solve this equation for x:

$$3x - 4 + 2x = 1,$$
$$5x = 5,$$
$$x = 1.$$

Therefore the value of y which corresponds to $x = 1$ is found by substituting $x = 1$ into either equation. Since the first has already been solved for y, we have

$$y = 4 - 2(1) = 2.$$

Thus the solution is $x = 1$ and $y = 2$. We check this by substituting both values into the other equation. This gives

$$3(1) - 2 = 1.$$

Therefore the solution checks.

Example B   Solve, by substitution, the system of equations

$$3x + 2y = 7, \qquad x - 3y = 6.$$

Inspection of the equations shows that the solution for x in the second equation appears best. Thus, solving the second equation for x, we have $x = 3y + 6$. Substituting this expression for x into the first equation, we have

$$3(3y + 6) + 2y = 7.$$

We now solve this equation for y:

$$9y + 18 + 2y = 7, \qquad 11y = -11, \qquad y = -1.$$

Substituting $y = -1$ into $x = 3y + 6$, we have

$$x = 3(-1) + 6 = -3 + 6 = 3.$$

The solution is $x = 3$ and $y = -1$. Checking this solution by substituting these values in the first equation, we have

$$3(3) + 2(-1) = 9 - 2 = 7.$$

These values therefore satisfy the first equation, and the solution is confirmed.

Example C   Solve, by substitution, the system of equations

$$2x - 4y = 23, \qquad 3x + 5y = -4.$$

There is little preference as to which unknown to solve for or which equation to use. Therefore, simply choosing to solve the first equation for x, we have $2x = 23 + 4y$, or

$$x = \frac{23 + 4y}{2}.$$

Substituting this expression into the second equation, and then solving for y, we have

$$3\left(\frac{23 + 4y}{2}\right) + 5y = -4,$$
$$3(23 + 4y) + 10y = -8,$$
$$69 + 12y + 10y = -8,$$
$$22y = -77,$$
$$y = -\tfrac{7}{2}.$$

Substituting this value into the solution for x, we have

$$x = \frac{23 + 4(-\frac{7}{2})}{2} = \frac{23 - 14}{2} = \frac{9}{2}.$$

Thus, the solution is $x = \frac{9}{2}$ and $y = -\frac{7}{2}$. Checking this solution in the second equation, we have

$$3(\tfrac{9}{2}) + 5(-\tfrac{7}{2}) = \tfrac{27}{2} - \tfrac{35}{2} = -\tfrac{8}{2} = -4.$$

This means that the solution checks.

When one is trying to solve a system which turns out to be dependent, one can reduce the equation to $0 = 0$ after substitution. This may be deemed reasonable, since $0 = 0$ regardless of the value of x, and the coordinates of all points which satisfy one equation of a dependent system also satisfy the other equation, regardless of the value of x. If the system is inconsistent, the equation after substitution may be reduced to $0 = a$, where a is not zero. This also may be deemed reasonable, since zero does not equal a nonzero number, and there are no points whose coordinates satisfy both equations.

Solve, by substitution, the system of equations   **Example D**

$$2x - y = 3, \qquad 4x - 2y = 6.$$

Solving the first equation for y and substituting this expression into the second equation, we have

$$y = 2x - 3,$$
$$4x - 2(2x - 3) = 6,$$
$$4x - 4x + 6 = 6,$$
$$6 = 6.$$

By subtracting 6 from each side, we have $0 = 0$. Therefore the system is dependent.

Solve the system of equations   **Example E**

$$3x - 2y = 4, \qquad 9x - 6y = 2.$$

Solving the first equation for x, we have

$$x = \frac{2y + 4}{3}.$$

Substituting this expression into the second equation, we have

$$9\left(\frac{2y + 4}{3}\right) - 6y = 2,$$
$$3(2y + 4) - 6y = 2,$$
$$6y + 12 - 6y = 2,$$
$$12 = 2,$$
$$10 = 0.$$

Since this cannot be true, the system is inconsistent.

EXERCISES   In the following exercises, solve the given systems of equations by substitution.

1. $y = 5 + x$
$2x - y = 1$

2. $s = 1 - t$
$2s - 8t = 1$

3. $x - y = 2$
$2x + y = 8$

4. $m - n = 5$
$m + 2n = -1$

5. $u + v = 10$
$u - v = 4$

6. $x = y - 1$
$x + y = 5$

7. $2x + y = 0$
$3x + 2y = 1$

8. $2x = 3y$
$x - 4y = 0$

9. $x - 2y = 0$
$2x - 3y = 1$

10. $a - 2b = 4$
$2a + b = 6$

11. $3x = 2y$
$-x + 4y = 0$

12. $2x + 3y = 6$
$x - y = 4$

13. $k - 8u = 4$
$2k + u = 2$

14. $x = y + 1$
$x - y = 5$

15. $z + 2u = 3$
$3z - u = 1$

16. $\frac{1}{2}x + y = 8$
$x + 4y = 7$

17. $\frac{1}{3}x + y = 9$
$x - \frac{1}{3}y = 6$

18. $2u + 3w = 6$
$4u + 2w = 8$

19. $3x - 4k = 12$
$4x + 5k = -7$

20. $3y - 2z = 6$
$2y + 9z = 8$

21. A man has two outboard motors for his boat. The sum of the powers p_1 and p_2 of the two motors is 17 hp, and one motor has 7 hp more than the other. We can find the power of each of the motors by solving the equations

$$p_1 + p_2 = 17, \qquad p_1 = p_2 + 7.$$

22. In order to determine how many cm^3 of a 30% solution of hydrochloric acid should be drawn off from 100 cm^3 and replaced by a 10% solution to give an 18% solution, one uses the equations

$$x + y = 100, \qquad 0.30x + 0.10y = 18.$$

Here y is the required unknown.

23. The voltage between two points in an electric circuit is 60 volts. The contact point of a voltage divider is placed between these two points so that the voltage is divided into two parts; one of these parts is twice the other. These two voltages V_1 and V_2 can be found by solving the equations

$$V_1 = 2V_2, \qquad V_1 + V_2 = 60.$$

24. A man invests a total of $5000 partly at 5% and the remainder at 4%. The total annual income from his investment is $230. The amounts x and y, invested at 5% and 4%, respectively, can be found by solving the equations

$$x + y = 5000, \qquad 0.05x + 0.04y = 230.$$

25. A roof truss is in the shape of an isosceles triangle. The perimeter of the truss is 50 ft, and twice the base is 9 ft more than three times the length of a rafter (neglecting overhang). The length of the base b and a rafter r can be found by solving the equations

$$b + 2r = 50, \qquad 2b = 3r + 9.$$

26. Under certain conditions, the tensions T_1 and T_2 (in pounds) supporting a derrick are found by solving the equations

$$0.68T_1 + 0.57T_2 = 750, \qquad 0.73T_1 - 0.82T_2 = 0.$$

15–3 SOLUTION BY THE ADDITION-SUBTRACTION METHOD

The second algebraic method of solving two simultaneous equations that we shall discuss is known as the *addition-subtraction* method. The basis of this method is that if one of the unknowns appears on the same side of each equation, and if the coefficients of this unknown are numerically the same, it is possible to add (or subtract) the left-hand sides as well as the right-hand sides in order to obtain an equation with only one of the unknowns remaining. The following example illustrates the basic method.

Solve, by the addition-subtraction method, the system of equations   Example A

$$2x - y = 1, \qquad 3x + y = 9.$$

We note that if the left-hand sides of the two equations are added, there will be a $+y$ and a $-y$, which means that the sum will not contain y. The two sides of each equation are equal. Hence, if the left-hand sides are added, the sum will equal the sum of the right-hand sides. Since y is not present, the resulting equation will contain only x, and thus can be solved for x. We may then find y by substituting the value of x into either equation, then solving for y. Thus, adding the left-hand sides and equating this sum to the sum of the right-hand sides, we have

$$
\begin{array}{r}
2x - y = 1 \\
3x + y = 9 \\
\hline
5x \quad\ = 10, \\
x = 2.
\end{array}
$$

Substituting $x = 2$ into the second equation, we have

$$3(2) + y = 9,$$
$$6 + y = 9,$$
$$y = 3.$$

The solution is $x = 2$ and $y = 3$. Checking this solution in the first equation, we have

$$2(2) - 3 = 1,$$

which means that the solution is correct.

Example B   Solve, by the addition-subtraction method, the system of equations

$$2x + 3y = 7, \qquad 2x - y = -5.$$

If we subtract the left-hand side of the second equation from the left-hand side of the first equation, x will not appear in the result. Thus, we may obtain the solution by subtracting the respective sides of the equations. Performing this operation, we have

$$
\begin{array}{rl}
2x + 3y = & 7 \\
2x - \ y = & -5 \qquad \text{(subtracting)} \\
\hline
4y = & 12, \\
y = & 3.
\end{array}
$$

Substituting $y = 3$ into the first equation, we have

$$
\begin{array}{rl}
2x + 3(3) = & 7, \\
2x + 9 = & 7, \\
2x = & -2, \\
x = & -1.
\end{array}
$$

The solution is $x = -1$, $y = 3$. Checking this solution in the second equation, we have

$$2(-1) - (3) = -2 - 3 = -5.$$

In many systems it is necessary to multiply one (or both) of the equations by constants so that the resulting coefficients of one unknown are numerically the same. The following two examples illustrate this procedure.

Solve, by the addition-subtraction method, the system of equations   Example C

$$2x + 3y = -5,$$
$$4x - y = 4.$$

If each term of the second equation is multiplied by 3, it will be possible to eliminate y by addition and continue to the solution. Thus, rewriting the equations, we have

$$2x + 3y = -5,$$
$$4x - y = 4,$$

and multiplying each term of the second equation by 3, we have

$$2x + 3y = -5,$$
$$12x - 3y = 12.$$

Adding the equations, we have

$$14x = 7,$$
$$x = \tfrac{1}{2}.$$

Substituting $x = \tfrac{1}{2}$ into the first equation, we have

$$2(\tfrac{1}{2}) + 3y = -5,$$
$$1 + 3y = -5,$$
$$3y = -6,$$
$$y = -2.$$

The solution is $x = \tfrac{1}{2}$, $y = -2$. Checking this solution by substituting in the second equation, we have

$$4(\tfrac{1}{2}) - (-2) = 2 + 2 = 4.$$

Example D   Solve, by the addition-subtraction method, the system of equations

$$2x - 4y = 5, \qquad 3x + 5y = 8.$$

It is not possible to multiply just one of these equations by an integer to make the coefficients of one of the variables numerically the same. Therefore we multiply both equations by appropriate integers. We can multiply the first equation by 3 and the second equation by 2 in order to make the coefficients of x equal, or we may multiply the first equation by 5 and the second one by 4 in order to eliminate y. Choosing this second method, we obtain the new set of equations

$$
\begin{aligned}
10x - 20y &= 25 \\
12x + 20y &= 32 \\
\hline
22x \quad\;\; &= 57,
\end{aligned}
$$

$$x = \tfrac{57}{22}.$$

$$2(\tfrac{57}{22}) - 4y = 5,$$

$$-4y = 5 - \tfrac{57}{11}$$

$$-4y = \frac{55 - 57}{11} = -\frac{2}{11},$$

$$y = \frac{-2}{-44} = \frac{1}{22}.$$

Checking, we have

$$3\left(\frac{57}{22}\right) + 5\left(\frac{1}{22}\right) = \frac{171}{22} + \frac{5}{22} = \frac{171 + 5}{22} = \frac{176}{22} = 8.$$

Therefore the solution is

$$x = \frac{57}{22}, \qquad y = \frac{1}{22}.$$

If the system is dependent or inconsistent, we have the same type of result as that mentioned in the last section. That is, if the system is dependent, the addition-subtraction method will result in $0 = 0$ after the equations are combined or the result will be $0 = a$ (a not zero) if the system is inconsistent.

Example E   Solve, by the addition-subtraction method, the system of equations

$$3x - 6y = 8, \qquad -x + 2y = 3.$$

Multiplying the second equation by 3 and adding equations, we have

$$3x - 6y = 8$$
$$\underline{-3x + 6y = 9}$$
$$0 = 17$$

Since this result is not possible, the system is inconsistent.

In the following exercises, solve the given systems of equations by the addition-   **EXERCISES**
subtraction method.

1. $x + y = 4$
   $x - y = 2$

2. $x + y = 5$
   $x - 2y = 1$

3. $2x + y = 16$
   $x - y = 2$

4. $x + y = 11$
   $2x - y = 1$

5. $m + n = 9$
   $2m - n = 0$

6. $2x = 7 - y$
   $2x = 1 + y$

7. $d + t = 3$
   $2d + 3t = 10$

8. $2r + s = 7$
   $r + 2s = -1$

9. $x + 2n = -3$
   $3x - 5n = -3$

10. $2x + y = 4$
    $5x + y = 13$

11. $x - 2y = 5$
    $2x + y = 20$

12. $4t - x = 5$
    $3t - x = 1$

13. $7x = 5 + y$
    $7x = 4 + y$

14. $2m = 10 - 3n$
    $3m = 12 - 4n$

15. $a + 7b = 15$
    $3a + 2b = 7$

16. $-8x + 7y = 2$
    $3x - 5y = 9$

17. $13p - 18q = 21$
    $4p + 12q = 5$

18. $11k + 15t = 1$
    $2k + 3t = 1$

19. $\frac{2}{7}x - \frac{1}{3}y = -3$
    $\frac{5}{14}x + \frac{5}{3}y = -10$

20. $62x - 4y = 43$
    $15x + 12y = 17$

21. $\frac{1}{x} + \frac{2}{y} = 3$

    $\frac{1}{x} - \frac{2}{y} = -1$

22. $\frac{7}{8}x + \frac{5}{12}y = -4$

    $x + y = 8$

23. One electronic data-processing card-sorter can sort a cards per minute; a second card-sorter can sort b cards per minute. They sort 7500 cards if the first sorts for two minutes and the second sorts for one minute. They can sort 9000 cards if the second sorts for two minutes and the first for one minute. We can determine the sorting rates a and b by solving the equations

$$2a + b = 7500, \qquad a + 2b = 9000.$$

24. While a pulley belt is making one complete revolution, one of the pulley wheels makes 6 revolutions and the other makes 15 revolutions. The

circumference of one wheel is 2 ft more than twice the circumference of the other wheel. The circumferences c_1 and c_2 can be found by solving the equations

$$6c_1 = 15c_2, \qquad c_1 - 2c_2 = 2.$$

25. A rocket is launched so that it averages 2000 mi/hr. An hour later, an interceptor rocket is launched along the same path at an average speed of 2500 mi/hr. In order to find the time of flights of the rockets t_1 and t_2 before the interceptor rocket overtakes the first rocket, one must solve the following equations:

$$2000t_1 = 2500t_2, \qquad t_1 = t_2 + 1.$$

26. A man wants to determine how many gallons m of milk containing 3% butterfat and how many gallons c of cream containing 15% butterfat should be mixed to give 20 gal of milk containing 6% butterfat. He can use the equations

$$m + c = 20, \qquad 0.03m + 0.15c = 1.2.$$

27. Under certain conditions two electric currents (in amps) I_1 and I_2 can be found by solving the equations

$$3I_1 + 4I_2 = 3, \qquad 3I_1 - 5I_2 = -6.$$

28. Under certain conditions, when balancing weights x and y on a board weighing 20 lb, we can find x and y by solving the equations

$$5x - 7y = 20, \qquad 4x - 3.2y = 40.$$

15–4 STATED PROBLEMS

In the first section of this chapter we mentioned that many types of stated problems lead to systems of two simultaneous equations. This has also been illustrated with several examples in each of the previous sections. Now that we have seen how such systems are solved, we shall set up equations from stated problems and then solve these equations. The following examples illustrate the method.

Example A

Two gears together have 102 teeth. One of the gears has 12 more than twice the number of teeth of the other. Find the number of teeth of each gear.

As in the solution of equations in one unknown, which we solved in Chapter 6, we first choose a letter to represent each of the unknown quantities. Thus we let x = number of teeth on the larger gear and

y = number of teeth on the smaller gear. Since the two gears together have 102 teeth, we have one equation, which is

$$x + y = 102.$$

Next, since one of the gears has 12 more than twice the number of teeth of the other, we have a second equation, which is

$$x = 2y + 12.$$

We have now established the necessary two equations. We can solve this system by any appropriate method. Choosing substitution, we substitute the expression for x from the second equation into the first equation. Therefore,

$$(2y + 12) + y = 102,$$
$$2y + 12 + y = 102,$$
$$3y = 90,$$
$$y = 30.$$

Also, $x = 2(30) + 12,$

$$x = 72.$$

Therefore the larger gear has 72 teeth and the smaller gear has 30 teeth. Checking this *with the statement of the problem* we see that the solution checks.

In a particular house, the living room (rectangular) has a perimeter of 78 ft. The length is 3 ft less than twice the width. Find the dimensions of the room.   Example B

First we let l = the length of the room and w = the width of the room. Since the perimeter is 78 ft, we know that

$$2l + 2w = 78.$$

Since the length is 3 ft less than twice the width, we have

$$l = 2w - 3.$$

Dividing through the first equation by 2, and rearranging the second equation, we have

$$l + w = 39,$$
$$l - 2w = -3.$$

Subtracting, we have

$$3w = 42,$$

$$w = 14 \text{ ft}.$$

Therefore

$$l = 2(14) - 3, \qquad l = 25 \text{ ft}.$$

Thus the length is 25 ft and the width is 14 ft. This is seen to check with the *statement* of the problem.

Example C   A man invests $7000, part of it at 4% and the remainder at 5%. How much is invested at each rate if the total annual income from the investment is $300?

We are asked to find the amount invested at each percentage. Thus we let $x =$ the amount invested at 4% and $y =$ the amount invested at 5%. We know that the total amount invested is $7000, which means that

$$x + y = 7000.$$

The income from any investment equals the percentage times the amount invested. This means that the income from the 4% part is $0.04x$ and the income from the 5% part is $0.05y$. Since the total income is $300, we have

$$0.04x + 0.05y = 300.$$

Repeating the first equation and multiplying the second equation through by 100, we have the system of equations

$$x + y = 7000, \qquad 4x + 5y = 30000.$$

Using the addition-subtraction method, we have

$$5x + 5y = 35000$$
$$\underline{4x + 5y = 30000}$$
$$x \qquad\quad = \$5000.$$

Substitution in the first equation gives us $y = \$2000$. Since 4% of $5000 is $200 and 5% of $2000 is $100, we see that the total annual income of $300 checks. Therefore $5000 is invested at 4% and $2000 is invested at 5%.

Example D   Two jet planes start at cities A and B, 6400 mi apart, traveling the same route toward each other. They pass each other 2 hr later; the jet which starts from city A travels 200 mi/hr faster than the other. How far are they from city A when they pass each other?

Since we wish to determine the distance from city A to the place at which they pass each other, we let $x =$ the distance from city A to the point at which they pass and $y =$ the distance from city B to the point at which they pass.

Since the cities are 6400 mi apart, we have

$$x + y = 6400.$$

The other information we have is that one jet travels 200 mi/hr faster than the other. Therefore it is necessary to set up the other equation in terms of speeds. The speed of each jet is the distance traveled divided by the time. Since the jet from city A travels x mi in 2 hr, its speed is $x/2$. In the same way, the speed of the other jet is $y/2$. Since the jet from city A travels 200 mi/hr faster, we have

$$\frac{x}{2} = \frac{y}{2} + 200.$$

We now have the necessary two equations.

Proceeding with the solution, we repeat the first equation and multiply through the second equation by 2. This gives

$$x + y = 6400,$$
$$x = y + 400.$$

Subtracting y from each side of the second equation, we have

$$x + y = 6400$$
$$\underline{x - y = 400}$$
$$2x \quad\;\; = 6800,$$
$$x = 3400 \text{ mi.}$$

This means that $y = 3000$ mi. Thus the faster jet traveled at 1700 mi/hr and the slower one at 1500 mi/hr. And therefore the solution checks with the statement of the problem.

An alternate method would be to let $u =$ the speed of the jet from city A and $v =$ the speed of the jet from city B.

Even though the required distance from city A is not one of the unknowns, if we find u, we may find the distance by multiplying u by 2, the time that elapses before the planes meet. Using these unknowns, we have the first equation $u = v + 200$ from the fact that the jet from city A travels 200 mi/hr faster. Also, since distance equals speed times time, the distance from city A to the meeting place is $2u$, and that from city B is $2v$. The total of these distances is 6400 mi. Therefore $2u + 2v = 6400$ is the other equation.

Example E   How many pounds of sand must be added to a mixture which is 50% cement and 50% sand in order to get 200 lb of a mixture which is 80% sand and 20% cement?

Since the unknown quantities are the amounts of sand and original mixture, we let $x =$ number of pounds of sand required and $y =$ number of pounds of original mixture required.

Now we know that the final mixture will have a total weight of 200 lb. Therefore

$$x + y = 200.$$

Next, the amount of sand, x, and the amount of sand present in the original mixture, $0.5y$, equals the amount of sand in the final mixture, $0.8(200)$. This gives us

$$x + 0.5y = 0.8(200).$$

Rewriting the first equation and multiplying the second equation by 2, we have

$$x + y = 200,$$
$$2x + y = 320.$$

Subtracting, we obtain

$$x = 120 \text{ lb},$$

which also gives us

$$y = 80 \text{ lb}.$$

Since half the original mixture is sand, the final mixture has 160 lb of sand, and this is 80% of the 200 lb. Therefore the solution checks, and the required answer is 120 lb of sand.

EXERCISES   In Exercises 1 through 12, verify the system of equations found in each of the indicated exercises from previous sections.

1. Exercise 21 of Section 15–1   **2.** Exercise 21 of Section 15–2

In Exercises 13 through 28, solve the given problems by first designating the unknown quantities by appropriate letters and then solving the system of equations which is found.

13. A board is 23 ft long. Where must it be cut so that the longer piece is 2 ft longer than the shorter piece?

14. The sum of two electric voltages is 100 volts. If the higher voltage is doubled and the other halved, the sum becomes 155 volts. What are the voltages?

15. In a particular type of process 5 drills of one type will last as long as 2 drills of another type. The sum of the average number of hours of operation for the two drills is 105 hr. What is the average number of hours each can be used?

16. Two spacecraft (on separate missions) spent a total of 22 days circling the earth. One spent 2 days less than twice the number of days the other spent in outer space. How long was each in space?

17. The side of one square metal plate is 5 mm longer than twice the side of another square plate. The perimeter of the larger plate is 52 mm more than that of the smaller. Find the sides of the two plates.

18. A rectangular field which is 100 ft longer than it is wide is divided into three smaller fields by placing two dividing fences parallel to those along the width. A total of 2600 ft of fencing is used. What are the dimensions of the field?

19. A man invests \$5000, partly at 3% and the remainder at 4%. The total annual income from both investments is \$170. How much is invested at each rate?

20. Part of \$6000 is invested at 5% and the remainder at 3%. The total annual income is \$244. How much is invested at each rate?

21. The relation between the celsius and fahrenheit temperature scales is that the number of fahrenheit degrees equals 32 more than $\frac{9}{5}$ the number of celsius degrees. At what reading are they equal?

22. The voltage across an electric resistor equals the current times the resistance. The sum of two resistances is 14 ohms. When a current of 3 amp passes through the smaller resistor and 5 amp through the larger resistor, the sum of the voltages is 60 volts. What is the value of each resistor?

23. The speed of one train is 5 mi/hr more than that of another train. They start at the same time at stations 425 mi apart and arrive at the same station at the same time 5 hr later. What is the speed of each?

24. Two trains travel at 40 mph and 36 mph, respectively. The faster train travels for a certain length of time and the slower train travels 2 hr longer. The total distance traveled by the two trains is 680 mi. Find the time each travels.

25. By weight, one alloy consists of 60% copper and 40% zinc. Another is 30% copper and 70% zinc. How many grams of each alloy are needed to make 120 lb of an alloy which consists of 50% of each metal?

26. How many gallons of a mixture containing 70% alcohol should be added to a mixture containing 20% alcohol to give 16 qt of a mixture containing 50% alcohol?

27. The specific gravity of an object may be defined as its weight in air divided by the difference between its weight in air and its weight when submerged in water. The sum of the weights in water and in air of an object of specific gravity equal to 10 is 30 lb. What is its weight in air?

28. After a laboratory experiment, a student reported that the difference between two resistances was 8 ohms and that twice one of the resistances was 3 ohms less than twice the other. Is this possible?

15–5 REVIEW EXERCISES

In Exercises 1 through 28, solve the given systems algebraically.

1. $2x + y = 6$
$3x - y = 6$

2. $3x + y = 12$
$3x - y = 24$

3. $x + 2y = 12$
$x + 3y = 16$

4. $x + 2y = 12$
$2x - y = 4$

5. $2x - y = 4$
$x + 3y = 16$

6. $y + 2x = -3$
$3y - 5x = -3$

7. $2p + 7q = 10$
$3p - 2q = 10$

8. $m = n + 3$
$m = 5 - 3n$

9. $2u - 3v = 5$
$-u + 4v = -5$

10. $4x + 3y = -1$
$5x + 2y = 4$

11. $3a + 7b = 15$
$2a - 5b = 39$

12. $2p = 4x + 1$
$2p = 2x - 3$

13. $3x = -16 - y$
$7x = -8 - 5y$

14. $3y = 11 - 5h$
$15y - 15h = 7$

15. $-6y + 4z = -8$
$5y + 6z = 2$

16. $7x + 9y = 3$
$5x + 4y = 1$

17. $3n + d = 20$
$6n + 2d = 40$

18. $x - 2y = 6$
$-2x + 4y = 5$

19. $3x + y = -5$
$6x + 8y = 2$

20. $4x - y = 7$
$8x + 3y = -26$

21. $2x - 3y = 8$
$5x + 2y = 9$

22. $8x - 9y = 3$
     $3x + 4y = 2$

23. $0.03x + 2y = 1$
     $0.02x - 3y = 5$

24. $17x - 9y = 10$
     $8x + 7y = -13$

25. $\frac{2}{3}x + \frac{3}{4}y = 26$
     $\frac{1}{3}x - \frac{3}{4}y = -14$

26. $\dfrac{4x + 5y}{20} = 3$
     $\frac{1}{2}x - \frac{1}{3}y = 2$

27. $\dfrac{9}{r} - \dfrac{5}{s} = 2$
     $\dfrac{7}{r} - \dfrac{3}{s} = 6$

28. $\dfrac{2}{x} - \dfrac{2}{y} = 4$
     $\dfrac{1}{x} - \dfrac{3}{y} = -2$

In Exercises 29 through 36, solve the given systems of equations graphically.

29. $x + 3y = 2$
     $6x - 3y = 5$

30. $2x + 3y = 0$
     $x + y = 2$

31. $3x - y = 6$
     $x - 2y = 4$

32. $4x - y = 9$
     $4x + 3y = 0$

33. $4u + v = 2$
     $3u - 4v = 30$

34. $r + 4s = 6$
     $r + 6s = 7$

35. $3x - y = 5$
     $-6x + 2y = 3$

36. $m + 3n = 7$
     $3m - 2n = 5$

Solve the applied problems in Exercises 37 through 40 by any appropriate method.

37. When one is analyzing a certain electric circuit, one obtains the following equations:

$$4i_1 - 10i_2 = 3,$$
$$-10i_2 - 5(i_1 + i_2) = 6.$$

Solve for the indicated electric currents i_1 and i_2 (in amperes).

38. The equation $s = v_0 t + \frac{1}{2}at^2$ is used to relate the distance s traveled by an object in time t, given that the initial velocity is v_0 and the acceleration is a. For an object moving down an inclined plane, it is noted that $s = 32$ ft when $t = 2$ sec, and $s = 63$ ft when $t = 3$ sec. Find v_0 (in feet/second) and a (in feet/second^2).

39. Two ropes support a given weight. The equations used to find the tensions in the ropes are

$$0.866T_2 - 0.500T_3 = 0,$$
$$0.500T_2 + 0.866T_3 = 50.$$

Find T_2 and T_3 (in pounds).

40. Nitric acid is produced from air and nitrogen compounds. To determine the size of the equipment required, one often uses a relationship between the air flow rate m (in moles/hour) and exhaust nitrogen rate n. For one particular operation, one encounters the following equations:

$$1.58m + 41.5 = 38.0 + 2.00n, \qquad 0.424m + 36.4 = 189 + 0.0728n.$$

Solve for m and n.

In Exercises 41 through 50, set up the appropriate systems of equations and solve.

41. A plumber worked for 3 hr on a particular job and his helper worked on it for 4 hr. Together they earned $25.50. If the hours worked were reversed, they would have earned $27.00 together. What is the hourly rate each receives?

42. Two men together make 120 castings in one day. If one of them turns out half again as many as the other, how many does each make in a day?

43. The circumference of a circular lawn area is 5.60 ft more than the perimeter of a nearby square area. The diameter of the circle is 10.0 ft more than the side of the square. Find the diameter of the circle and the side of the square. (Use $\pi = 3.14$ and three significant figures in working this problem.)

44. Two thermometer readings differ by 48°F. Four times the smaller reading exceeds twice the larger reading by 2°F. What are the readings?

45. A man has $1.10 in nickels and dimes. There are 15 coins in all. How many of each has he?

46. While a 40-ft pulley belt is making one complete revolution, one of the pulley wheels makes one more revolution than the other. The smaller wheel is replaced by another wheel which has half the radius; the replacement wheel makes 6 revolutions more than the larger wheel for each revolution of the belt. What are the circumferences of the two original wheels?

47. A car travels 355 mi by going at one speed for 3 hr and at another speed for 4 hr. If it had traveled 3 hr at the second speed and 4 hr at the first speed, it would have gone 345 mi. Find the two speeds.

48. An airplane travels 1120 mi in 7 hr with the wind. The trip takes 8 hr against the wind. Determine the speed of the plane relative to the air and the speed of the wind.

49. Mr. Jones invested $5000, partly at 5% and the remainder at 3%. He earns $180 each year from the investments. What is the amount invested at each rate?

50. How many cm^3 of each of a 10% solution and a 25% solution of nitric acid must be used to make 95 cm^3 of a 20% solution?

Additional Topics from Geometry

16

16–1 BASIC CONCEPTS

In this chapter we shall be concerned primarily with certain basic topics from geometry, although we shall have occasion to use algebra as a tool. Since several concepts of geometry were introduced in Chapter 7, some of the material in this chapter will be familiar. However, a number of those concepts are included here for reasons of continuity and completeness.

This section will be devoted to introducing terminology from geometry and showing how it is used to describe geometric figures and their various parts. The remaining sections will be devoted to introducing other important topics in the study of geometry. The study of geometry included in this chapter is not complete, but it is sufficient to give you a good idea of the basic topics of the subject.

As we stated in Chapter 7, geometry deals with the properties and measurement of angles, lines, surfaces, and volumes, and the basic figures which are formed. We also mentioned that certain concepts, such as a *point*, a *line*, and a *plane* are in general accepted as being known intuitively. Therefore we shall make no attempt to define these quantities, although we shall use them in defining and describing other quantities. This in itself points out an important aspect in developing a topic: that is, not everything can be defined or proved; some concepts must be accepted and used as a basis for the study.

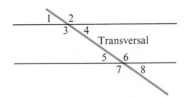

Figure 16–1

In a plane, if a line crosses two given *parallel* or nonparallel lines, it is called a *transversal*. If a transversal crosses a pair of parallel lines, certain pairs of equal *angles* result. In Fig. 16–1, the *corresponding angles* are equal. (That is, $\angle 1 = \angle 5$, $\angle 2 = \angle 6$, $\angle 3 = \angle 7$, and $\angle 4 = \angle 8$.) Also, the *alternate interior angles* are equal ($\angle 3 = \angle 6$ and $\angle 4 = \angle 5$), and the *alternate exterior angles* are equal ($\angle 1 = \angle 8$ and $\angle 2 = \angle 7$).

There are many special names given to angles and pairs of angles, depending on their size, relative position, and so on. *Adjacent angles*

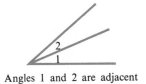

Angles 1 and 2 are adjacent

Figure 16–2

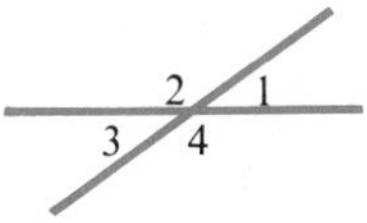

Angles 1 and 3 are vertical
Angles 2 and 4 are vertical

Figure 16–3

have a common *vertex* and a side common to them (see Fig. 16–2). Two lines that cross form two pairs of equal angles "across" the point of intersection; these angles are called *vertical angles* (see Fig. 16–3). *Perpendicular* lines are defined to be a pair of lines which cross and form equal adjacent angles (see Fig. 16–4).

Equal adjacent angles 1 and 2

Figure 16–4

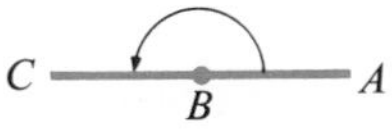

Straight angle *ABC*

Figure 16–5

Since one complete rotation about a point is 360°, the angle about a point on one side of a straight line, called a *straight angle*, equals 180° (see Fig. 16–5). *Supplementary angles* are two angles whose sum is 180°. A *right angle* has 90°. *Complementary angles* are two angles whose sum equals 90°. An angle less than 90° is an *acute angle* (see Fig. 16–6). An angle greater than 90° but less than 180° is an *obtuse angle* (see Fig. 16–7).

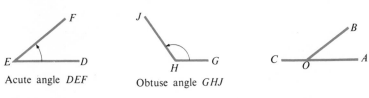

Acute angle *DEF*

Obtuse angle *GHJ*

Figure 16–6   **Figure 16–7**   **Figure 16–8**

In Fig. 16–8, ∠*AOB* is an acute angle, ∠*AOC* is a straight angle, ∠*BOC* is an obtuse angle, and angles *AOB* and *BOC* are supplementary angles.

Example A

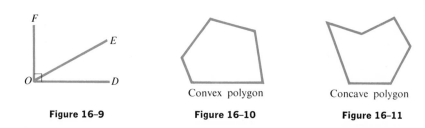

Convex polygon

Concave polygon

Figure 16–9   **Figure 16–10**   **Figure 16–11**

In Fig. 16–9, $\angle DOE$ is an acute angle, $\angle DOF$ is a right angle, and angles DOE and EOF are complementary angles.

When a part of the plane is bounded and closed by straight line segments, it is called a *polygon*. In general, polygons are named according to the number of sides they have. A *triangle* has three sides, a *quadrilateral* has four sides, a *pentagon* has five sides, and so on. We shall consider here only *convex* polygons, i.e., those in which none of the *interior angles* equals or is greater than 180° (see Fig. 16–10). If a polygon is not convex, it is concave (see Fig. 16–11). In a *regular* polygon, all the sides and interior angles are equal in length. (See Fig. 16–12, which is a regular *octagon:* 8 sides.)

In a polygon, a line segment that joins any two nonadjacent vertices is called a *diagonal.* From this definition, we can see that a triangle cannot have any diagonals, but that polygons with four or more sides do have diagonals.

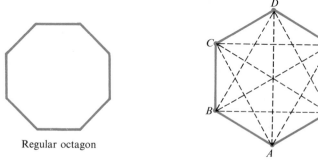

Regular octagon

Figure 16–12   **Figure 16–13**

Example B   Figure 16–13 shows a *hexagon* (6 sides). We can see that three diagonals may be drawn from vertex A (AC, AD, and AE). Also, three may be drawn from vertex B (BD, BE, and BF). From vertex C three may be drawn, although only two (*CE* and *CF*) are different from those already drawn, since diagonal *AC* has already been included. From vertex *D* three may be drawn, although only one is different from those already drawn (*DF*). No other diagonals not already included can be drawn from vertices *E* and *F*. Therefore it is possible to draw three different diagonals from any vertex, and nine diagonals in all.

The polygons of greatest general importance are the triangle and the quadrilateral. In Chapter 7 we discussed the important types of triangles (*equilateral, isosceles,* and *right* triangles). We also introduced the important quadrilaterals (*parallelograms, rectangles, squares, trapezoids,* and *rhombuses*). We presented the figures, as well as the formulas for finding their *perimeters* and *areas.* Therefore we shall not discuss these topics here.

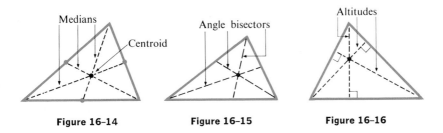

Figure 16–14   Figure 16–15   Figure 16–16

There are certain basic properties of triangles which we shall mention here. One very important property is that *the sum of the three angles of any triangle is* 180°. Also, the three *medians* (line segments drawn from a vertex to the *midpoint* of the opposite side) meet at a single point (see Fig. 16–14). This point of intersection of the medians is called the *centroid* of the triangle. It is also true that the three *angle bisectors* meet at a common point (see Fig. 16–15), as do the three *altitudes* (heights) which are drawn from a vertex perpendicular to the opposite side (or its extension). See Fig. 16–16.

We shall conclude this section with an extension of the discussion of the circle. In Chapter 7 we defined the *circumference, diameter,* and *radius* of the circle, and gave formulas for finding the area and the circumference. Also associated with the circle is the *chord,* which is a line segment having its endpoints on the circumference. A *tangent* is a line that touches a circle (does not pass through) at one point. A *secant* is a line that passes through two points of a circle. An *arc* is a part of the circumference. When two radii form an angle at the center, the angle is called a *central angle*. An *inscribed angle* of an arc is one for which the endpoints of the arc are points on the sides of the angle, and for which the vertex is a point of the arc, although not an endpoint.

Example C   In Fig. 16–17, line segment *AB* is a diameter, and line segments *AO*, *CO*, and *BO* are radii. Line segments *DE* and *BF* are chords (and so is *AB* actually). Line *S*, which passes through *D* and *E*, is a secant, and line *T*, which touches the circle at *D*, is a tangent. Radii *CO* and *AO* form a central angle at *O*, where arc *AC* is part of the circumference. The $\angle ABF$ is an inscribed angle of arc *ADEBF*.

There are two important properties of a circle which we shall mention here.

1)   *A tangent to a circle is perpendicular to the radius drawn to the point of contact.*
2)   *An angle inscribed in a semicircle is a right angle.*

These statements are illustrated in the following example.

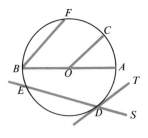
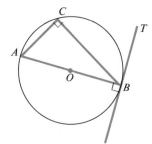

| Figure 16–17 | Figure 16–18 |

Example D   In Fig. 16–18, tangent line *T* is perpendicular to the radius *OB*, since it is tangent to the circle at point *B*. Also, $\angle ACB$, which is inscribed in arc *ACB*, where *AB* is a diameter, is a right angle, since arc *ACB* is a semicircle.

EXERCISES   In Exercises 1 through 4, refer to Fig. 16–19 and identify the listed pairs of angles. Use only angles 1 through 5.

1. The alternate interior angles
2. The alternate exterior angles
3. The corresponding angles
4. The vertical angles

Figure 16–19

In Exercises 5 through 10, refer to Fig. 16–20 and identify at least two of each of the listed types of angles.

5. Straight angles

6. Right angles

7. Acute angles

8. Obtuse angles

9. Complementary angles (2 pairs)

10. Supplementary angles, one of which starts at *A* (2 pairs)

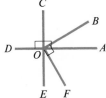

Figure 16–20

In Exercises 11 through 14, refer to Fig. 16–21, in which $\angle ABD = 30°$, $\angle SBK = 30°$, and $EK \perp$ (is perpendicular to) AC, and determine the indicated angles.

11. $\angle DBE$ **12.** $\angle DBC$ **13.** $\angle ABS$ **14.** $\angle EBS$

Figure 16–21

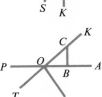

Figure 16–22

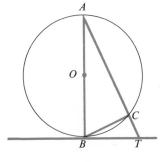

Figure 16–23

In Exercises 15 through 18, refer to Fig. 16–22, in which *AOP* and *KOT* are straight lines, $\angle TOP = 40°$, $\angle OBC = 90°$, and $\angle AOL = 55°$. Determine the indicated angles.

15. $\angle LOT$ **16.** $\angle POL$ **17.** $\angle KOP$ **18.** $\angle KCB$

In Exercises 19 through 22, refer to Fig. 16–23, where *AB* is a diameter, line *TB* is tangent to the circle at *B*, and $\angle ABC = 65°$. Determine the listed angles.

19. $\angle CBT$ **20.** $\angle BCT$ **21.** $\angle CAB$ **22.** $\angle BTC$

In Exercises 23 through 28, answer the given questions.

23. What is the maximum number of acute angles a triangle may contain?

24. What is the maximum number of acute angles a quadrilateral may contain?

25. What is the maximum number of right angles a pentagon may contain?

26. How many diagonals does a pentagon have?

27. How many diagonals does a *septagon* (7 sides) have?

28. How many diagonals can be drawn from a single vertex of an octagon?

In Exercises 29 through 32, you are asked to draw figures and then use the figures to arrive at certain conclusions. Hence it is important that you draw the figures reasonably accurately.

29. Draw a rhombus and its diagonals. How do the diagonals cross each other?

30. Draw a scalene triangle, along with its medians and altitudes. Is the point of intersection of the medians the same as that of the altitudes?

31. Draw a circle with two tangent lines that are perpendicular. What is your conclusion about the arc of the circle between the points of tangency?

32. Inscribe an angle in an arc of 300°. What is the relation between the angle between the chords and the remaining arc?

In Exercises 33 through 35, solve the given problems.

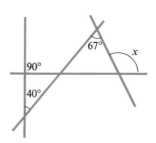

Figure 16–24

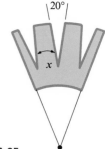

Figure 16–25

33. The streets in a certain city meet at the angles shown in Fig. 16–24. Find the angle between the indicated streets.

34. The velocity of an object moving in a circular path is always directed tangent to the circle in which it is moving. A boy whirls a stone on the end of a string in a vertical circle. The string was initially in a vertical position, and the stone makes $5\frac{1}{2}$ revolutions before the string breaks. In what direction does the stone travel at that instant?

35. The gear in Fig. 16–25 has 24 teeth. Find the indicated angle.

There is one property of a right triangle which is of such importance that we shall devote this section to developing it and showing some of its applications. It is the *Pythagorean theorem*, which states that

in a right triangle, the square of the length of the hypotenuse equals the sum of the squares of the lengths of the other two sides.

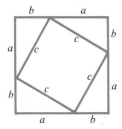

Figure 16–26

First we shall show a proof of this theorem which makes use of both geometry and algebra. In Fig. 16–26, a square of side c is inscribed in a square of side $a + b$ as shown. The area of the outer square $(a + b)^2$ minus the area of the four triangles of sides a, b, and c equals the area of the inner square. This leads to

$$(a + b)^2 - 4(\tfrac{1}{2}ab) = c^2,$$
$$a^2 + 2ab + b^2 - 2ab = c^2,$$
$$a^2 + b^2 = c^2. \qquad \textbf{16–1}$$

We see that this result is the Pythagorean relation for each of the four triangles of sides a, b, and c. Therefore, in any right triangle with sides a, b, and c, where c is the hypotenuse, Eq. (16–1) is valid.

We now present five examples illustrating the use of the Pythagorean theorem.

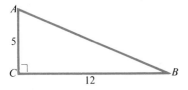

Figure 16–27

For a right triangle ABC, with the right angle at C, $AC = 5$ and $BC = 12$,   Example A
find AB (see Fig. 16–27).

Letting AC, BC, and AB denote the sides, we find that the Pythagorean theorem, applied to this triangle, is

$$(AC)^2 + (BC)^2 = (AB)^2.$$

Substituting the values for AC and BC, we have

$$5^2 + 12^2 = (AB)^2,$$
$$25 + 144 = (AB)^2,$$
$$169 = (AB)^2,$$
$$13 = AB.$$

We find the final value $AB = 13$ by taking the square root of both sides. Since lengths are in general considered positive, we shall use the positive square root.

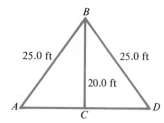

Figure 16–28

Example B   A pole is on level ground area and is perpendicular to the ground. Guy wires, which brace the pole on either side, are attached at the top of the pole. Each guy wire is 25.0 ft long and the pole is 20.0 ft high. How far are the grounded ends of the guy wires from each other? (See Fig. 16–28.)

From the figure we see that we are to find AD. In order to find AD we shall find AC, which in turn equals CD, and therefore $AD = 2AC$. From the Pythagorean theorem, we have $(AC)^2 + (BC)^2 = (AB)^2$. Substituting the known values of AB and BC, we have

$$(AC)^2 + (20.0)^2 = (25.0)^2,$$
$$(AC)^2 + 400 = 625,$$
$$(AC)^2 = 225,$$
$$AC = 15.0 \text{ ft.}$$

Therefore $AD = 30.0$ ft.

SIGNED NUMBER

① $(+4)+(-6)$

$+4-6=-2$

② $(+2)+(-9)+(-1)$

$+2-9-1=$

$+2-10=-8$

⑤ $(-5)-(+8)$

$-5-8=-13$

⑦ $(-3)-(-9)+(+4)$

$-3+9+4=$

$-3+13=+10$

⑨ $(-2)(-6)(+8)$

$12×+8=-96$

⑪ $(-36)÷(+9)$

$-36÷+9=-4$

⑬ $(+5)(+3)(+2)(-1)$

$+30×-1=-30$

⑮ $(-2)^2-(-1)^2$

$+4+1=+3$

(17) $\dfrac{(-5)(-6)}{+3} = \dfrac{+30}{+3} = +10$

(19) $\dfrac{(-1)(-5)(+45)}{(+9)(+5)(+1)} =$ $\qquad$ $+5 \times +45 = 225$

$\dfrac{+225}{+45} = +5$

(21) $(-2)(+4) - \dfrac{(-6)}{+2} - (-5)$

$-8 + (-3) + 5$

$-8 + 3 + 5 = +10$

(23) $-\dfrac{(-2)(-3)}{(-6)} + (-4)(+2) - \dfrac{(-8)}{(+4)}$

$-\dfrac{(+6)}{(-6)} + (-4)(+2) - \dfrac{(-8)}{+4}$

$+1 + (-8) - (-2)$

$+1 - 8 + 2$

$+3 - 8 = -5$

$2(x-4) - 5(x+1) =$

Find the general formula for the length of a diagonal of a square of side s Example C
(see Fig. 16–29).

From the statement of the problem, we know that we wish to find d in
terms of s. From the Pythagorean theroem, we have

$$d^2 = s^2 + s^2 = 2s^2, \qquad d = \sqrt{2s^2} = s\sqrt{2}.$$

The diagonal is therefore equal to the length of a side of the square times
$\sqrt{2}$.

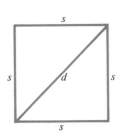

Figure 16–29

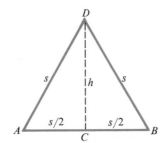

Figure 16–30

Find the general formula for the area of an equilateral triangle of side s Example D
in terms of s (see Fig. 16–30).

In order to find the area, we must first find the height h in terms of s.
Once this is done, we can find the area as one-half the product of h (in
terms of s) and s. Since the triangle is equilateral, the altitude divides AB
into two equal parts at C. This means that $AC = s/2$. Using the Pythagorean theorem, we have (using triangle ACD)

$$s^2 = h^2 + \left(\frac{s}{2}\right)^2,$$

$$h^2 = s^2 - \left(\frac{s}{2}\right)^2 = s^2 - \frac{s^2}{4} = \frac{3s^2}{4},$$

$$h = \frac{s}{2}\sqrt{3}.$$

This, in turn, means that the area A is found by

$$A = \tfrac{1}{2}(s)\left(\frac{s}{2}\sqrt{3}\right) = \frac{s^2\sqrt{3}}{4}.$$

Example E   A rope is attached to the top of a 22.0 ft pole. A man holding the rope
moves a certain distance from the pole and notes that there are 30.0 ft
of rope from the ground to the top of the pole. He then moves another
10.0 ft from the pole. How long must the rope be in order to reach the
ground at his feet? (See Fig. 16–31.)

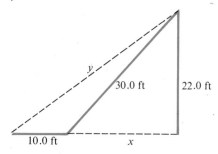

Figure 16–31

From the figure, we see that if we first find his original distance x
from the pole, we can then determine the required distance y. First
applying the Pythagorean theorem to the triangle with sides x, 22.0, and
30.0, we have

$$x^2 + (22.0)^2 = (30.0)^2,$$
$$x^2 + 484 = 900,$$
$$x^2 = 416,$$
$$x = 20.4 \text{ ft.}$$

Now we add 10.0 to 20.4 and apply the Pythagorean theorem to the
triangle with sides 30.4, 22.0, and y. This gives

$$(30.4)^2 + (22.0)^2 = y^2,$$
$$924 + 484 = y^2,$$
$$y^2 = 1408,$$
$$y = 37.5 \text{ ft,}$$

which means that the rope must be at least 37.5 ft long.

EXERCISES   In Exercises 1 through 18, use the Pythagorean theorem to solve for the unknown
side of the right triangle. In each case, c is the hypotenuse. If the answer is
not exact, round off to three digits.

	a	*b*	*c*		*a*	*b*	*c*
1.	3	4	?	**2.**	9	12	?
3.	8	15	?	**4.**	24	10	?
5.	6	?	10	**6.**	2	?	4
7.	5	?	7	**8.**	3	?	9
9.	?	12	16	**10.**	?	10	18
11.	?	15	32	**12.**	?	5	36
13.	56	?	82	**14.**	?	125	230
15.	5.62	40.5	?	**16.**	23.5	4.33	?
17.	0.709	?	2.76	**18.**	?	0.0863	0.145

In Exercises 19 through 32, set up the given problems and solve by use of the Pythagorean theorem.

19. What is the length of a diagonal of a square of side 4?

20. What is the area of an equilateral triangle of side 8?

21. The shortest side of a triangle whose angles are 30°, 60°, and 90° (the shortest side is one-half the hypotenuse) is 8.00 in. Find the perimeter and the area of the triangle.

22. A square is inscribed in a circle (all four vertices of the square touch the circle). Find the length of the side of the square if the radius of the circle is 8.00 in.

23. The hypotenuse of a right triangle is 24.0 ft, and one side is twice the other. Find the perimeter of the triangle.

24. How long is the side of an isosceles right triangle whose hypotenuse is *s*?

25. A man rows across a river that is 600 ft wide. The current carries him downstream 30.0 ft from the point directly across from his starting point. How far did he actually travel?

26. The guy wires bracing a telephone pole on a level ground area and the line along the ground between the grounded ends of the wires form an equilateral triangle whose side is 20.0 ft. Find the height of the point at which the wires are attached to the pole.

27. Figure 16–32 shows a roof truss. The rafters are 21.0 ft long, including a 1.5 ft overhang, and the height of the truss is 6.50 ft. Determine the length of the base of the truss.

21.0 ft

6.50 ft

Figure 16-32

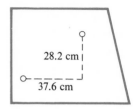

Figure 16-33

28. Figure 16–33 shows a metal plate with two small holes bored in it. What is the center-to-center distance between the holes?

29. In an alternating current circuit containing a resistor and a capacitor, the capacitor contributes an effective resistance to the current, called the *reactance*. The total effective resistance in the circuit, called the *impedance Z*, is related to the resistance R and reactance X in exactly the same way that the hypotenuse of a right triangle is related to the sides. Find Z for a circuit in which $R = 17.0$ ohms and $X = 8.25$ ohms.

30. The electric intensity at point P due to an electric charge Q is in the direction from the charge shown in Fig. 16–34. The electric intensity E at P is equivalent to the two intensities, E_h and E_v, which are horizontal and vertical, respectively. Given that $E = 35,000$ units and $E_h = 17,300$ units, find E_v.

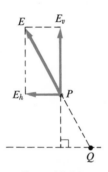

Figure 16-34

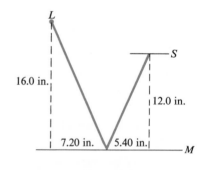

Figure 16-35

31. Two forces, F_1 and F_2, which are acting on an object are at right angles to each other. Their net resultant force F on the object is related to F_1 and F_2 in the same way that the hypotenuse of a right triangle is related to the sides. Given that $F_1 = 865$ lb and $F_2 = 255$ lb, find F.

32. A source of light L, a mirror M, and a screen S are situated as shown in Fig. 16–35. Find the distance a light ray travels in going from the source to the mirror and then to the screen.

33. A rectangular room is 12.0 ft long, 10.0 ft wide, and 8.00 ft high. What is the distance from a corner on the floor to the opposite corner at the ceiling?

34. Figure 16–36 shows four streets of a city. What is the indicated distance?

35. Figure 16–37 shows a quadrilateral tract of land. What is the length of the indicated side?

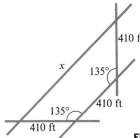

Figure 16–36

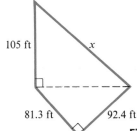

Figure 16–37

36. A ship 28.0 mi due west of a lighthouse travels 18.0 mi toward the lighthouse and then turns. After traveling another 14.0 mi in a straight line, it is due north of the lighthouse. How far, on a direct line, is the ship from its starting point?

16–3 SIMILAR FIGURES

In our discussion of geometry in the preceding sections, we studied several important basic properties of geometric figures, such as—among others— the concepts of perimeter and area that deal with the actual size of a figure. Also we saw that the length of the sides and the size of the angles, respectively, are of importance in defining the properties of figures. In this section we shall consider the properties of figures which are of the same basic shape, although not necessarily of the same size.

We shall devote most of the section to triangles. However, we shall first introduce the terminology that is appropriate for polygons in general. *Corresponding sides* and *corresponding angles*, one each from two different polygons, are those which have the same relative position with respect to the other parts of the polygon.

In Fig. 16–38 the quadrilaterals shown are lettered so that corresponding   Example A
angles have the same letters. That is, angles A and A' are corresponding angles, B and B' are corresponding angles, and so on. Also, the sides

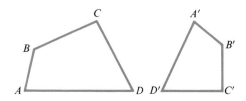

Figure 16-38

between these vertices are corresponding sides. That is, side AB corresponds to side $A'B'$, and so forth. Even though the quadrilaterals are not drawn so that corresponding parts are in the same position relative to the page, both have the largest angle between the shortest and second-shortest sides, with other relative positions the same.

If the corresponding angles of two polygons are equal and the corresponding sides are proportional, the polygons are said to be *similar*.

Example B   The two quadrilaterals in Fig. 16–38 have been drawn in such a manner that the corresponding angles are equal. Also, the corresponding sides are proportional, or

$$\frac{AB}{A'B'} = \frac{BC}{B'C'} = \frac{CD}{C'D'} = \frac{DA}{D'A'}.$$

If the corresponding angles of two polygons are equal and the corresponding sides are equal, then the two polygons are said to be *congruent*. As a result of this definition, the areas and perimeters of congruent figures are also equal.

Example C   One rectangle of width 2 in. and length 4 in. is congruent to any other rectangle of width 2 in. and length 4 in. However, it is similar to any rectangle of width 5 in. and length 10 in., since the ratios of corresponding sides are equal.

One equilateral triangle of side 6 in. is congruent to any other equilateral triangle of side 6 in., and is similar to any other equilateral triangle, regardless of the length of the side.

From our discussion, we can see that *similar triangles* have two basic properties. These are:

1) corresponding angles are equal, and
2) corresponding sides are proportional.

If we wish to show that two triangles are similar, we must show that one of these conditions is valid. (If one is valid, so is the other in the case of triangles.) Also, if we know that two triangles are similar, we use these properties to determine unknown parts of one triangle from known parts of the other. The following examples illustrate the use of the properties of similar triangles.

In Fig. 16–39, given triangle ABC, where DE is parallel to BC, show that triangle ADE is similar to triangle ABC.   **Example D**

We shall introduce a few symbols which are commonly used in geometry. The symbol $\triangle$ denotes "triangle," $\parallel$ denotes "parallel," and $\sim$ denotes "similar." Therefore the above statement can be rephrased as: Given $\triangle ABC$, where $DE \parallel BC$, show that $\triangle ADE \sim \triangle ABC$.

To show that the triangles are similar, we recall that corresponding angles of parallel lines cut by a transversal are equal. This means that $\angle ADE = \angle ABC$ and that $\angle AED = \angle ACB$. Since $\angle DAE$ is common to both triangles, we have one angle in each triangle equal to one angle in the other triangle. Since the corresponding angles are equal, $\triangle ADE \sim \triangle ABC$.

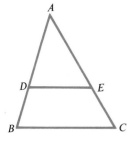

Figure 16–39

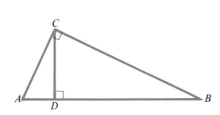

Figure 16–40

In Fig. 16–40, in right $\triangle ABC$, with right angle at C, $CD \perp AB$ ($\perp$ means "perpendicular"). Show that $\triangle ADC \sim \triangle CDB$.   **Example E**

First, both triangles contain a right angle. That is, $\angle CDA = \angle CDB$. Since the sum of the angles in a triangle is 180°, the sum of the other two angles in $\triangle ADC$ is 90°, or $\angle CAD + \angle ACD = 90°$. Also, angles ACD and DCB are complementary, which means that $\angle ACD + \angle DCB = 90°$. These two equations can be written as

$$\angle CAD = 90° - \angle ACD, \qquad \angle DCB = 90° - \angle ACD.$$

Since the right-hand sides of these equations are equal, we conclude that $\angle CAD = \angle DCB$. We have now shown that two angles are respectively equal in the two triangles. Since, in any triangle, the sum of the angles is 180°, the remaining angles must also be equal. Therefore, $\angle ACD = \angle CBD$. The triangles are therefore similar. We do note, however, that the corresponding sides appear in different positions with respect to the page. This is indicated by writing the ratio of corresponding sides as

$$\frac{AD}{DC} = \frac{DC}{DB} = \frac{AC}{CB},$$

where the sides of $\triangle ADC$ are written in the numerators, and the corresponding sides of $\triangle CDB$ are written as denominators.

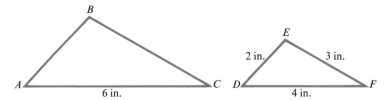

Figure 16–41

Example F   In Fig. 16–41, $\triangle ABC \sim \triangle DEF$, where $AC = 6$ in., $DF = 4$ in., $FE = 3$ in., and $ED = 2$ in. Find the lengths of sides CB and AB.

Since the triangles are similar, the corresponding sides are proportional. This means that

$$\frac{AC}{DF} = \frac{CB}{FE} = \frac{BA}{ED}.$$

Substituting the known values, we have

$$\frac{6}{4} = \frac{CB}{3} = \frac{BA}{2}.$$

Since the middle and right ratios are both equal to $\frac{6}{4}$, we can solve for the unknown side each contains. Therefore

$$\frac{CB}{3} = \frac{6}{4}, \qquad CB = \frac{6(3)}{4} = \tfrac{9}{2} \text{ in.}$$

$$\frac{BA}{2} = \frac{6}{4}, \qquad BA = \frac{6(2)}{4} = 3 \text{ in.}$$

On level ground, a tree casts a shadow 24 ft long. At the same time, a   **Example G**
pole 4.0 ft high casts a shadow 3.0 ft long. How high is the tree? See
Fig. 16–42.

The rays of the sun are essentially parallel. Hence the two triangles
indicated in Fig. 16–42 are similar, since each has a right angle, and the
angles at the tops are equal. The lengths of the hypotenuses are of no
importance in this problem. We shall therefore use only the other sides
in stating the ratios of corresponding sides. Thus

$$\frac{h}{4.0} = \frac{24}{3.0}, \qquad h = 32 \text{ ft.}$$

We conclude that the tree is 32 ft high.

One of the most practical uses of similar figures is that of *scale
drawings*. Maps, charts, blueprints, and most drawings which appear in
books are familiar examples of scale drawings. Actually there have been
numerous scale drawings used in this book in the previous sections.

In any scale drawing, all distances are drawn a certain ratio of the
distances they represent, and all angles equal the angles they represent.
Consider the following example.

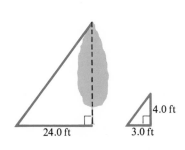

Figure 16–42

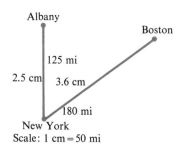

Figure 16–43

A man who is drawing a map of the area indicated in Fig. 16–43 uses a   **Example H**
scale of 1 cm = 50 mi. Therefore, if the actual distance between Albany
and New York is 125 mi, the distance *d* between these cities on the map
would be found by use of the proportion

$$\frac{125}{50} = \frac{d}{1},$$

which, when solved for d, gives

$$d = 2.5 \text{ cm.}$$

Also, if we measure the distance between New York and Boston on the map to be 3.6 cm, we can find the actual distance x between these cities by the proportion

$$\frac{x}{50} = \frac{3.6}{1},$$

which tells us that $x = 180$ mi (see Fig. 16–43).

In Exercises 1 through 6, determine whether or not the given figures are (1) similar, and (2) congruent. Angles which are equal are marked in the same way, and so are sides which are equal. Unless parts are actually marked in the same way, do not assume that they are equal.

1. The quadrilaterals in Fig. 16–44   **2.** The quadrilaterals in Fig. 16–45

3. The triangles in Fig. 16–46   **4.** The triangles in Fig. 16–47

5. The quadrilaterals in Fig. 16–48   **6.** The trapezoids in Fig. 16–49

In Exercises 7 through 12, solve for the unknown side by use of an appropriate proportion. All line segments are straight.

7. In Fig. 16–50, $KM = 6$, $MN = 9$, and $MO = 12$. Find LM.

8. In Fig. 16–51, $BD = 5$, $BE = 8$, and $BA = 10$. Find BC.

9. In Fig. 16–52, $BK = 8$, $HT = 4$, and $HD = 5$. Find BA.

10. In Fig. 16–53(a), $LK = 6$ and $KO = 8$. In Fig. 16–53(b), $L'K' = 8$. Find $K'O'$ if the pentagons are similar.

11. In Fig. 16–54, $AB = 3$, $BF = 8$, and $ED = 3$. Find EC.

12. In Fig. 16–55, $AD = 4$, and $DB = 12$. Find CD.

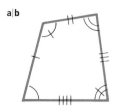
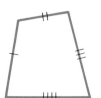
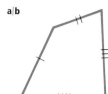

Figure 16–44   Figure 16–45

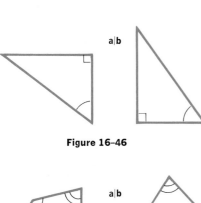

Figure 16–46

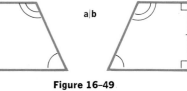

Figure 16–47

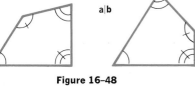

Figure 16–48

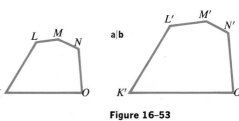

Figure 16–49

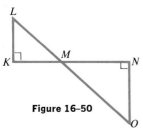

Figure 16–50

Figure 16–51

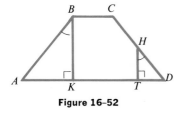

Figure 16–52

Figure 16–53

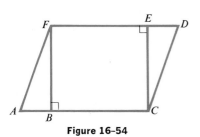

Figure 16–54

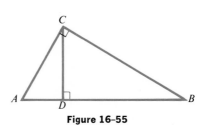

Figure 16–55

In Exercises 13 through 16, construct appropriate figures.

13. Draw △*ABC* such that *AB* ⊥ *BC* and ∠*ACB* = ∠*CAB*.

14. Draw △*ABC* with *D* on *AB* and *E* on *AC* such that *DE* ∥ *BC*.

15. Draw quadrilateral *ABCD* such that *AB* ⊥ *BC*, *AB* ∥ *CD*, and ∠*DAB* is acute.

16. Draw quadrilateral *ABCD* such that *AB* ∥ *CD*, *AD* ∥ *BC*, and *DC* ⊥ *CB*.

In Exercises 17 and 18, find the required values.

17. Two triangles are similar, and the sides of the larger triangle are 3.0 in., 5.0 in., and 6.0 in., and the shortest side of the other triangle is 2.0 in. Find the remaining sides of the smaller triangle.

18. Two triangles are similar. The angles of the smaller triangle are 50°, 100°, and 30°, and the sides of the smaller triangle are 7.00 in., 9.00 in., and 4.57 in. The longest side of the larger triangle is 15.0 in. Find the other two sides and the three angles of the larger triangle.

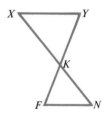

Figure 16–56

In Exercises 19 and 20, show that the required triangles are similar.

19. In Fig. 16–56, show that △*XYK* ~ △*NFK*. (*XY*∥*FN*)

20. In Fig. 16–55, show that △*ACB* ~ △*ADC*.

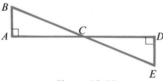

Figure 16–57

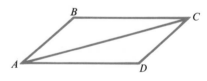

Figure 16–58

In Exercises 21 and 22, find the required values.

21. In Fig. 16–57, △*ABC* ≅ △*EDC* (≅ means "congruent"). If *AD* = 16 in., how long is *AC*?

22. In Fig. 16–58, △*ABC* ≅ △*ADC*. If ∠*CAD* = 40°, how many degrees are there in ∠*CAB* + ∠*ABC*?

In Exercises 23 through 34, solve the given problems.

23. A man casts a shadow 5.0 ft long. His son casts a shadow 3.0 ft long. If the son is 4.0 ft tall, how tall is the father?

24. The shadow of a pole standing 4.0 ft from a street light is 2.0 ft long. The pole is 5.0 ft tall. How high is the street light?

25. A certain house blueprint has a scale of $1\frac{1}{4}$ in. = 10 ft. The living room is 18 ft long. What distance on the blueprint represents this length?

26. On a map, 12 cm = 100 mi. What is the distance between two cities if the distance between them on the map is 7.5 cm?

27. A 4.0 ft wall stands 2.0 ft from a building. The ends of a straight pole touch the building and the ground 6.0 ft from the wall. A point on the pole touches the wall's top. How high on the building does the pole touch?

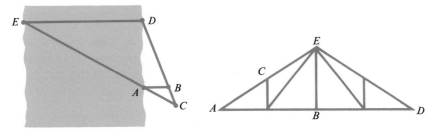

Figure 16–59   Figure 16–60

28. To find the width ED of a river, a surveyor places markers at A, B, C, and D (see Fig. 16–59). He places them so that $AB \parallel ED$, $BC = 50.0$ ft, $DC = 300$ ft, and $AB = 80.0$ ft. How wide is the river?

29. A 30.0-ft pole on level ground is supported by two 60.0-ft guy wires attached at its top. The guy wires are on opposite sides of the pole. How far is it between the grounded ends of the wires?

30. Town B is due east of town A, and town E is due east of town D. The direct routes from A to E and B to D cross at town C. The route DC is 15 mi, DB is 45 mi, and DE is 24 mi. How far is it from town A to town B?

31. Figure 16–60 shows a roof truss. Assume that all parts that appear equal *are* equal, and that $AC = 6.72$ ft and $BE = 6.70$ ft. Find the base of the truss AD.

32. Using an appropriate scale, represent a proton (as a dot), an electron (as a dot) which is 10^{-12} cm from the proton, a second electron which is 3×10^{-12} cm from the proton, and a third electron which is 10^{-10} cm from the electron.

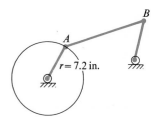

Figure 16–61

33. Figure 16–61 shows a crank-lever mechanism. From the figure determine the scale and then determine the length AB.

34. A photograph 6.00 in. by 9.00 in. is enlarged so that the length of the enlargement is 15.0 in. Find the ratio of the area of the enlargement to that of the original photograph.

16–4 SOME IMPORTANT FORMULAS FROM SOLID GEOMETRY

Except for a brief mention of rectangular solids in Chapter 7, we have restricted our attention to plane geometry. There are, however, a number of important geometric solid figures. It is the purpose of this section to briefly discuss the determination of surface area and volume of the most important of these figures.

We defined the volume of a rectangular solid of length l, width w, and height h as $V = lwh$. If we call the lower base of the solid which is of length l and width w the *base* of the solid, we can state that the volume is

$$V = Bh, \qquad \qquad \text{16–2}$$

where B is the area of the base. The reason for this change of form of the formula for the volume is that Eq. (16–2) can be used to find the volume of any solid which has parallel bases and vertical sides. Solids of this kind are called *prisms*.

Example A The prism shown in Fig. 16–62 has a regular hexagon as a base. If we are able to determine the area of the hexagon, we can use Eq. (16–2) to find the volume. If, for example $B = 12 \text{ in}^2$ and $h = 5.0$ in., the volume is

$$V = (12)(5.0) = 60 \text{ in}^3.$$

We can use Eq. (16–2) as a basis for determining the volume of a *right circular cylinder* (Fig. 16–63). Since the base of the cylinder is a circle, and the area of a circle is $A = \pi r^2$, we conclude that $B = \pi r^2$.

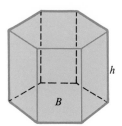

Figure 16-62

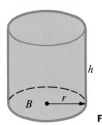

Figure 16-63

This means that the volume of a right circular cylinder is

$$V = \pi r^2 h,$$ 16-3

where r is the radius of the base and h is the altitude.

If the radius of the base of a right circular cylinder is 6.00 in. and the   Example B
height is 4.00 in., the volume of the right circular cylinder is

$$V = \pi(6.00)^2(4.00) = (3.14)(36.0)(4.00) = 452 \text{ in}^3.$$

The surface area of a rectangular solid is the total area of the six faces. Or we can say that it is the sum of the areas of the bases (top and bottom) and the area of the vertical sides. In just the same way we can find the surface area of the right circular cylinder. The total surface area is the sum of the areas of the bases and curved portion of the surface which is known as the *lateral surface area*. Since each base is a circle, the sum of the areas of the bases is $2\pi r^2$. We can see that the lateral surface area is the circumference times the altitude, or $(2\pi r)(h)$. Therefore the total surface area of the right circular cylinder is

$$A = 2\pi r^2 + 2\pi rh.$$ 16-4

The surface area of the cylinder of Example B, where $r = 6.00$ in. and   Example C
$h = 4.00$ in., is

$$A = 2\pi(6.00)^2 + 2\pi(6.00)(4.00)$$
$$= (6.28)(36.0) + (6.28)(24.0) = (6.28)(60.0)$$
$$= 377 \text{ in}^2.$$

The remaining formulas which we present are of a form similar to those already seen. However, due to the type of figures, we shall not attempt to derive the formulas.

The volume of the *pyramid* (Fig. 16–64) and the volume of the *right circular cone* (Fig. 16–65) can be found by use of the formula

$$V = \tfrac{1}{3}Bh,$$ 16–5

where B is the area of the base and h is the altitude. The base of the pyramid may be any polygon. The base of the cone is a circle, which means that $B = \pi r^2$. For the cone, therefore, we may write

$$V = \tfrac{1}{3}\pi r^2 h.$$ 16–6

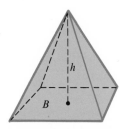

Figure 16–64

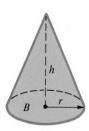

Figure 16–65

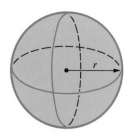

Figure 16–66

Example D   The volume of a pyramid whose base is a square of side 4.0 in. and whose altitude is 9.0 in. is

$$V = \tfrac{1}{3}(4.0)^2(9.0) = 48 \text{ in}^3.$$

Here the area of the base is seen to be $(4.0)^2 = 16 \text{ in}^2$.

If the base of the pyramid is a right triangle of base 4.0 in. and height 7.0 in., the base area B is $\tfrac{1}{2}(4.0)(7.0) = 14 \text{ in}^2$. If the altitude were again 9.0 in., the volume would be

$$V = \tfrac{1}{3}(14)(9.0) = 42 \text{ in}^3.$$

The volume of a right circular cone whose base radius is 4.00 in. and whose altitude is 9.00 in. is

$$V = \tfrac{1}{3}\pi(4.00)^2(9.00) = 151 \text{ in}^3.$$

The final solid figure we shall consider is the *sphere* (Fig. 16–66). The volume of the sphere is

$$V = \tfrac{4}{3}\pi r^3$$ 16–7

and the surface area of the sphere is

$$A = 4\pi r^2,$$ **16-8**

where r is the radius of the sphere.

The radius of the earth (which is approximately a sphere) is about 3960 mi.   Example E
The volume of the earth is

$$V = \tfrac{4}{3}\pi(3960)^3 = 2.60 \times 10^{11} \text{ mi}^3.$$

The area of the earth is

$$A = 4\pi(3960)^2 = 1.97 \times 10^8 \text{ mi}^2.$$

In Exercises 1 through 10, find the volume of the indicated figure for the given   EXERCISES
values.

1. Prism, square base of side 2.0 ft, altitude 5.0 ft

2. Prism, trapezoidal base (bases 4.0 in. and 6.0 in. and height 3.0 in.), altitude 6.0 in.

3. Cylinder, radius of base 7.00 in., altitude 6.00 in.

4. Cylinder, diameter of base 6.36 ft, altitude 18.0 in.

5. Pyramid, rectangular base 12.5 in. by 8.75 in, altitude 4.20 in.

6. Pyramid, equilateral triangular base of side 3.00 in., altitude 4.25 in.

7. Cone, radius of base 2.66 ft, altitude 1.22 yd

8. Cone, diameter of base 16.3 in., altitude 18.4 in.

9. Sphere, radius 5.48 ft

10. Sphere, diameter 15.7 yd

In Exercises 11 through 16, find the total surface area of the indicated figure
for the given values.

11. Prism, rectangular base 4.00 in. by 8.00 in., altitude 6.00 in.

12. Prism, parallelogram base (base 16.0 in., height 4.25 in., perimeter 42.0 in.), altitude 6.45 in.

13. Cylinder, radius of base 8.58 in., altitude 1.38 ft

14. Cylinder, diameter of base 12.5 ft, altitude 4.60 ft

15. Sphere, radius 16.0 ft

16. Sphere, diameter 15.3 in.

In Exercises 17 through 20, derive the required formula.

17. The total surface area of a hemispherical volume of radius r. (Curved surface and flat surface.)

18. The total surface area of a volume formed by placing a hemisphere of radius r on a cylinder of radius r and altitude h.

19. The volume formed by placing a hemisphere of radius r on a cone of radius r and altitude h.

20. The volume formed by placing a pyramid of square base (edge e) and altitude h on a cube of edge e.

In Exercises 21 through 32, solve the given problems.

21. When built, the Great Pyramid of Egypt had a square base, approximately 250 yd on a side. Its height was about 160 yd. What was its volume?

22. The circumference of a basketball is about 29.8 in. What is its volume?

23. A conical cistern 10.0 ft high has a radius at the top of 6.00 ft. Water weighs 62.4 lb/ft^3. How many pounds of water does the cistern hold?

24. A cylindrical grain storage container 82.0 ft high has a radius of 24.3 ft. One bushel of grain occupies about 1.24 ft^3. How many bushels can be stored in the container?

25. A swimming pool is 50.0 ft wide, 80.0 ft long, 3.00 ft deep at one end, and 8.00 ft deep at the other end. How many cubic feet of water will it hold? (Assume that the slope on the bottom is constant.)

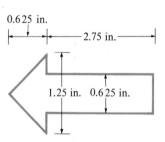

Figure 16–67

26. A certain type of rivet is shaped as shown in Fig. 16–67 (a conical part on a cylindrical part). Find the volume of the rivet shown.

27. At \$0.25 per yd^2, how much would it cost to paint the outside of the storage container of Exercise 24? (The bottom is not to be painted.)

28. The diameter of the moon is about 2160 mi. What is the surface area of the moon? Compare the radius of the moon with that of the earth, and then compare the areas.

29. The base of a glass prism is an equilateral triangle, 1.00 in. on a side. If the prism is 4.00 in. long, what is the total surface area?

30. An oil storage tank is in the shape of hemispheres on each end of a cylinder. The total length of the tank is 45.0 ft, and the diameter of the cylinder (or sphere) is 12.5 ft. What is the volume, in gallons, of the tank? ($1 \text{ ft}^3 = 7.48$ gal.)

31. How much does a wire 0.250 in. in diameter weigh if it is 1.00 mi long? Assume that the density of the wire is 550 lb/ft^3.

32. A tent has the shape of a pyramid on a square base. The side of the square is 9.25 ft and the height of the pyramid is 10.5 ft. What is the area of the canvas needed for the four sides and the floor?

16–5 REVIEW EXERCISES

In Exercises 1 through 8, use Fig. 16–68 and identify all the listed types of angles. ($FD \parallel AC$)

1. Pairs of alternate interior angles   **2.** Pairs of corresponding angles

3. Pairs of vertical angles   **4.** Right angles

5. Acute angles   **6.** Obtuse angles

7. Adjacent complementary angles   **8.** Adjacent supplementary angles

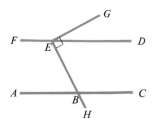

Figure 16–68

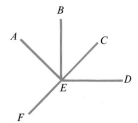

Figure 16–69

In Exercises 9 through 12, use Fig. 16–69 and determine the indicated angles. Given: $BE \perp DE$, $AE \perp CF$, $\angle CED = 35°$.

9. $\angle BEC$ **10.** $\angle AEB$ **11.** $\angle AED$ **12.** $\angle DEF$

In Exercises 13 through 16, a, b, and c are the sides of right triangles, where c is the hypotenuse. Determine the required sides.

	a	b	c		a	b	c
13.	8	?	17	**15.**	36	?	60
14.	4	9	?	**16.**	?	5	19

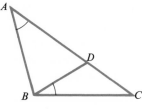

Figure 16-70

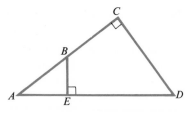

Figure 16-71

In Exercises 17 and 18, solve for the unknown side of the given triangle by use of an appropriate proportion.

17. In Fig. 16–70, $AC = 12$, $BC = 8$, $BD = 5$. Find AB.

18. In Fig. 16–71, $AB = 4$, $BC = 4$, $CD = 6$. Find BE.

In Exercises 19 and 20, use Fig. 16–72 and find the indicated sides. Given: BF is a diameter, CE is tangent at D, $AB = 2.0$ in, $BC = 4.0$ in., $AE = 18.0$ in. ($BF \parallel CE$)

19. $BF = $?   **20.** $CE = $?

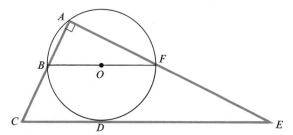

Figure 16-72

In Exercises 21 through 28, find the required quantities.

21. The volume of a prism of base area 12 ft^2 and altitude 6.0 ft

22. The volume of a pyramid of base area 12 ft^2 and altitude 6.0 ft

23. The volume of a right circular cylinder of base radius 7.32 ft and altitude 3.85 ft

24. The volume of a right circular cone of base diameter 22.0 ft and altitude 8.17 ft

25. The lateral surface area of the cylinder of Exercise 23

26. The radius of a sphere whose volume is $9\pi/2$

27. The surface area of a sphere whose radius is $1/\sqrt{\pi}$

28. The volume of a regular tetrahedron (four faces are all equilateral triangles) of edge 1.25 ft

In Exercises 29 through 53, solve the given problems.

29. The hypotenuse of a right triangle is 24.0 ft, and one side is twice the other. Find the perimeter of the triangle.

30. The hypotenuse of a right triangle is 3.00 ft longer than one of the sides, which in turn is 5.00 ft longer than the other side. How long are the sides and the hypotenuse?

31. One of the acute angles of a right triangle is three times the other. How many degrees are there in each angle?

32. In a given triangle, the second angle is three times the first and the third angle is twice the first. How many degrees are there in each angle?

33. The areas of a triangle and a square are equal. The base of the triangle is 4.0 in. and its altitude is 9.0 in. What is the side of the square?

34. Is it possible that sides of 9, 40, and 41 could be the sides of a right triangle?

35. If two sides and an angle of one triangle are equal respectively to two sides and an angle of another triangle, the triangles are congruent. Is this statement always true?

36. Determine a general formula for the length of the diagonal of a cube (from one corner to the opposite corner).

37. In a certain pulley system, the center of pulley A is 18.0 in. above and 14.5 in. to the right of the center of pulley B. How far is it between the centers of the pulleys?

38. The base of a 20.0 ft ladder is 6.25 ft from the base of a vertical wall. How far up on the wall does the ladder touch?

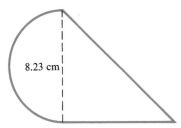

8.23 cm

Figure 16–73

39. A loop of wire is in the shape shown in Fig. 16–73 (the two geometric figures are a semicircle and an isosceles right triangle). Find the length of the wire loop.

40. The impedance of a certain alternating current circuit is 16.5 ohms and the capacitive reactance is 3.75 ohms. Find the resistance in the circuit. (See Exercise 29 of Section 16–2.)

41. A tree casts a shadow of 12 ft and the distance from the end of the shadow to the top of the tree is 13 ft. How high is the tree?

42. A tree and a telephone pole cast shadows as shown in Fig. 16–74. Find the height of the telephone pole.

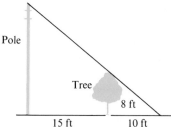

Figure 16–74

43. The diameter of the sun is 860,000 mi, the diameter of the earth is 7920 mi, and the distance from the earth to the sun (center to center) is 93,000,000 mi. What is the distance from the center of the earth to the end of the shadow due to the rays from the sun?

44. Light is reflected from a mirror so that the angle of incidence i (see Fig. 16–75) equals the angle of reflection r. Suppose that a light source is 6.38 in. from a mirror, and a particular ray of light strikes the mirror at the point shown. How far is the screen S from the mirror?

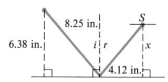

Figure 16–75

45. A drafting student is making a drawing with a scale of $2\frac{3}{4}$ in. $=$ 5 ft. What distance on his drawing should be used to represent 18 ft 3 in.?

46. On the blueprint of a certain building, a certain hallway is 38.5 in. long. The scale is $1\frac{1}{8}$ in. $=$ 6 ft. How long is the hallway?

47. The circumference of a cylindrical water tank is 152 ft, and its height is 48.5 ft. How many gallons of water can it hold? (1 ft^3 $=$ 7.48 gal.)

48. What is the volume of darkness of the earth's shadow? (Assume that it is a right circular cone with the base through the center of the earth; see Exercise 43.) Compare this with the volume of the earth.

49. How many in^3 of metal are there in a length of pipe 15.5 ft long when the inside diameter is 8.00 in. and the metal is 0.500 in. thick?

50. A concrete base for a piece of machinery is in the shape of a *frustrum* of a pyramid (a frustrum is formed by cutting off the top by a plane parallel to the base). The top of the frustrum is a rectangle 18.0 ft by 12.5 ft. The length of the base is 24.0 ft and the depth of the frustrum is 3.25 ft. How many cubic feet of concrete were used in making the base?

51. A wedge is in the shape of a prism with a right triangular base. The base has a width of 4.00 in. and a length of 14.5 in. What is the total surface area of the wedge, given that its altitude is 5.38 in.?

52. How many square inches of material are used to make a tennis ball whose circumference is 8.25 in.?

53. A hot water tank is the shape of a right circular cylinder surmounted by a hemisphere. The total height of the tank is 6.75 ft and the diameter of the base is 2.50 ft. How many gallons does the tank contain? (See Exercise 47.)

17 Introduction to Trigonometry

Many distances that are either extremely difficult or actually impossible to measure directly can be determined by means of *indirect measurement*. Examples of such distances are the widths of rivers, heights of mountains, and distances from the earth to other points in the universe. The basic geometric figure used in indirect measurement is the triangle. This chapter is devoted to a brief introduction to the subject of *trigonometry*, the literal meaning of which is "triangle measurement."

In developing the basic methods of trigonometry, we use the properties of similar triangles. In particular, we use the property that corresponding sides of similar right triangles are proportional.

Since the corresponding sides of similar triangles are proportional, it is also true that the ratio of one side to another in any given triangle is the same as the ratio of the corresponding sides in a triangle which is similar.

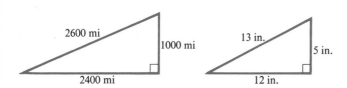

Figure 17–1

The two right triangles in Fig. 17–1 are similar, although the distances   Example A
represented are of very different magnitudes. Since they are similar, we know that

$$\frac{13}{2600} = \frac{5}{1000}.$$

However, we can also see that the ratio of the shortest side to the hypotenuse is the same in each. That is,

$$\frac{5}{13} = \frac{1000}{2600}.$$

Ratios of other pairs of corresponding sides can also be set up and shown to be equal.

We shall now define the trigonometric ratios. These definitions are based on ratios of sides of similar right triangles and the property that corresponding angles of similar triangles are equal.

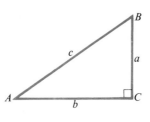

Figure 17–2

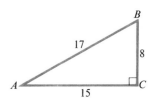

Figure 17–3

In Fig. 17–2, we define the

$$\text{sine of angle } A = \frac{\text{side opposite angle } A}{\text{hypotenuse}},$$

$$\text{cosine of angle } A = \frac{\text{side adjacent to angle } A}{\text{hypotenuse}},$$

$$\text{tangent of angle } A = \frac{\text{side opposite angle } A}{\text{side adjacent to angle } A}.$$

For convenience of notation, the names of the ratios are usually abbreviated, and the sides are designated by the letters shown in Fig. 17–2. Therefore we write

$$\sin A = \frac{a}{c}, \qquad \cos A = \frac{b}{c}, \qquad \tan A = \frac{a}{b}. \qquad \text{17–1}$$

The definitions given above can be used to find the trigonometric ratios of any acute angle in a right triangle. That is,

$$\sin B = \frac{\text{side opposite angle } B}{\text{hypotenuse}} = \frac{b}{c}$$

and

$$\cos B = \frac{a}{c}, \qquad \tan B = \frac{b}{a}.$$

Example B   In the triangle shown in Fig. 17–3, we have

$$\sin A = \tfrac{8}{17}, \qquad \cos A = \tfrac{15}{17}, \qquad \tan A = \tfrac{8}{15},$$
$$\sin B = \tfrac{15}{17}, \qquad \cos B = \tfrac{8}{17}, \qquad \tan B = \tfrac{15}{8}.$$

In a given right triangle, if two of the sides are known, the third may be found by use of the Pythagorean theorem. Then, in turn, the trigonometric ratios may be found for the angles. The following example illustrates the method.

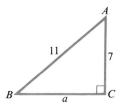

Figure 17-4

In Fig. 17–4, one side and the hypotenuse of the triangle are given. To find the other side, a, we use the Pythagorean theorem, which gives

Example C

$$a = \sqrt{11^2 - 7^2} = \sqrt{121 - 49} = \sqrt{72} = 8.485.$$

We are now in a position to find any of the ratios associated with the triangle. For example,

$$\sin A = \frac{8.485}{11} = 0.771 \quad \text{and} \quad \tan B = \frac{7}{8.485} = 0.825.$$

In any right triangle there are in all six possible ratios which may be set up. So far, we have named three of them. The others are called the *cotangent*, *secant*, and *cosecant*. Referring to Fig. 17–2 and using the abbreviations for these ratios, we make the following definitions:

$$\cot A = \frac{b}{a}, \quad \sec A = \frac{c}{b}, \quad \csc A = \frac{c}{a}. \qquad \textbf{17-2}$$

Using the general definitions implied in Eqs. (17–2), we can find the trigonometric ratios for any acute angle in a right triangle.

Referring to Fig. 17–3, we have

Example D

$$\cot A = \tfrac{15}{8}, \quad \sec A = \tfrac{17}{15}, \quad \csc A = \tfrac{17}{8},$$
$$\cot B = \tfrac{8}{15}, \quad \sec B = \tfrac{17}{8}, \quad \csc B = \tfrac{17}{15}.$$

If one of the trigonometric ratios for a given angle is known, it is possible to determine the values of the other five. The following example illustrates how this may be done.

If we know that the sine of an angle is $\tfrac{2}{3}$, we know that the ratio of the side opposite that angle to the hypotenuse is 2 to 3. Therefore, for purposes of finding the other ratios, we may assume that the lengths of these two sides are 2 units and 3 units. For convenience, we may draw a triangle with these two sides, as shown in Fig. 17–5. The third side may

Example E

be found by use of the Pythagorean theorem. Therefore, calling this side x, we have

$$x = \sqrt{3^2 - 2^2} = \sqrt{5}.$$

We now determine the other trigonometric ratios of the angle, A, whose sine $\frac{2}{3}$ is given. They are

$$\cos A = \frac{\sqrt{5}}{3},$$

$$\tan A = \frac{2}{\sqrt{5}} = \frac{2\sqrt{5}}{5}, \qquad \cot A = \frac{\sqrt{5}}{2},$$

$$\sec A = \frac{3}{\sqrt{5}} = \frac{3\sqrt{5}}{5}, \qquad \csc A = \frac{3}{2}.$$

Decimal equivalents can also be easily determined.

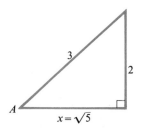

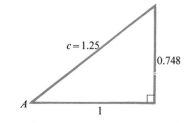

Figure 17-5   **Figure 17-6**

Example F Given that $\tan A = 0.748$, we know that the ratio of the side opposite angle A to the side adjacent to it is 0.748. This means that we may assume a triangle of sides 0.748 and 1, as shown in Fig. 17-6. Using the Pythagorean theorem to find the hypotenuse c, we have

$$c = \sqrt{1^2 + 0.748^2} = \sqrt{1.560} = 1.25.$$

Therefore the other trigonometric ratios for this angle are

$$\sin A = \frac{0.748}{1.25} = 0.598, \qquad \cos A = \frac{1}{1.25} = 0.800,$$

$$\cot A = \frac{1}{0.748} = 1.34, \qquad \sec A = \frac{1.25}{1} = 1.25,$$

$$\csc A = \frac{1.25}{0.748} = 1.67.$$

In Exercises 1 through 4, find the indicated trigonometric ratios from Fig. 17–7. **EXERCISES**

1. sin A, tan A, cos B

2. cos A, sin B, cot A

3. cot B, sec A, tan B

4. sec B csc A, csc B

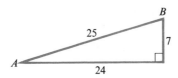

Figure 17-7

In Exercises 5 through 8, find the indicated trigonometric ratios from Fig. 17–8.

5. sin A, sec B, cot A

6. csc A, sin B, cot B·

7. tan A, cos B, sec A

8. tan B, csc B, cos A

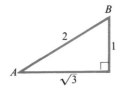

Figure 17-8

In Exercises 9 through 12, find the indicated trigonometric ratios from Fig. 17–9.

9. cos A, tan A, csc B

10. sin B, sec A, cot B

11. sin A, cos B, cot A

12. csc A, tan B, sec B

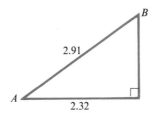

Figure 17-9

In Exercises 13 through 20, determine the indicated trigonometric ratios. The listed sides are those shown in Fig. 17–10.

13. $a = 3$, $b = 4$. Find sin A and tan B.

14. $a = 5$, $c = 13$. Find cos A and csc B.

15. $b = 9$, $c = 41$. Find cot A and cos B.

16. $a = 8$, $c = 19$. Find sin A and sec B.

17. $a = 1$, $b = 1$. Find tan A and sin B.

18. $a = 2$, $c = 4$. Find sec A and tan B.

19. $b = 14$, $c = 23$. Find csc A and cos B.

20. $a = 132$, $b = 75$. Find cos A and cot B.

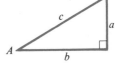

Figure 17-10

In Exercises 21 through 26, using the given trigonometric ratios, find the indicated trigonometric ratios.

21. tan $A = 1$. Find sin A.

22. sin $A = \frac{1}{2}$. Find cos A.

23. cos $A = 0.7$. Find csc A.

24. sec $A = 1.6$. Find sin A.

25. cot $A = 0.563$. Find cos A.

26. csc $A = 2.64$. Find tan A.

In Exercises 27 through 32, answer the given questions.

27. State the definitions of the cotangent, secant, and cosecant in terms of adjacent side, opposite side, and hypotenuse.

28. From the definitions of the trigonometric ratios, it can be seen that csc A is the reciprocal of sin A. What ratio is the reciprocal of cos A? of cot A?

29. From the definitions of the trigonometric ratios, it can be seen that sin $A =$ cos B. What ratio associated with angle B equals tan A? csc A?

30. Draw three right triangles: (1) with sides 3 in., 4 in., and 5 in., (2) with sides 6 in., 8 in., and 10 in., (3) with sides 4.5 in., 6.0 in., and 7.5 in. For each triangle determine the sine and tangent of the smallest angle. What is the relationship of the three triangles? What is true of the trigonometric ratios found?

17-2 VALUES OF THE TRIGONOMETRIC RATIOS

In the first section of this chapter we defined the trigonometric ratios of an angle, but we did not mention the size of the angle. For an angle of a specified number of degrees, there is a specific set of values of trigonometric ratios. The actual method used to determine these values for the purpose of setting up tables requires the use of more advanced mathematics than we can discuss here. However, by using certain basic geometric properties we can establish the values of the trigonometric ratios for certain angles.

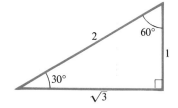

Figure 17-11

A basic geometric fact is that in a 30°-60°-90° triangle, the side opposite the 30° angle is one-half the hypotenuse (see Fig. 17-11). We can easily verify this statement by referring to the equilateral triangle shown in Fig. 16-30, which has been divided into two smaller congruent triangles by the altitude. Each of the smaller triangles has angles of 30° (at top), 60°, and 90°.

In Fig. 17-11, the hypotenuse has been given the value 2, the side opposite the 30° angle has been given the value 1, and from the Pythagorean theorem we determine that the third side has the value $\sqrt{3}$. Therefore, for the 30° angle and the 60° angle, the trigonometric ratios may be established as shown in the table below.

Angle	sin	cos	tan	cot	sec	csc
30°	1/2	$\sqrt{3}/2$	$\sqrt{3}/3$	$\sqrt{3}$	$2\sqrt{3}/3$	2
60°	$\sqrt{3}/2$	1/2	$\sqrt{3}$	$\sqrt{3}/3$	2	$2\sqrt{3}/3$

The following example illustrates the use of another geometric property to establish the values of the trigonometric ratios of 45°.

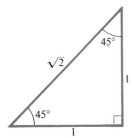

Figure 17–12

To find the trigonometric ratios for 45°, we construct an isosceles right triangle, as shown in Fig. 17–12. Since the triangle is isosceles, both acute angles are 45°, and the legs are equal. Therefore each is given the value 1. From the Pythagorean theorem, we find that the hypotenuse is $\sqrt{2}$. Therefore we have   **Example A**

$$\sin 45° = \sqrt{2}/2, \qquad \cos 45° = \sqrt{2}/2, \qquad \tan 45° = 1,$$
$$\cot 45° = 1, \qquad \sec 45° = \sqrt{2}, \qquad \csc 45° = \sqrt{2}.$$

Combining the values from the above table for 30° and 60°, and the values from Example A for 45°, we can set up the following short table of values of the trigonometric ratios (in decimal form).

Angle	sin	cos	tan	cot	sec	csc
30°	0.500	0.866	0.577	1.732	1.155	2.000
45°	0.707	0.707	1.000	1.000	1.414	1.414
60°	0.866	0.500	1.732	0.577	2.000	1.155

A more complete table, showing the values of the trigonometric ratios for each degree from 0° to 90°, is given in the Appendix. It will be noted that from 0° to 45° the values of the angle are found in the left column, and from 45° to 90° they are found in the right column. This arrangement is chosen because the values of each of the cofunctions (cosine, cotangent, cosecant) from 0° to 45° or from 45° to 90° are the same as those of the corresponding functions (sine, tangent, secant) from 45° to 90° or from 0° to 45°. The reason for this is brought out in the following example.

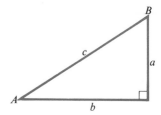

Figure 17–13

Example B   In the right triangle shown in Fig. 17–13, the two acute angles add up to 90°. Since $\sin A = a/c$ and $\cos B = a/c$, we see that $\sin A = \cos B$. Also, since $A + B = 90°$,

$$B = 90° - A \quad \text{or} \quad \sin A = \cos (90° - A).$$

If $A = 32°$, for example, then

$$\sin 32° = \cos 58°.$$

Therefore, in the table, all the values are included for the ratios from 0° to 45°, and it is only necessary to relabel the columns (as is done at the bottom) to obtain the values for the ratios from 45° to 90°.

The following examples illustrate how the table of trigonometric ratios is used to find values of the ratios and to find the angle when one of the ratios is given.

Example C   To find cot 34° we look under the column labeled "cot" and to the right of 34 in the degrees column to find the value 1.483.

To find the value of cos 73° we must look *above* the "cos" at the bottom, since 73° is greater than 45°. Also we must look to the *left* of the 73 in the degree column at the right. We thus find the value 0.2924.

The value of tan 48° is found above the "tan" at the bottom and to the left of the 48 in the right column. We thus find the value 1.111.

Given that $\sin \alpha = 0.5446$ (α is the Greek letter "alpha" and is often   **Example D**
used to designate angles, as are many of the Greek letters), find α. First
we look for 0.5446 in one of the columns labeled "sin." Finding this
value *under* the "sin," we then look to the left column and determine
that $\alpha = 33°$.

Given that $\sec \alpha = 1.589$, find α. This time we note that 1.589 is
above "sec," and therefore we look to the right column to determine
that $\alpha = 51°$.

If two sides of a right triangle are known, using the definitions of the
trigonometric ratios along with the table allows us to determine the angles
of the triangle. Consider the following example.

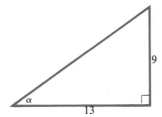

Figure 17-14

For the triangle in Fig. 17–14, find α.   **Example E**

Since we know the two legs of the triangle, we can directly determine the
value of the tangent of α. Thus

$$\tan \alpha = \tfrac{9}{13} = 0.6923,$$

which means that $\alpha = 35°$ (to the nearest degree), since 0.6923 is closer
to 0.7002 than any other value in the tangent column.

In Exercises 1 through 12, determine the value of the indicated trigonometric   **EXERCISES**
ratio from Table 3 of the Appendix.

1. $\sin 39°$ **2.** $\tan 17°$ **3.** $\sec 8°$ **4.** $\csc 44°$

5. $\cos 68°$ **6.** $\cot 87°$ **7.** $\sin 56°$ **8.** $\tan 64°$

9. $\cot 49°$ **10.** $\sin 78°$ **11.** $\cos 51°$ **12.** $\sec 77°$

In Exercises 13 through 24, determine the value of the angle α, to the nearest
degree, from Table 3 of the Appendix.

13. $\sin \alpha = 0.4067$ **14.** $\tan \alpha = 0.2126$ **15.** $\sec \alpha = 1.150$

16. $\cos \alpha = 0.9910$ **17.** $\cot \alpha = 2.891$ **18.** $\csc \alpha = 6.200$

19. $\cos \alpha = 0.2752$ **20.** $\sin \alpha = 0.8475$ **21.** $\tan \alpha = 5.670$

22. $\cot \alpha = 0.2867$ **23.** $\sin \alpha = 0.9986$ **24.** $\sec \alpha = 9.567$

In Exercises 25 through 28, for the given trigonometric ratio, find the indicated trigonometric ratio from Table 3 of the Appendix.

25. $\sin \alpha = 0.6428$, $\sec \alpha$ **26.** $\cos \alpha = 0.5736$, $\tan \alpha$

27. $\tan \alpha = 1.036$, $\csc \alpha$ **28.** $\cot \alpha = 0.1051$, $\sin \alpha$

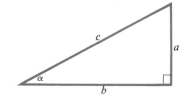

Figure 17–15

In Exercises 29 through 36, find, to the nearest degree, angle α in Fig. 17–15, for the given sides of the triangle.

29. $a = 3$, $c = 5$ **30.** $a = 2$, $b = 5$

31. $b = 5$, $c = 7$ **32.** $a = 5.6$, $b = 1.9$

33. $a = 16$, $c = 21$ **34.** $b = 0.076$, $c = 0.152$

35. $a = 8700$, $b = 960$ **36.** $a = 6.7$, $c = 56$

In Exercises 37 through 40, draw a right triangle, including the indicated angle (use a protractor). Draw the side adjacent to the angle 10 cm long. By measuring the other sides and using the definitions of the ratios, verify the values of the ratios with the values from the table.

37. $\sin 32°$ **38.** $\tan 56°$

39. $\cos 13°$ **40.** $\csc 78°$

In Exercises 41 and 42, solve the given problems.

41. When a light ray enters glass from the air, it bends somewhat toward a line perpendicular to the surface. The *index of refraction* of a medium (in this case glass) is defined as

$$n = \frac{\sin i}{\sin r},$$

where i is the angle between the perpendicular and the ray in air and r is the angle between the perpendicular and the ray in the medium. A typical case for glass is $i = 60°$ and $r = 35°$. Determine the index of refraction for this case.

42. The work W done by a force F is defined as

$$W = Fd \cos \theta,$$

where F is the magnitude of the force, d is the distance through which it acts, and θ (the Greek theta) is the angle between the direction of the force and the direction of motion. Given that a 25.0 lb force acts through 20.0 ft, and the angle between the force and motion is 32°, how much work is done by the force?

17-3 TRIGONOMETRIC SCALES ON THE SLIDE RULE

Values of the trigonometric ratios can be found on most slide rules to three significant digits. Generally the trigonometric scales, ST, S, and T are read in conjunction with the C (or D) and CI scales. [If a slide rule does not have an ST scale, the S and T scales are used together with the B (or A) scale.] Although any of the six ratios can be found on the slide rule, we shall restrict our attention to finding values of the sine, cosine, and tangent of acute angles.

To find values of the sine of angles from about 0.6° to about 5.7°, one places the hairline over the angle on the ST scale and reads the value on the C scale (or D scale if they are lined up). All such values are in the range 0.01 to 0.1. To find values of the sine from about 5.7° to 90°, one places the hairline over the angle on the S scale, and reads the value on the C scale. All such values are in the range from 0.1 to 1.0.

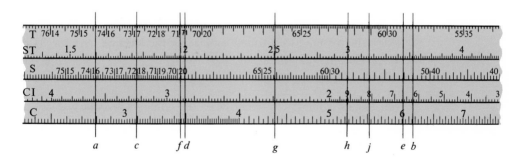

Figure 17-16

The value of sin 1.60° is found by placing the hairline over 1.6 on the ST scale and reading the answer 0.0279 on the C scale. See setting a in Fig. 17-16.

Example A

The value of sin 38° is found by placing the hairline over 38 on the S scale and reading the result, 0.616, on the C scale. See setting *b* in Fig. 17–16.

To find values of the cosine we read the sine values "backward." On the S scale we read cosine values from right to left (they are usually marked on the *left* side of the divisions of the S scale). The S scale is used for angles from 0° to about 84.3°. The ST scale is used for angles from about 84.3° to about 89.4°.

Example B The value of cos 72° is found by placing the hairline over the left 72 of the S scale and reading the result, 0.309, on the C scale. See setting *c* in Fig. 17–16.

The value of cos 88° is found by placing the hairline over the 2 (90 − 88 = 2) of the ST scale and reading the result, 0.0349, on the C scale. See setting *d* in Fig. 17–16.

The values of the sine and tangent are very nearly equal for small angles. For that reason values of the sine and tangent are found for such angles by use of the ST scale. Therefore, to find values of the tangent for angles from about 0.6° to about 5.7°, we follow the same procedure as for values of the sine. To find values of the tangent for angles from about 5.7° to 45°, one places the hairline over the angle on the T scale, and reads the value on the C scale.

Example C The value of tan 1.60° is the same as sin 1.60°. See setting *a* in Fig. 17–16.

The value of tan 31° is found by placing the hairline over the 31 of the T scale and reading the result, 0.601, on the C scale. See setting *e* in Fig. 17–16.

For angles from 45° to about 84.3° the numbers are marked on the left side of the divisions on the T scale. To find the tangents of these angles, place the hairline over the appropriate angle (being sure to read from right to left), and read the result on the CI scale. All such values are from 1.00 to 10.0. Also note that the CI scale is read from right to left. For angles from about 84.3° to about 89.4° the angle is found on the ST scale by subtracting the angle from 90°, and setting the hairline over this difference. The result is read on the CI scale, with values ranging from 10.0 to 100.

The value of tan 71° is found by placing the hairline over the 71 (on the left of the division) on the T scale and reading the result, 2.90, on the CI scale. See setting f in Fig. 17–16.

 The value of tan 87.5° is found by placing the hairline over the 2.5 $(90 - 87.5 = 2.5)$ of the ST scale and reading the result, 22.9, on the CI scale. See setting g in Fig. 17–16.

 Just as with tables, if we know values of trigonometric ratios, we can determine the angles by using the slide rule. We must be careful, however, to note the decimal point of the ratio and to use the proper scales. This procedure is illustrated in the following example.

If we know that $\sin \alpha = 0.523$, we set the hairline over 523 on the C   **Example E** scale, and read $\alpha = 31.5°$ on the S scale. If we knew that $\sin \alpha = 0.0523$, we would still set the hairline over 523 on the C scale, but we would read $\alpha = 3.00°$ on the ST scale. See setting h in Fig. 17–16.

 If we know that $\tan \alpha = 1.81$, we place the hairline over 181 on the CI scale, not the C scale. The result, $\alpha = 61.1°$, is read on the T scale, reading right to left. See setting j in Fig. 17–16.

 Since the trigonometric scales are read directly, it is not possible to include values for all angles. Those for which the ratios are less than 0.01 or greater than 100 are not included.

In Exercises 1 through 16, find the indicated trigonometric ratios by using a   **EXERCISES** slide rule.

1. $\sin 26°$	**2.** $\tan 37°$	**3.** $\cos 14°$	**4.** $\sin 15.5°$
5. $\sin 3.40°$	**6.** $\cos 5°$	**7.** $\tan 4.75°$	**8.** $\cos 86.2°$
9. $\tan 58°$	**10.** $\sin 83°$	**11.** $\cos 71.5°$	**12.** $\tan 89.1°$
13. $\sin 1.72°$	**14.** $\tan 5.48°$	**15.** $\tan 48.2°$	**16.** $\cos 61.3°$

In Exercises 17 through 32, find the angle α from a slide rule.

17. $\sin \alpha = 0.652$	**18.** $\cos \alpha = 0.219$
19. $\tan \alpha = 0.492$	**20.** $\sin \alpha = 0.927$
21. $\sin \alpha = 0.0873$	**22.** $\tan \alpha = 0.0759$
23. $\cos \alpha = 0.0233$	**24.** $\tan \alpha = 25.6$
25. $\tan \alpha = 7.82$	**26.** $\sin \alpha = 0.107$
27. $\cos \alpha = 0.408$	**28.** $\cos \alpha = 0.0617$

29. $\sin \alpha = 0.0996$ **30.** $\tan \alpha = 2.79$

31. $\tan \alpha = 85.0$ **32.** $\cos \alpha = 0.0851$

In Exercises 33 and 34, solve the given problems by use of a slide rule.

33. One end of a 25.0-m metal rod lies on a flat surface; the rod makes an angle of 17° with the surface. The length of the shadow of the rod due to a light shining vertically down on it is (25.0)(cos 17°). Find the length of the shadow.

34. The coefficient of friction between an object on an inclined plane and the plane equals the tangent of the angle that the plane makes with the horizontal if the object moves down the plane with a constant speed. The coefficient of friction between a wooden crate and a wooden plank is 0.340 when the crate is moving with a constant speed. At what angle is the plank inclined?

17-4 ELEMENTARY RIGHT TRIANGLE APPLICATIONS

In this section we shall indicate, by means of examples and exercises, many of the applications of the trigonometric ratios. These will include those of indirect measurement, which was mentioned in the first section of this chapter. First, however, we shall briefly consider the general idea of *solving a triangle*.

In every triangle there are three angles and three sides. If three of these six parts are known, the other three can be determined, so long as at least one of the known parts is a side. By solving a triangle, we mean finding the unknown parts of a triangle by using the known parts so that the result is that all six parts are known.

In a right triangle we must know only two parts other than the right angle in order to solve it. The following two examples illustrate solving right triangles.

Example A   Given that the hypotenuse of a right triangle is 16.0, and that one of the acute angles is 35°, find the other acute angle and the two sides. See Fig. 17-17.

Since the angles of a triangle contain a total of 180°, and the right angle contains 90°, the two acute angles must total 90°. Therefore the unknown angle α must be 55°.

Next, since $\sin 35° = b/16.0$, we have

$$b = 16.0 \sin 35° \quad \text{or} \quad b = 16.0(0.5736) = 9.18.$$

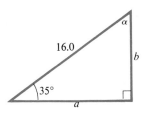

Figure 17-17

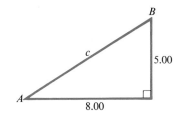

Figure 17-18

Also, since cos 35° = $a/16.0$, we have

$$a = 16.0 \cos 35° = 16.0(0.8192) = 13.1.$$

Therefore the required angle is 55° and the required sides are 9.18 and 13.1.

In a right triangle, the two legs are 5.00 and 8.00. Find the hypotenuse and the two acute angles. See Fig. 17-18.　　　　　　　　**Example B**

From the figure we see that tan A = 5.00/8.00, which means that tan A = 0.6250. From the table we then determine that $\angle A = 32°$ (to the nearest degree). This in turn means that $\angle B = 58°$.

We can find side c by either the Pythagorean theorem or by using a ratio of one of the angles just determined. The Pythagorean theorem is preferable, since it does not involve derived numbers, which could conceivably be in error. Thus

$$c = \sqrt{(5.00)^2 + (8.00)^2} = \sqrt{89.0} = 9.43.$$

The application of the trigonometric ratios is essentially the same as solving triangles, although it is usually one specific part of the triangle that we are asked to determine. The following four examples illustrate some of the basic applications.

A ladder 22.0 ft long leans against the wall of a house. It makes an angle　　**Example C**
of 50° with the ground. How high on the house does the ladder reach?
See Fig. 17-19.

Since the side opposite the known angle is to be determined, and the hypotenuse is known, the solution is most easily found by use of the sine. Thus

$$\sin 50° = \frac{x}{22.0}, \quad x = 22.0 \sin 50° = 22.0(0.7660) = 16.9 \text{ ft.}$$

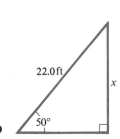

Figure 17-19

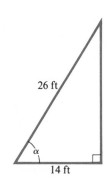

Figure 17-20

Example D   A guy wire attached to the top of a telephone pole is 26.0 ft long. The grounded end of the wire is 14.0 ft from the base of the pole. What is the angle between the wire and the ground? See Fig. 17–20.

Since we know the hypotenuse and the adjacent side of the desired angle, we can easily find the solution by using the cosine. Thus

$$\cos \alpha = \tfrac{14.0}{26.0} = 0.538.$$

From Table 3, the cosine nearest 0.538 is that of 57°. Thus

$$\alpha = 57°.$$

Example E   A lighthouse is 200 ft high. The *angle of elevation* (the angle between the horizontal and the line of sight, upward with respect to the observer) from a point on the shore to the top of the lighthouse is 20°. Find the distance from the point on shore to the base of the lighthouse. See Fig. 17–21.

Figure 17-21

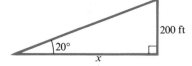

Since the known side is that which is opposite to the known angle, and the side to be determined is adjacent, the solution can be completed by using the tangent or the cotangent. We shall use the cotangent:

$$\cot 20° = \frac{x}{200}, \qquad x = 200 \cot 20° = 200(2.747) = 549 \text{ ft.}$$

If we had used the tangent, it would have involved dividing 200 by tan 20°, which would make the arithmetical operation slightly more involved.

The pilot in an airplane checks the *angle of depression* (the angle between   Example F
the horizontal and the line of sight, downward with respect to the observer) to the control tower of an airport to be 28°. If the plane is 10,000 ft
high, what is its horizontal distance from the tower? See Fig. 17–22.

Since the opposite and adjacent sides are involved, we can use the tangent
or cotangent. Here we shall use the tangent. Thus

$$\tan 28° = \frac{10,000}{x}, \qquad x = \frac{10,000}{0.5317} = 18,800 \text{ ft.}$$

If we had used the cotangent, it would have involved multiplying 10,000
by cot 28°, which would actually have made the arithmetical operation
slightly easier.

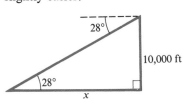

Figure 17–22

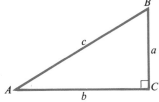

Figure 17–23

In Exercises 1 through 12, solve the triangles with the given parts. The parts   EXERCISES
given refer to Fig. 17–23.

1. $\angle A = 30°$, $a = 12$ 2. $\angle A = 45°$, $b = 16$

3. $\angle B = 60°$, $c = 22$ 4. $\angle B = 50°$, $a = 15$

5. $\angle A = 65°$, $c = 30$ 6. $\angle B = 23°$, $b = 1.45$

7. $a = 0.65$, $c = 1.30$ 8. $a = 4.7$, $b = 4.7$

9. $b = 5.8$, $c = 45$ 10. $a = 734$, $b = 129$

11. $a = 9.72$, $c = 10.8$ 12. $\angle A = 7°$, $a = 1960$

In Exercises 13 through 30, solve each for the appropriate part of a triangle.

13. The angle of elevation to the top of a statue is 20° from a point 200 ft from
the base of the statue. Find the height of the statue.

14. The angle of elevation of the sun is 50° at the time a tree casts a shadow 42.0 ft
long. Find the height of the tree.

15. A guy wire whose grounded end is 16.0 ft from the pole it supports makes
an angle of 56° with the ground. How long is the wire?

16. Along the shore of a river, from a rock at a height of 300 ft above the river,
the angle of depression of the closest point on the opposite shore is 12°.

What is the distance across the river from the base of the height to the closest point on the opposite shore?

17. A roadway rises 150 ft for every 2000 ft along the road. Find the angle of inclination of the roadway.

18. A searchlight is 520 ft from a building. The beam lights up the building at a point 150 ft above the ground. What angle does the beam make with the ground?

19. A draftsman sets the legs of a pair of dividers so that the angle between them is 36°. What is the distance between the points if each leg is 4.75 in. long?

20. In a scale drawing, the angle between the impedance and the resistance is 19°. If the impedance of the circuit is 38.5 ohms, what is the resistance? (See Exercise 29 of Section 16–2.)

21. The total angle through which a pendulum 40 in. long swings is 6°. Find the horizontal distance between the extreme positions of the pendulum.

22. A television antenna is 600 ft high. If the angle between the guy wires (attached at the top) and the antenna is 55°, how long are the guy wires?

23. An observer in a helicopter 800 ft above the ground notes that the angle of depression of an enemy position is 26°. How far from directly below the helicopter is this position?

Figure 17–24

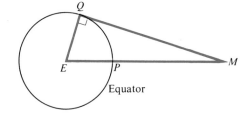

24. One way of finding the distance from the earth to the moon is indicated in Fig. 17–24. From point P the moon is directly overhead, and from point Q the moon is just visible. Both points are on the equator. The angle at E is almost 89°. Given that the radius of the earth is 4000 mi, how far is it to the moon (PM)?

25. An astronaut observes two cities which are 30 mi apart; the angle between the lines of sight is 10°. Given that he is the same distance from each, how high above the surface of the earth is he?

26. From an airplane 5000 ft above the surface of the water, a pilot observes two boats directly ahead. The angles of depression are 20° and 12°. How far apart are the boats?

27. A jet cruising at 610 mi/hr climbs at an angle of 12°. What is its gain in altitude in 3 min?

28. What is the distance between two points on a wheel 38° apart on the circumference, given that the diameter of the wheel is 28.0 in.?

29. Eight bolt holes (spaced equally) are drilled on the circumference of a circle whose diameter is 16.6 in. What is the center-to-center distance between holes?

30. A surveyor wishes to measure the width of a large lake. He sights a point B on the opposite side of the lake from point A. He then measures off 200 ft from point A to point C, such that $CA \perp AB$. He then determines that $\angle ABC = 8.50°$. How wide is the lake?

17–5 VECTORS

In the previous sections of this book we have been able to fully describe most quantities by specifying their magnitudes. Generally, one can describe areas, lengths of objects, time intervals, monetary amounts, temperatures, and numerous other quantities by specifying a number: the magnitude of the quantity. Such quantities are known as *scalar* quantities.

Numerous other quantities are fully described only when both their magnitude and direction are specified. Such quantities are known as *vectors*. Examples of vectors are velocity, force, and momentum. Vectors are of utmost importance in many fields of science and technology. The following example illustrates a vector quantity and the distinction between scalars and vectors.

A jet leaves New York and travels 300 mi. From this statement alone we know only the *distance* traveled. Therefore the distance here is a scalar quantity.

Example A

If we were to add the phrase "toward Los Angeles" to the above sentence about the jet, we would be specifying the direction of the jet, as well as the distance it traveled. We now know the *displacement* of the jet; that is, we know the direction of travel as well as the distance traveled. Displacement is a vector quantity.

In order to add scalar quantities, we simply find the sum of the magnitudes. However, this procedure generally does not work with vector quantities. Consider the following example.

Example B   A jet leaves New York, travels 300 mi due west, then turns and travels
400 mi due north.

Common sense tells us that the jet has traveled 700 mi, but that it is
not 700 mi from New York. In fact, we see by using the Pythagorean
theorem that the jet is 500 mi from New York (see Fig. 17–25). Therefore
the magnitude of the displacement is 500 mi, which means that the jet is
actually 500 mi from New York. The direction of the displacement is
indicated by the arrow shown in Fig. 17–25. Measuring the angle, we
find that it is directed at an angle of 53° north of west. Here we have added
vectors with magnitudes of 300 and 400 and the result is a vector of
magnitude of 500. The "discrepancy" is due to the directions involved.

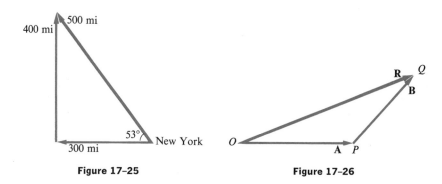

Figure 17–25   **Figure 17–26**

We see that the sum of two vectors must take the direction of the
vectors into account as well as their magnitudes. Reasoning along lines
suggested by Example B, we shall now define the sum of two vectors.

Boldface type (example: **A**) is commonly used to denote vectors;
in handwriting, one usually places an arrow over the letter (example: $\vec{A}$).
In Fig. 17–26, **A** represents the vector from O to P, **B** represents the vector
from P to Q, and **R**, the *resultant* vector, is the sum of vectors **A** and **B**
from O to Q. Note that the vectors are placed head to tail, and that the
resultant is drawn from the tail of the first vector to the head of the last
vector.

The above method of adding vectors is equivalent to making the two
vectors being added the sides of a parallelogram, with the diagonal being
the resultant. In general, a resultant vector is a single vector which can
replace any number of other vectors and still produce the same physical
effect.

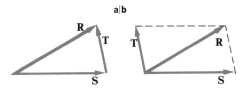

a|b

Figure 17–27

The addition of vectors **S** and **T** is shown in Fig. 17–27(a). In Fig. 17–27(b)   Example C
we see the parallelogram method of addition.

We shall now show how the trigonometric ratios are used to add two
vectors which are at right angles. In finding the resultant we must
determine its magnitude and its direction. As a matter of notation, we
shall denote the magnitude of a vector by using the same letter, but in
ordinary italic type. Consider the following example.

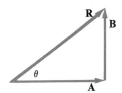

Figure 17–28

Add vectors **A** and **B**, with $A = 12$ and $B = 9$, which are at right angles,   Example D
as shown in Fig. 17–28.
One can find the magnitude of **R**, which is R, by using the Pythagorean
theorem. Thus

$$R = \sqrt{A^2 + B^2} = \sqrt{(12)^2 + 9^2} = \sqrt{225} = 15.$$

One can find the direction of **R** by using the trigonometric ratios.
Specifying the direction as the angle θ which **R** makes with **A**, we find
that

$$\tan \theta = \frac{B}{A} = \frac{9}{12} = 0.75.$$

To the nearest degree, $\theta = 37°$. Thus **R** is a vector with magnitude
$R = 15$ and is directed at an angle of $37°$ from vector **A**.

In addition to being able to add vectors, we often need to consider
a given vector as the sum of two other vectors. These two vectors, when

added, give the original vector. The method is called *resolving* the vector into its *components*. It is usually done within the framework of the rectangular coordinate system, as in the following example.

Example E   Resolve the vector **A**, with $A = 10$, which makes an angle of 56° with the positive *x*-axis, into two components, one directed along the *x*-axis (the *x*-component) and the other along the *y*-axis (the *y*-component). See Fig. 17–29.

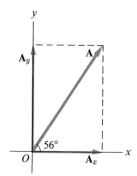

Figure 17-29

In the figure we see that the magnitude of the *x*-component, A_x, divided by the magnitude of **A**, equals the cosine of 56°, or

$$\frac{A_x}{A} = \cos 56°.$$

Solving for A_x, we have

$$A_x = A \cos 56°.$$

Since $A = 10$ and $\cos 56° = 0.5592$, we have

$$A_x = (10)(0.5592) = 5.6$$

rounded off to two significant digits.

Also from the figure we see that the side opposite the 56° angle is equal to the magnitude of the *y*-component, $A_y/A = \sin 56°$, we have

$$A_y = A \sin 56° = (10)(0.8290) = 8.3$$

rounded off to two significant digits.

Therefore we have resolved vector **A** into two components, one directed along the positive *x*-axis with a magnitude of 5.6, and the other directed along the positive *y*-axis with a magnitude of 8.3.

The following two examples show how two vectors, not at right angles, are added. The basic procedure is to resolve each into its x- and y-components. These components are added for each direction, thus giving the x- and y-components of the resultant. Then, by using the Pythagorean theorem and the tangent, we find the magnitude and direction of the resultant.

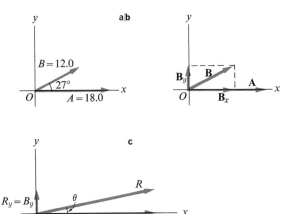

Figure 17–30

Example F

Add vectors **A** and **B** as shown in Fig. 17–30(a).

Since vector **A** is directed along the x-axis, it is not necessary to resolve it into components. In fact, $A_x = A = 18.0$ and $A_y = 0$. However, it is necessary to resolve vector **B** into its components. Following the same procedure as in Example E, by using the trigonometric ratios, we have

$$B_x = B \cos 27° \quad \text{and} \quad B_y = B \sin 27°.$$

Substituting $B = 12.0$, $\cos 27° = 0.8910$, and $\sin 27° = 0.4540$, we find that

$$B_x = 10.7 \quad \text{and} \quad B_y = 5.45.$$

See Fig. 17–30(b).

Now the only component in the y-direction is B_y, which means that $R_y = B_y$. Also, since both **A** and B_x are directed along the positive x-axis, we may add them to get the x component of the resultant. Therefore, $R_x = A + B_x$. [See Fig. 17–30(c).] Therefore

$$R_x = A + B_x = 18.0 + 10.7 = 28.7, \quad R_y = B_y = 5.45.$$

We get the magnitude R by using the Pythagorean theorem:

$$R = \sqrt{R_x^2 + R_y^2} = \sqrt{(28.7)^2 + (5.45)^2} = 29.2.$$

The direction of **R**, as specified by θ, is found by

$$\tan \theta = \frac{R_y}{R_x} = \frac{5.45}{28.7} = 0.190.$$

Therefore

$$\theta = 11°.$$

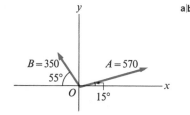 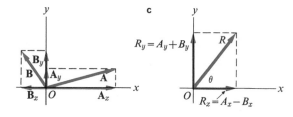

Figure 17–31

Example G   Add vectors **A** and **B** as shown in Fig. 17–31(a).

Since neither vector is directed along an axis, it is necessary to resolve both vectors into their x- and y-components.   Following the same procedure as in previous examples, we have (see Fig. 17–31b)

$$A_x = A \cos 15° \quad \text{and} \quad A_y = A \sin 15°$$

and

$$B_x = B \cos 55° \quad \text{and} \quad B_y = B \sin 55°.$$

Substituting the appropriate values, we have

$$A_x = (570)(0.9659) = 551,$$
$$A_y = (570)(0.2588) = 148,$$
$$B_x = (350)(0.5736) = 201,$$
$$B_y = (350)(0.8192) = 287.$$

Since both A_y and B_y are directed upward, the magnitude R_y is the sum of A_y and B_y.   Also, since A_x and B_x are directed oppositely, it is necessary to subtract B_x from A_x.   Therefore

$$R_x = A_x - B_x = 551 - 201 = 350,$$
$$R_y = A_y + B_y = 148 + 287 = 435.$$

Again using the Pythagorean theorem and the tangent of θ, we have

$$R = \sqrt{R_x^2 + R_y^2} = \sqrt{(350)^2 + (435)^2} = \sqrt{311700} = 558,$$

$$\tan \theta = \frac{R_y}{R_x} = \frac{435}{350} = 1.24,$$

$$\theta = 51°.$$

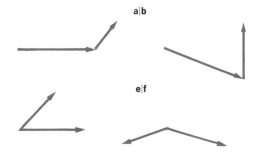

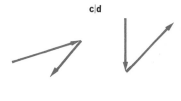

Figure 17-32

In Exercises 1 through 6, add the indicated vectors by means of diagrams.   **EXERCISES**

1. The vectors in Fig. 17-32(a).   **2.** The vectors in Fig. 17-32(b).

3. The vectors in Fig. 17-32(c).   **4.** The vectors in Fig. 17-32(d).

5. The vectors in Fig. 17-32(e).   **6.** The vectors in Fig. 17-32(f).

In Exercises 7 through 12, add the indicated vectors by using the Pythagorean theorem and the tangent. In all cases the vectors are at right angles.

7. The vectors in Fig. 17-33(a).   **8.** The vectors in Fig. 17-33(b).

9. The vectors in Fig. 17-33(c).   **10.** The vectors in Fig. 17-33(d).

11. The vectors in Fig. 17-33(e).   **12.** The vectors in Fig. 17-33(f).

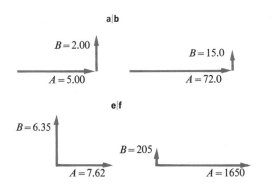

Figure 17-33

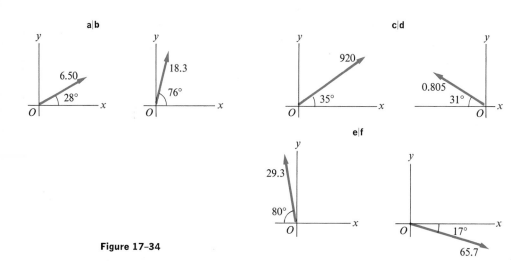

Figure 17-34

In Exercises 13 through 18, find the *x*-and *y*-components of the indicated vectors by using trigonometric ratios.

13. The vector in Fig. 17–34(a).   **14.** The vector in Fig. 17–34(b)

15. The vector in Fig. 17–34(c).   **16.** The vector in Fig. 17–34(d).

17. The vector in Fig. 17–34(e).   **18.** The vector in Fig. 17–34(f).

In Exercises 19 through 24, add the indicated vectors by using the Pythagorean theorem and the trigonometric ratios.

19. The vectors in Fig. 17–35(a).   **20.** The vectors in Fig. 17–35(b).

21. The vectors in Fig. 17–35(c)   **22.** The vectors in Fig. 17–35(d).

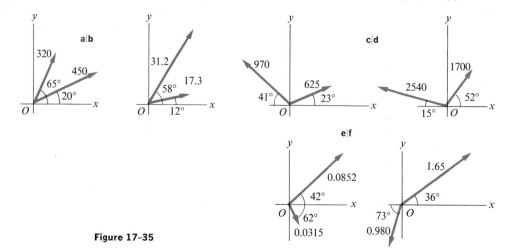

Figure 17-35

23. The vectors in Fig. 17–35(e).   **24.** The vectors in Fig. 17–35(f).

In Exercises 25 through 32, solve the given vector problems by using the Pythagorean theorem and the trigonometric ratios.

25. A ship travels 38 mi due east from a port and then turns south for 26 mi farther. What is the displacement of the ship from the port?

26. A motorboat which travels 7.0 mi/hr in still water heads directly across a stream which flows at 3.2 mi/hr. What is the resultant velocity of the boat? (*Velocity* has both magnitude and direction and is a vector, whereas *speed* has only magnitude and is a scalar.)

27. A rocket is fired at an angle of 80° with the horizontal with a speed of 2500 mi/hr; find the horizontal and vertical components of the velocity.

28. If an electron passes through a magnetic field, a force acts on it which is proportional to $v \sin \alpha$, where v is the velocity of the electron and α is the angle between the velocity and the direction of the magnetic field. Given that an electron passes through a magnetic field at 3.5×10^9 cm/sec at an angle of 80° to the field, find the component proportional to the force.

29. A 50-lb object is suspended from the ceiling by a rope. It is then pulled to the side by a horizontal force of 20 lb, and held in place. What is the tension in the rope? (In order that the object be in equilibrium there should be no net force in any direction. This means that the tension in the rope must equal the resultant of the two forces acting on it. The forces in this case are the 20-lb force and its own weight.)

30. A plane is headed due north at a speed of 550 mi/hr with respect to the air. There is a tail wind blowing from the southeast at 75.0 mi/hr. What is the resultant velocity of the plane with respect to the ground?

31. A 90-lb object is on the floor. Two forces are acting on the object. The first force, of 110 lb, acts at an angle of 30° upward from the horizontal to the right. The second force, of 75 lb, acts at an angle of 20° upward from the horizontal to the left. Will the object move? (Neglect frictional effects.)

32. A wooden block is on an inclined plane, as shown in Fig. 17–36. The block will slip down the plane if the component acting downward along the plane is greater than the frictional force acting upward along the plane. Given that the block weighs 85 lb, and the plane is inclined at 13°, will the block slip if the frictional force is 18 lb?

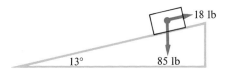

13°   85 lb   **Figure 17–36**

17-6 RADIANS

For many problems in which the trigonometric ratios are used, the degree measurement of angles is sufficient. However, in numerous practical and theoretical discussions, another measure of angle is more convenient. This unit of measurement of an angle is the *radian*. A radian is the measure of an angle, with vertex at the center of a circle, whose intercepted arc on the circle is equal in length to the radius of the circle.

Since the circumference of any circle, in terms of its radius, is given by $c = 2\pi r$, the ratio of the circumference to the radius is 2π. This means that the radius may be laid off 2π times along the circumference, regardless of the length of the radius. Therefore we see that radian measure is independent of the length of the radius of the circle (see Fig. 17-37).

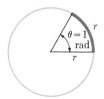

Figure 17-37

We may use the formula $c = 2\pi r$ to develop the relationship between degrees and radians. One complete rotation is measured as 360° or 2π radians. Therefore 360° is equivalent to 2π radians. It then follows that the relation between degrees and radians may be written as

$$\pi \text{ rad} = 180°.\qquad\qquad \textbf{17-3}$$

From Eq. (17-3) we find that

$$1° = \frac{\pi}{180} \text{ rad} = 0.01745 \text{ rad}\qquad\qquad \textbf{17-4}$$

and that

$$1 \text{ rad} = \frac{180°}{\pi} = 57.3°.\qquad\qquad \textbf{17-5}$$

Example A

$$18° = \frac{\pi}{180}\,(18) = \frac{\pi}{10} = 0.314 \text{ rad},$$

$$18° = (18)(0.01745) = 0.314 \text{ rad},$$

$$0.5 \text{ rad} = \frac{180}{\pi}\,(0.5) = \frac{90}{\pi} = 28.6°,$$

$$0.5 \text{ rad} = (0.5)(57.3) = 28.6°.$$

It will be noted that Eq. (17–3) can be used in all cases for converting to and from radian measure. It is a good practice to do so, for it is the basic relation between radians and degrees.

Due to the nature of the definition of the radian, it is very common to express radians in terms of π. Also, since a radian is the ratio of a distance to a distance, it actually has no dimensions. Therefore, when radians are being used, it is customary that no unit of measurement is indicated for the angle. When no unit appears, radians are understood to be the unit of angle measurement.

Example B

Since $30° = \frac{1}{6}(180°)$, we see that $30° = \frac{\pi}{6}$ rad. Also, since $45° = \frac{1}{4}(180°)$, we have $45° = \frac{\pi}{4}$ rad. In the same way, $90° = \frac{\pi}{2}$ rad.

Following the policy that no unit is used when radians are used, these relations would be written as

$$30° = \frac{\pi}{6}, \qquad 45° = \frac{\pi}{4}, \qquad 90° = \frac{\pi}{2}.$$

One point should be emphasized here. Since π is simply a special way of writing the number which is the ratio between the circumference and the diameter of a circle, which again means that radians really have no units, *radian measure amounts to measuring angles in terms of numbers.* It is this property that makes radians useful in certain situations.

Example C

Since $30° = \frac{\pi}{6} = 0.524$, we see that

$$\sin 30° = \sin \frac{\pi}{6} = \sin 0.524.$$

Also, since $12° = \frac{\pi}{180}(12) = \frac{\pi}{15} = 0.209$, we see that

$$\tan 12° = \tan 0.209 = 0.2126.$$

Often when one first encounters radian measure, expressions such as $\sin 1$ and $\sin \theta = 1$ are confused. The first is equivalent to $\sin 57.3°$, since $57.3° = 1$ (radian). The second means that θ is the angle for which the sine is 1. Since $\sin 90° = 1$, we can say that $\theta = 90°$, or $\theta = \pi/2$. The following example gives some final illustrations of evaluating expressions involving radians.

Example D

Since $36° = \frac{\pi}{5} = 0.628$, we find that

$$\cos 36° = \cos 0.628 = 0.8090.$$

Since $0.8090 = \frac{180°}{\pi}(0.8090) = 46.4°$, we find that

$$\cos 0.8090 = \cos 46.4° = 0.690 \quad \text{(slide rule)}.$$

If $\sin\theta = 0.771$, $\theta = 50.4° = 0.88$. If $\tan\theta = 1.70$, $\theta = 1.04$. If $\cos\theta = 0.889$, $\theta = 0.475$.

EXERCISES In Exercises 1 through 6, express the given angles in terms of π.

1. 15°	**2.** 75°	**3.** 80°
4. 120°	**5.** 135°	**6.** 300°

In Exercises 7 through 12, express the given numbers in terms of degrees.

7. $\pi/5$	**8.** $\pi/20$	**9.** $3\pi/10$
10. $5\pi/4$	**11.** $7\pi/12$	**12.** $4\pi/3$

In Exercises 13 through 18, express the given angles in radian measure.

13. 23°	**14.** 54.6°	**15.** 82°
16. 104.4°	**17.** 27.5°	**18.** 275°

In Exercises 19 through 24, express the given numbers in degrees.

19. 2	**20.** 1.5	**21.** 0.82
22. 0.074	**23.** 3/4	**24.** 5/2

In Exercises 25 through 36, find the indicated trigonometric functions.

25. $\sin\dfrac{\pi}{3}$	**26.** $\cos\dfrac{\pi}{6}$	**27.** $\tan\dfrac{5\pi}{12}$
28. $\sin\dfrac{7\pi}{18}$	**29.** $\cos\dfrac{7\pi}{20}$	**30.** $\tan\dfrac{2\pi}{5}$
31. $\sin 0.7$	**32.** $\cos 0.3$	**33.** $\tan 0.65$
34. $\cot 1.25$	**35.** $\sec 1.5$	**36.** $\csc 1.35$

In Exercises 37 through 42, find θ in radians.

37. $\sin\theta = 0.5878$	**38.** $\cos\theta = 0.9848$	**39.** $\tan\theta = 1.376$
40. $\sin\theta = 0.9336$	**41.** $\cot\theta = 0.7002$	**42.** $\sec\theta = 4.445$

17–7 APPLICATIONS OF RADIAN MEASURE

There are numerous applications of radian measure. In this section we shall briefly discuss certain geometric and technical applications.

Recalling our discussion of the circle, we can see that the length of an arc on a circle is proportional to the central angle. Since the length of the arc of a complete circle is the circumference, we can state that $s = 2\pi r$, where we have let s represent the arc length (of the entire circle) and r is the radius. Now 2π is also the central angle (in radians) of the entire circle. Therefore, for any arc of the circle, we have

$$s = \theta r, \qquad\qquad\qquad 17\text{-}6$$

where θ is the central angle measured in radians (see Fig. 17–38).

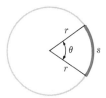

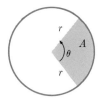

Figure 17-38   **Figure 17-39**

If $\theta = \pi/6$ and $r = 3.00$ in., we have   Example A

$$s = \left(\frac{\pi}{6}\right)(3.00) = \frac{\pi}{2} = 1.57 \text{ in.}$$

If we know the arc length $s = 7.20$ ft for a central angle of $150°$ of a circle, we can find the radius of the circle by

$$7.20 = (150)\left(\frac{\pi}{180}\right)r = \frac{5\pi}{6}r \quad \text{or} \quad r = \frac{6(7.20)}{5(3.14)} = 2.75 \text{ ft.}$$

Another geometric application is finding the area of a *sector* of a circle. A sector of a circle is the area enclosed by two radii and an arc of the circle (see Fig. 17–39). We can see that the area of a sector is proportional to the central angle. The area of a complete circle is $A = \pi r^2$. This formula can be written as $A = \frac{1}{2}(2\pi)r^2$. Since the central angle for a complete circle is 2π, we can write the area of any sector of a circle in terms of the radius and the central angle as

$$A = \tfrac{1}{2}\theta r^2. \qquad\qquad\qquad 17\text{-}7$$

The area of a sector whose central angle is $18°$ and radius is 5.00 in. is   Example B

$$A = \frac{1}{2}(18)\left(\frac{\pi}{180}\right)(5.00)^2 = \frac{1}{2}\left(\frac{\pi}{10}\right)(25.0) = 3.93 \text{ in}^2.$$

Given that the area of a sector is 75.5 ft^2 and the radius is 12.2 ft, we can find the central angle by

$$75.5 = \tfrac{1}{2}\theta(12.2)^2, \qquad \theta = \tfrac{151}{149} = 1.01.$$

This means that the central angle is 1.01 radians, or 57.9°.

The next illustration we shall present deals with velocity. We know that the magnitude of the average velocity is $v = s/t$, where v is the average velocity, s is the distance traveled, and t is the elapsed time. If an object is moving around a circular path with constant speed, the actual distance traveled is the length of arc traversed. Therefore, if we divide both sides of Eq. (17–6) by t, we obtain

$$\frac{s}{t} = \frac{\theta}{t}r \qquad \text{or} \qquad v = \omega r. \qquad\qquad \textbf{17-8}$$

In Eq. (17–8), v is the magnitude of the *linear velocity* and ω (the Greek omega) is the *angular velocity* of an object moving around a circle of radius r. The units of ω are radians per unit of time. However, in practice, ω is often given in revolutions per unit of time, and for such cases it is necessary to convert ω to radians per unit of time before substitution in Eq. (17–8).

Example C   The linear velocity of an object moving about a circle, whose radius is 6.00 in., with an angular velocity of 4.00 rad/sec is

$$v = (6.00)(4.00) = 24.0 \text{ in./sec.}$$

(Remember that radians are numbers and are not included in the final set of units.) This means that the object is moving along the circumference of the circle at 24.0 in./sec.

Example D   A flywheel rotates with an angular velocity of 20.0 rev/min. Its radius is 18.0 in. Find the linear velocity of a point on the rim.

$$20.0 \text{ rev/min} = \left(20.0 \frac{\text{rev}}{\text{min}}\right)\left(2\pi \frac{\text{rad}}{\text{rev}}\right) = 40.0\pi \frac{\text{rad}}{\text{min}},$$

$$v = (40.0)(3.14)(18.0) = 2260 \text{ in./min.}$$

Therefore the linear velocity is 2260 in./min, which is equivalent to 188 ft/min or 3.13 ft/sec.

Due to their nature, many phenomena are described in terms of the sine and cosine. Usually it is necessary to use these ratios with radian measure in such cases. The following example illustrates a problem from electricity.

The current at any time t in a certain alternating current circuit is given by   Example E

$$i = I \sin 60t.$$

Here I is the maximum possible current and t is the time in seconds. Given that $I = 0.020$ amp, find i for $t = 0.010$ sec.

Substituting, we have

$$i = (0.020) \sin (0.60) = (0.020)(0.565) = 0.0113 \text{ amp}.$$

1. In a circle of radius 10.0 in., find the length of arc subtended on the cir-   EXERCISES
   cumference by a central angle of 60°.

2. In a circle of diameter 4.50 ft, find the length of arc subtended on the circumference by a central angle of 42°.

3. Find the area of a sector of a circle, given that the central angle is 75° and the radius is 6.50 in.

4. Find the area of a sector of a circle, given that the central angle is 120° and the diameter is 56.0 cm.

5. Find the radius of a circle, given that the arc length is 34.0 in. for a central angle of 65°.

6. Find the central angle of a circle, given that the arc length is 780 mm and the radius is 520 mm.

7. Find the central angle of a circle, given that the area is 46.5 in^2 and the radius is 6.90 in.

8. Two concentric (same center) circles have radii of 5.00 in. and 6.00 in., respectively. Calculate the portion of the area of the sector of the larger circle which is outside the smaller circle, given that the central angle is 30°.

9. A pendulum 3.00 ft long oscillates through an angle of 5°. Find the distance through which the end of the pendulum swings in going from one extreme position to the other.

10. The radius of the earth is about 3960 mi. What is the length, in miles, of an arc of the earth's equator for a central angle of 1°?

11. In turning, an airplane traveling at 540 mi/hr moves through a circular arc for 2 min. What is the radius of the circle, given that the central angle is 8°?

12. An ammeter needle is deflected 52° by a current of 0.20 amp. The needle is 3.0 in. long and a circular scale is to be used. How long is the scale for a maximum current of 1.00 amp?

13. A flywheel whose radius is 5.28 in. rotates at 300 rev/min. Through what total distance does a point on the rim travel in 30 sec?

14. For the flywheel in Exercise 13, how far does a point halfway out, along a radius, move in one second?

15. An automobile whose tires are 28.0 in. in diameter is traveling at 60.0 mi/hr. What is the angular velocity of the tires in rad/sec?

16. Find the velocity, due to the rotation of the earth, of a point on the surface of the earth at the equator (see Exercise 10).

17. An astronaut in a spacecraft circles the earth once each 1.50 hr. If his altitude is constant at 240 mi, what is his velocity? (See Exercise 10.)

18. What is the linear velocity of the point in Exercise 13?

19. The displacement of a certain water wave (height above that which it would have if the water were calm) is given by $d = 2.5 \sin 2t$, where d is measured in ft and t in sec. Find d, given that $t = 0.60$ sec.

20. The voltage in a certain alternating electric current circuit is given by $v = V \cos 25t$, where V is the maximum possible voltage and t is the time in seconds. Find v for $t = 0.010$ sec and $V = 140$ volts.

21. A pulley belt 8.60 ft long takes 2.00 sec to make one complete revolution. The radius of the pulley is 6.00 in. What is the angular velocity, in revolutions per minute, of the pulley?

22. The moon is about 240,000 mi from the earth. What is its angular velocity about the earth in radians per second? It takes the moon about 28 days to make one revolution.

23. A phonograph record 6.90 in. in diameter rotates 45.0 times per minute. What is the linear velocity of a point on the rim in feet/second?

24. A circular sector whose central angle is 210° is cut from a circular piece of sheet metal of diameter 12.0 in. A cone is then formed by bringing the two radii of the sector together. What is the lateral surface area of the cone?

17–8 REVIEW EXERCISES

In Exercises 1 through 6, determine the indicated trigonometric ratios. The listed sides are those shown in Fig. 17–40. Do not use Table 3.

1. $a = 12$, $b = 5$. Find $\cos A$ and $\tan B$.

2. $b = 9$, $c = 15$. Find $\sec A$ and $\cot B$.

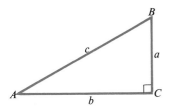

Figure 17–40

3. $a = 8.7$, $b = 2.3$. Find $\tan A$ and $\cos B$.

4. $a = 125$, $c = 148$. Find $\sin A$ and $\sec B$.

5. $a = 0.089$, $c = 0.098$. Find $\cot A$ and $\sin B$.

6. $b = 1670$, $c = 4200$. Find $\csc A$ and $\csc B$.

In Exercises 7 through 12, use Table 3 to find, to the nearest degree, the indicated angle. The parts of the triangle are those of Fig. 17–40.

7. $a = 8$, $c = 13$. Find $\angle A$.   **8.** $b = 51$, $c = 58$. Find $\angle A$.

9. $a = 5.6$, $b = 1.3$. Find $\angle B$.   **10.** $a = 0.78$, $c = 2.4$. Find $\angle B$.

11. $b = 3420$, $c = 7200$. Find $\angle B$.   **12.** $a = 0.0067$, $b = 0.0156$. Find $\angle A$.

In Exercises 13 through 20, find the indicated values on a slide rule.

13. $\sin 24°$ **14.** $\cos 18°$ **15.** $\tan 63.8°$ **16.** $\sin 48.5°$

17. $\sin \alpha = 0.785$; find α **18.** $\tan \alpha = 2.56$; find α

19. $\cos \alpha = 0.156$; find α **20.** $\sin \alpha = 0.0852$; find α

In Exercises 21 through 26, convert the radians to degrees, or the degrees to radians.

21. $12°$ **22.** $78°$ **23.** 0.639

24. 1.42 **25.** $110°$ **26.** 5

In Exercises 27 through 30, determine the values of the given trigonometric ratios.

27. $\sin 0.4$ **28.** $\cos 1.3$ **29.** $\tan 0.451$ **30.** $\cot 0.086$

In Exercises 31 through 40, solve the triangles with the given parts. The given parts are shown in Fig. 17–40.

31. $\angle A = 48°$, $a = 18$ **32.** $\angle A = 68°$, $b = 39$

33. $\angle A = 21°$, $c = 6.93$ **34.** $\angle B = 18°$, $a = 0.36$

35. $\angle B = 82°$, $b = 45.9$ **36.** $\angle B = 72°$, $c = 1890$

37. $a = 8.7$, $b = 5.2$ **38.** $a = 0.0076$, $b = 0.012$

39. $a = 97$, $c = 108$ **40.** $b = 17.4$, $c = 54.0$

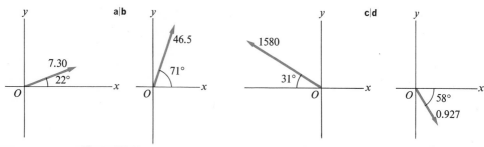

Figure 17–41

In Exercises 41 through 44, find the x- and y-components of the indicated vectors by using the trigonometric ratios.

41. The vector in Fig. 17–41(a)   **42.** The vector in Fig. 17–41(b)

43. The vector in Fig. 17–41(c)   **44.** The vector in Fig. 17–41(d)

In Exercises 45 through 48, add the indicated vectors by using the Pythagorean theorem and the trigonometric ratios.

45. The vectors in Fig. 17–42(a)   **46.** The vectors in Fig. 17–42(b)

47. The vectors in Fig. 17–42(c)   **48.** The vectors in Fig. 17–42(d)

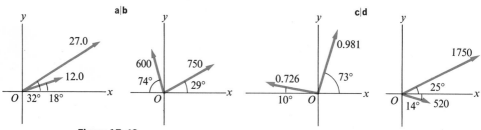

Figure 17–42

In Exercises 49 through 74, solve the given problems.

49. When the angle of elevation of the sun is 40°, what is the length of the shadow of a tree 65 ft tall?

50. The distance from a point on the shore of a lake to an island is 3500 ft. From a point directly above the shore on a cliff the angle of depression to the island is 15°. How high is the cliff?

51. The distance from point B to point C along the shore of a river is 500 ft. Point A is directly across from point C on the opposite shore. Given that $\angle ABC$ is 40°, how wide is the river?

52. A guy wire supporting a television tower is grounded 750 ft from the base of the tower. Given that the wire makes an angle of 30° with the ground, how high up on the tower is it attached?

53. The span of a roof is 30 ft. Its rise is 8 ft at the center of the span. What is the angle the roof makes with the horizontal?

54. A roadway rises 85 ft for every 1000 ft along the road. Determine the angle of inclination of the roadway.

55. A jet climbs at an angle of 35° while traveling at 600 mph. How long will it take to climb to an altitude of 10,000 ft?

56. An observer 3000 ft from the launch pad of a rocket measures the angle of inclination to the rocket soon after liftoff to be 65°. How high is the rocket, assuming it has moved vertically?

57. St. Louis has a latitude of 38.7° north. How far is it from the equator? The radius of the earth is about 3960 mi.

58. A thermometer needle passes through 55° for a temperature change of 40°. If the needle is 5.0 in. long and a circular scale is to be used, how long is the scale for a maximum temperature change of 150°?

59. The displacement of a particle moving with simple harmonic motion is given by $d = A \cos 5t$, where A is the maximum displacement and t is the time. Find d given that $A = 12.0$ ft and $t = 0.15$ sec.

60. The armature of a dynamo is 1.25 ft in diameter and is rotating at the rate of 1250 rev/min. What is the linear velocity of a point on the outside of the armature?

61. A plane travels 50 mi east from an airfield and then travels another 35 mi north. What is the plane's displacement from the airfield?

62. Two forces, 16 lb and 34 lb, act on the same object and at right angles to each other. What is the resultant force on the object?

63. A ship is traveling at 15.0 mi/hr. What is the velocity of a person walking across the deck, at right angles to the direction of the ship, at 3.00 mi/hr with respect to the sea?

64. A balloon is rising at the rate of 15.0 ft/sec and at the same time is being blown horizontally by the wind at the rate of 22.5 ft/sec. Find the resultant velocity.

65. An astronaut, traveling toward the moon, notes that the moon's diameter subtends an angle of 4° when he is 31,000 mi from it. What is the diameter of the moon?

66. The distance from ground level to the underside of a cloud is called the *ceiling*. One observer 1000 ft from a searchlight notes that the angle of

elevation of the spot of light on a cloud from a vertical beam is 76°. What is the ceiling?

67. A person observes an object drop from a window 20 ft away and directly opposite him. Given that the distance the object drops as a function of time is $s = 16t^2$, how far is the object from the observer (on a straight line) after 2.0 sec?

68. A picture 8.0 ft in height is on a wall with the lower edge 5.0 ft above an observer's eye. The observer is 15 ft from the wall. What angle does the picture subtend at the observer's eye?

69. A pulley of radius 3.60 in. is belted to another pulley of radius 5.75 in. The smaller pulley rotates at 35.0 rev/sec. What is the angular velocity of the larger pulley?

70. A lathe is to cut material at the rate of 350 ft/min. Calculate the radius of a cylindrical piece that is turned at the rate of 120 rev/min.

71. The side of an equilateral triangle is 24 in. How long is its altitude?

72. A certain machine part is a regular hexagon (6 sides) 0.844 in. on a side. What is the distance across from one side to the opposite side?

73. Given that A and B are acute angles, is $\cos A > \cos B$ if $A > B$? Is $\tan A > \tan B$ if $A > B$?

74. Show, by means of the definitions, that $\tan A = \sin A/\cos A$. Also show that $(\sin A)^2 + (\cos A)^2 = 1$, using the definitions and the Pythagorean theorem.

Answers to
Odd-Numbered
Exercises

Section 1–2   **1.** 161   **3.** 1636   **5.** 2694   **7.** 24,672   **9.** 25,295
11. 139,639   **13.** 581   **15.** 949   **17.** 9798   **19.** 95,682
21. 10 ft 3 in.   **23.** 29 yd 1 ft   **25.** 11 in.   **27.** 8 yd 2 ft
29. 3301 mi   **31.** 10 gal 3 qt   **33.** 4 hr 41 min 30 sec
35. 6824 sq mi   **37.** $2686   **39.** 10 hr 44 min

Section 1–3   **1.** 6993   **3.** 2,337,545   **5.** 15,830,199   **7.** 251,387,772
9. 243   **11.** 326   **13.** 1423, rem. 13   **15.** 1570, rem. 374
17. 47,804   **19.** 72,220   **21.** 238 sq in.   **23.** 6 sq ft
25. 108 ft   **27.** 10,115 mi   **29.** 19 mi/gal   **31.** 67,664 sq ft
33. 15,920 mi/hr   **35.** 36 mi

Section 1–4   **1.** $1\frac{2}{3}$ **3.** $4\frac{25}{62}$ **5.** $\frac{13}{5}$ **7.** $\frac{344}{19}$ **9.** $\frac{6}{14}$ **11.** $\frac{4}{5}$
13. $\frac{24}{78}$ **15.** $\frac{5}{13}$ **17.** $\frac{91}{175}$ **19.** $\frac{32}{2}$ **21.** $\frac{1}{3}$ **23.** $\frac{6}{13}$
25. $\frac{3}{5}$ **27.** $\frac{6}{7}$ **29.** $\frac{3}{11}$ **31.** $\frac{13}{9}$ **33.** $\frac{11}{5}$ **35.** $\frac{17}{19}$
37. $\frac{17}{27}$ **39.** $\frac{220}{43}$ **41.** $\frac{1}{7}$ **43.** $\frac{2}{7}$ **45.** $\frac{77}{20}$ min   **47.** $\frac{9}{5}$

Section 1–5   **1.** 23, 29   **3.** 41, 43, 47, 53, 59   **5.** 4   **7.** 24   **9.** 72
11. 300   **13.** $\frac{4}{5}$ **15.** $\frac{4}{3}$ **17.** $\frac{11}{4}$ **19.** $\frac{1}{3}$ **21.** $\frac{83}{24}$
23. $\frac{47}{40}$ **25.** $\frac{73}{72}$ **27.** $\frac{73}{42}$ **29.** $8\frac{1}{2}$ in.   **31.** $4\frac{7}{12}$ ft
33. $7\frac{263}{360}$ ohms   **35.** $\frac{4}{15}$

Section 1–6   **1.** $\frac{6}{77}$ **3.** $\frac{6}{5}$ **5.** $\frac{21}{20}$ **7.** $\frac{5}{27}$ **9.** $\frac{5}{18}$ **11.** $\frac{3}{2}$
13. $\frac{14}{9}$ **15.** $\frac{2}{17}$ **17.** 2   **19.** $\frac{2}{15}$ **21.** $\frac{27}{64}$ **23.** $\frac{5}{4}$
25. $\frac{16}{9}$ **27.** $\frac{1}{5}$; $\frac{1}{13}$ **29.** $\frac{9}{2}$, $\frac{7}{3}$ **31.** 75 volts   **33.** $\frac{7}{6}$ in.
35. 12 articles   **37.** $\frac{13}{22}$ acres/hr   **39.** $7\frac{7}{40}$ bu

Section 1–7   **1.** $4(10) + 7(1) + \frac{3}{10}$
3. $4(100) + 2(10) + 9(1) + \frac{4}{10} + \frac{8}{100} + \frac{6}{1000}$ **5.** 27.3
7. 57.54   **9.** 8.03   **11.** 17.4   **13.** 0.4   **15.** 0.21
17. 1.7   **19.** 0.499   **21.** $\frac{9}{20}$ **23.** $\frac{267}{50}$ **25.** 31.295

27. 2817.256 **29.** 8.763 **31.** 13.99952 **33.** 124.992
35. 12.5 **37.** 0.34 **39.** 28.5 ohms **41.** \$235.88
43. 15.96 sq in. **45.** 43.8 mi/hr **47.** 8.5

1. 0.08 **3.** 2.36 **5.** 0.003 **7.** 27% **9.** 321% Section 1–8
11. 0.64% **13.** $\frac{3}{10}$ **15.** $\frac{1}{40}$ **17.** $\frac{6}{5}$ **19.** 60%
21. 57.1% **23.** 22.9% **25.** 13 **27.** 5.304 **29.** 25%
31. 7.5% **33.** 50 **35.** 400 **37.** \$15.12 **39.** \$15.30
41. 35% **43.** 18% **45.** 11 amps

1. 2^4 **3.** 10^5 **5.** $3 \times 3 \times 3 \times 3 \times 3 \times 3$ Section 1–9
7. $7 \times 7 \times 7 \times 7 \times 7 \times 7$ **9.** 4 **11.** 3 **13.** 2 **15.** 108
17. 4500 **19.** 891 **21.** 6.856 **23.** 2.571 **25.** 46,656
27. 27 **29.** 0.99 **31.** 2.7 **33.** 1.94 **35.** 40,000,000 ft
37. 2.48 sec **39.** 27.9 ft **41.** 0.759 atm

1. 3 **3.** 9 **5.** 108 **7.** 305 **9.** 110 **11.** 10001 Section 1–10
13. 101110 **15.** 1001111 **17.** 1111 **19.** 101101
21. 11011001 **23.** 110 **25.** 1110101 **27.** 100011011010
29. 11101

1. 13,330 **3.** 2779 **5.** 121.112 **7.** 1876.96 Section 1–11
9. 4,365,872 **11.** 428 **13.** 72.312 **15.** 0.014
17. 37.11312 **19.** $\frac{5}{13}$ **21.** $\frac{19}{10}$ **23.** $\frac{71}{60}$ **25.** $\frac{401}{525}$
27. $\frac{22}{5}$ **29.** $\frac{11}{6}$ **31.** $\frac{4}{3}$ **33.** $\frac{215}{33}$ **35.** 7 **37.** 10
39. 48 **41.** 49 **43.** $\frac{9}{2}$; $\frac{7}{22}$ **45.** 0.28125 **47.** $\frac{14}{25}$
49. 0.82; $\frac{41}{50}$ **51.** 0.0055; $\frac{11}{2000}$ **53.** 93.4% **55.** 8%
57. 6.557 **59.** 4096 **61.** 0.734 **63.** 3.06 **65.** 5
67. 18 **69.** 1110 **71.** 1000010 **73.** 17.98 in.
75. 29.54 in. **77.** 21.5 ft **79.** 20.6 ohms **81.** $\frac{7}{32}$ in.
83. $\frac{3}{10}$ pt **85.** \$6.21 **87.** 0.01 lb **89.** 15.3% **91.** 2.5%
93. 9.5 ohms **95.** $20\frac{9}{16}$ in.

Section 2–1   **1.** 1760 yd/mi   **3.** 100,000 cm/km
5. (12 in./ft)(12 in./ft) = 144 sq in./sq ft   **7.** 12.7 cm
9. 64 pints   **11.** 9.46 l.   **13.** 0.163 lb   **15.** 13.59 l.
17. 130 tons   **19.** 37 mi/hr   **21.** 770 mi/hr   **23.** 345 lb/ft^3
25. 1030 g/cm^2 **27.** 0.47 l/sec

Section 2–2   **1.** 24 is exact   **3.** 3 is exact, 74.6 is approx.   **5.** 1063 is approx.
7. 100 and 200 are approx.; 3200 is exact   **9.** 3, 4   **11.** 3, 4
13. 3, 3   **15.** 1, 6   **17.** (a) 3.764, (b) 3.764
19. (a) 0.01, (b) 30.8   **21.** (a) same, (b) 78.0
23. (a) 0.004, (b) same   **25.** (a) 4.93, (b) 4.9
27. (a) 57900, (b) 58000   **29.** (a) 861, (b) 860
31. (a) 0.305, (b) 0.31   **33.** 18.5 gal, 19.5 gal   **35.** 3.68 min

Section 2–3   **1.** 51.2   **3.** 1.70   **5.** 431.4   **7.** 30.9   **9.** 62.1
11. 270   **13.** 160   **15.** 27,000   **17.** 5.7   **19.** 4.39
21. 10.2   **23.** 22   **25.** 17.62   **27.** 18.85   **29.** 21.0 lb
31. First plane, 70 mi/hr   **33.** 62.1 lb/ft^3 **35.** 850,000 lb
37. 115 ft/sec

Section 2–4   **1.** 2, 3   **3.** 4, 2   **5.** (a) 9.82, (b) same
7. (a) 0.0023, (b) 23.685   **9.** 3.83, 3.8   **11.** 368,000, 370,000
13. 57000, 57000   **15.** 5550, 5500   **17.** 438.7   **19.** 10.89
21. 0.12   **23.** 0.057   **25.** 6.9   **27.** 7.6   **29.** 13 cm
31. 35.62 pints   **33.** 760 l   **35.** 740 in^3 **37.** 1.10 m/sec
39 1.06 tons/ft^2 **41.** 30,630,000 cm^3/min   **43.** 0.00038 in^2
45. 0.67 kg/l   **47.** 0.2845 in., 0.2855 in.   **49.** 146.5 g
51. 0.43 in.   **53.** Did not record fact that time was 2.0 sec; no.

Section 3–1   **1.** 1080   **3.** 442   **5.** 1670   **7.** 524   **9.** 388   **11.** 1360

13, 15,
17, 19:

21, 23, 25, 27:

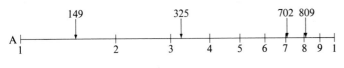

149   325   702 809

A

1   2   3   4   5   6 7 8 9   1

29. 400   **31.** 30,000,000   **33.** 8 (or 9)   **35.** 15

Section 3–2

1. 6.00   **3.** 180   **5.** 0.00856   **7.** 5.27   **9.** 0.00338

11. 740   **13.** 7   **15.** 0.50   **17.** 311   **19.** 389

21. 1,465,000   **23.** 1518   **25.** 4170   **27.** 227,000   **29.** 751

31. 4.01   **33.** 548 in^2 **35.** 53.4 mi/hr   **37.** 99.6 lb

39. 121 turns   **41.** 39.4 cm   **43.** $447

Section 3–3

1. 196   **3.** 2120   **5.** 0.000400   **7.** 45.0   **9.** 98.8

11. 4,380,000,000   **13.** 2,400,000   **15.** 0.194   **17.** 6.40

19. 0.117   **21.** 23.9   **23.** 0.756   **25.** 218   **27.** 0.255

29. 4.73   **31.** 95.2   **33.** 29.0   **35.** 5820   **37.** 3960 cm^2

39. 154 ft

Section 3–4

1. 6.22   **3.** 3.31   **5.** 2.07   **7.** 1.36   **9.** 9.81

11. 0.116   **13.** 3.67   **15.** 65.3   **17.** 0.0855   **19.** 452

21. 0.0369   **23.** 0.000944   **25.** 731 rev/min   **27.** 99.2 cm^2

29. 230 ft/sec   **31.** 6.64 acres

Section 3–5

1. 17.0   **3.** 18,800   **5.** 74,500   **7.** 2,480,000   **9.** 33.6

11. 32.9   **13.** 8.49   **15.** 0.679   **17.** 139   **19.** 2780

21. 0.511   **23.** 14.4   **25.** 2.62   **27.** 67.2   **29.** 28.0

31. 428   **33.** 5.44   **35.** 0.960   **37.** 6420   **39.** 14.2

41. 18.6   **43.** 664   **45.** 215 mi   **47.** $6750   **49.** 681 in.

51. 204 mi   **53.** 3850 mi/hr   **55.** 299 cm^2 **57.** 0.181 mi/sec

Section 4–1

1. Add 7 to 2   **3.** Add +9 to +5   **5.** Add −3 to −4

7. Subtract +2 from −5

9, 11, 13, 15:

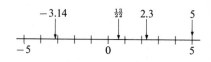

17. 4   **19.** -2 **21.** $6 > 2$ **23.** $0 < 4$ **25.** $-3 > -7$
27. $|6| = |-6|$ **29.** 6   **31.** $\frac{6}{7}$ **33.** -100
35. -25 volts   **37.** -2600 **39.** -7 (as of 1969)
41. $-30°F < -5°F$

Section 4–2   **1.** $+10$ **3.** -15 **5.** -6 **7.** -4 **9.** $+4$ **11.** -2
13. -8 **15.** $+1$ **17.** -17 **19.** -6

21 and 23:

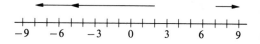

25. $+15°F$ **27.** 20 min   **29.** \$70   **31.** A statement containing
a double negative is equivalent to a positive statement.

Section 4–3   **1.** -28 **3.** $+16$ **5.** 0   **7.** -168 **9.** -4 **11.** 0
13. -27 **15.** $+2$ **17.** $+30$ **19.** -3 **21.** -5
23. $+5$ **25.** 98 cm   **27.** 40,000 ft   **29.** 1.05 amps

Section 4–4   **1.** -2 **3.** -8 **5.** -13 **7.** $+10$ **9.** $+96$ **11.** -4
13. -30 **15.** $+3$ **17.** $+10$ **19.** $+5$ **21.** 0   **23.** -5

25 and 27:

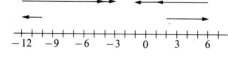

29. $+4 > -5$ **31.** $-8 < -2$ **33.** $+1, -1$
35. Profit was made   **37.** 71°F   **39.** \$80   **41.** 14,500 mi/hr
43. 1650 lb/in^2

Section 5–1   **1.** b, c **3.** $9, p, q, r$ **5.** i^2, R **7.** a, b, c, d, e **9.** 6
11. $8a^2$ **13.** $4e$ **15.** mw^2 **17.** ab **19.** x^2 **21.** $2w^2$

23. a^3b^2 **25.** $x = 2y$ **27.** $V = 7.48\ lwd$ **29.** $s = \frac{1}{2}gt^2$

31. $A = s^2$ **33.** $N = 24n$ **35.** 1,800,000 mi   **37.** 90 gal

39. 1000 cm^2 **41.** 680 ft

1. $a^2, -3ab, 7b$ **3.** $3, -6ab, 7a, -8/b$ **5.** $-x$ and $3x$ Section 5–2

7. x and $2x$ **9.** $-2mn$ and $-mn$ **11.** $3x^3, -5x^3$ and $-x^3$

13. $6a(a - x)$ **15.** $x^2(a - x)(a + x)$ **17.** $\dfrac{2}{5a}$ **19.** $\dfrac{6}{a - b}$

21. $p = 2l + 2w$ **23.** $A = 2x^2 + 4xl$ **25.** $V = I(R + r)$

27. $A = \dfrac{a + b + c + d + e}{5}$ **29.** $T = 6.28\sqrt{l/g}$ **31.** 20 in.

33. 0.357 volt   **35.** 0.647

1. $3a - b$ **3.** $7a + 4b^2$ **5.** $5x + 5y$ **7.** $4ax + 2ay$ Section 5–3

9. $x - y$ **11.** $3x - 2y$ **13.** $3a + 3x + bx$ **15.** $5x^2 + 14xy$

17. $ax + 3ac - 2c^2$ **19.** $7ax + 3bx - 3a^2$ **21.** $3abc - c^2 + b$

23. $5abc + b - 10$ **25.** $4x + 5a$ ft   **27.** $2xy + 5y + 15$

29. $3ay$ gal   **31.** 60   **33.** -4 **35.** 848 in^2 **37.** 846

1. $3x + 2y$ **3.** $6a^2 - 2ax$ **5.** $3x + y$ **7.** $2a - b$ Section 5–4

9. $3a + 11b - ab$ **11.** $2ax + 2a$ **13.** $2a - ax$

15. $3ab + a - 2b$ **17.** $3 + 5a + ax$ **19.** $13a + 3b$

21. $5a + 4b$ **23.** $4ax - 5xy + 2ay$ **25.** 98   **27.** -26

29. 218,448   **31.** $p = 3s$ **33.** $I = 300ar + 2a$

35. $V = 40n + 145$ **37.** $d = 6at + 8a$ **39.** $C = 2ad - 10a$

41. 21 in.   **43.** 5580 ft^2 **45.** (a) 400 mi, (b) 723 mi

47. (a) \$600, (b) \$2200

1. 5   **3.** 3   **5.** 8   **7.** 35   **9.** -4 **11.** 3   **13.** 8   Section 6–1

15. -12 **17.** 7   **19.** 1/2   **21.** 2/3   **23.** -5 **25.** 13

27. 11   **29.** 3   **31.** 22/3   **33.** 3   **35.** First has no solution

1. $\dfrac{Id^2}{5300E}$ **3.** $v_2 - at$ **5.** $\dfrac{PV}{R}$ **7.** $\dfrac{yd}{ml}$ **9.** $\dfrac{L - 3.14r_2 - 2d}{3.14}$ Section 6–2

11. $\dfrac{L - L_0}{L_0 t}$ **13.** $\dfrac{p - p_a + dgy_1}{dg}$ **15.** $\dfrac{f_s u - fu}{f}$ **17.** $a - bc$

19. $\dfrac{f - 3y}{a}$ **21.** $\dfrac{3y - 2ay}{2a}$ **23.** $2b + 4$ **25.** $\dfrac{x_1 - x_2 - 3a}{a}$

27. $\dfrac{3y + 6 - 7ay}{7a}$ **29.** $\dfrac{x - 3a - ax}{a}$ **31.** $3A - a - b$

33. $\dfrac{y - 200}{85}$ **35.** $\dfrac{b - 5t}{2t}$

Section 6–3   **1.** 7 in., 13 in.   **3.** 24 mm   **5.** 43 in., 53 in.
7. 300 cards/min, 750 cards/min   **9.** 13 nickels, 8 quarters   **11.** 8
13. After 6.5 hr   **15.** 6.6 hr, 5.4 hr   **17.** $\frac{20}{3}$ qt   **19.** 240 g
21. 5 in., 8 in.   **23.** 50 acres at \$200; 90 acres at \$300   **25.** 315 mi
27. 5.6 qt

Section 6–4   **1.** $y = kt$ **3.** $y = ks^2$ **5.** $t = k/y$ **7.** $y = kst$
9. $y = ks/t$ **11.** $x = \dfrac{kyz}{t^2}$ **13.** $y = 5s$ **15.** $s = 2t^3$
17. $u = 272/d^2$ **19.** 16   **21.** 32/5   **23.** 72/5   **25.** $v = 32t$
27. $E = 15V^2$; grams   **29.** 13.5 hp   **31.** $P = RT/V$
33. $l = Rd^2/k$

Section 6–5   **1.** 8   **3.** 9   **5.** -2 **7.** $R - R_1 - R_2$ **9.** ms_1/r
11. 4   **13.** -2 **15.** 10   **17.** $\dfrac{d_m + A}{A}$ **19.** $\dfrac{W + H_1 - H_2}{S_1 - S_2}$
21. $\dfrac{2a + ax}{3}$ **23.** $\dfrac{ax + ab - bx}{b}$ **25.** $\dfrac{6 - x - a^2}{a}$ **27.** $\dfrac{2 - 3a}{6}$
29. 3   **31.** 2   **33.** -3 **35.** $y = kx^2$ **37.** $v = kst^2$
39. $f = k\sqrt{t}$ **41.** 4 in.   **43.** 12 hp, 10 hp, 4 hp   **45.** 5750 ft
47. 31 6¢ stamps, 21 10¢ stamps   **49.** 1350 mi/hr, 1650 mi/hr
51. 22.5 qt   **53.** $x = yz/9$ **55.** 9 lb   **57.** 3.33 sec

Section 7–1   **1.** 26°   **3.** 104°   **5.** 17.1°   **7.** 73.91°   **9.** $\angle CBD, \angle DBA$
11. 65°   **13.** 135°   **15.** 3 in.

17.
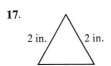

19.
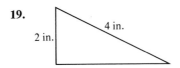

21.
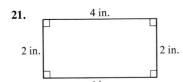

23.
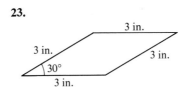

25. (a) Yes, (b) No   **27.** Two equal isosceles triangles   **29.** 54°

1. 36 ft   **3.** 23.00 cm   **5.** 25 ft   **7.** 10 yd   **9.** 18.46 in.   Section 7–2
11. 62.4 m   **13.** 62.8 ft   **15.** 45.36 in.   **17.** $p = 2s + a$
19. $p = 2r + \pi r$ **21.** $p = 5s$ **23.** $p = 2a + b_1 + b_2$
25. $a = p - b - c$ **27.** $r = c/2\pi$ **29.** $b = p - a - r - \pi r/2$
31. 42 ft   **33.** \$9.00   **35.** 2680 ft   **37.** 106 yd

1. 28 in^2 **3.** 13 yd^2 **5.** 24 ft^2 **7.** 154 in^2 Section 7–3
9. 36 in., 60 in^2 **11.** 30 in., 30 in^2 **13.** 26 in., 32 in^2
15. 216 ft^3 **17.** 169 in^3 **19.** $A = bh_1 + \frac{1}{2}bh_2$
21. $A = \frac{1}{2}ar + \frac{1}{4}\pi r^2$ **23.** $A = r^2 + 2rh + \frac{1}{2}\pi r^2$ **25.** $l = V/wh$
27. $h = \dfrac{2A - \pi r^2}{4r}$ **29.** 784 in^2 **31.** \$48   **33.** 41.1 ft^2
35. 6160 lb   **37.** 155 in^2 **39.** 3010 gal

1. 52 ft   **3.** 50 ft   **5.** 75.4 yd   **7.** 73.1 ft   **9.** 144 ft^2 Section 7–4
11. 120 ft^2 **13.** 452 yd^2 **15.** 156 ft^2
17. 10,700 cm^3; 2900 cm^2 **19.** 210 ft^3 **21.** $p = 2b + 2c$
23. $p = 3a + \pi a$ **25.** $A = \frac{1}{2}ac$ **27.** $A = \frac{1}{2}\pi a^2 + \frac{3}{2}ah$
29. 300 yd   **31.** 13.6 in.   **33.** 5 in., 5 in., 5 in., 8 in.
35. 10.4 in.   **37.** 1690 ft^2 **39.** 30,700 lb   **41.** 19 lb
43. 5730 in.   **45.** 6500 mi, 6220 mi

Section 8–1 **1.** $3s - xy - a$ **3.** $9y - 3x - 4a - 9xy$ **5.** $3x + 2xy$
7. $-3x^2 + 3xy - 2s$ **9.** $2a + 3$ **11.** $-4 - 4x$
13. $2s - 1$ **15.** $4y - 9$ **17.** $10x + 1$
19. $7t - 5x - 5p^2 + 9$ **21.** 1 **23.** $3/2$ **25.** $5 - 4a$
27. $6/5$ **29.** 3 **31.** $-32M - 1270$ **33.** $\dfrac{mv_0 - I}{m}$
35. $V - iR - ir + E$

Section 8–2 **1.** x^{10} **3.** y^8 **5.** x^{21} **7.** y^{15} **9.** $-6a^3x^2y$
11. $-45\,a^2ct^7$ **13.** $-84r^2s^2t^4$ **15.** $-8s^3t^9x^3$ **17.** $2a^2 + 6ax$
19. $-2s^2tx + 2st^3y$ **21.** $-3x^3y^2 + 9ax^2y^7$ **23.** $2x^2 + x - 1$
25. $a^2 - 3ax + 2x^2$ **27.** $2x^2 + 18x - 5tx - 45t$
29. $4a^2 - 81p^2y^2$ **31.** $a^2 + 2axy - 4ax - 2x^2y + 3x^2$
33. $x^3 - 3x^2 - 10x + 24$ **35.** $x^2 + 4xy + 4y^2$
37. $x^3 + 3x^2 + 3x + 1$ **39.** $x^2 - y^2$ **41.** $v = 6t^2 - 36t + 48$
43. $(10)(2) = 4(9) - (16)$ **45.** $mv_2^2 - mv_1^2$

Section 8–3 **1.** x^3 **3.** a **5.** $1/p^{10}$ **7.** $4n^3$ **9.** $-ax$
11. $\dfrac{2at^4}{c^2}$ **13.** $-\dfrac{x}{4r^2}$ **15.** $\dfrac{7t^2u}{6}$ **17.** $-a^2x^2 + ax$
19. $y^2 - 2xy^3$ **21.** $bc - ab^3c^4 - 2a$ **23.** $-ab^2 + 2a^2b^3 + 1 + b$
25. $x - 3$ **27.** $2x + 1$ **29.** $2x^2 - x + 3$
31. $2x^3 - x^2 + 2x + 1 - 2/(3x - 1)$ **33.** -1 **35.** $6/17$
37. $a + 5$ **39.** $\dfrac{1}{R_1} + \dfrac{1}{R_2} + \dfrac{1}{R_3}$ **41.** $6, 9$

Section 8–4 **1.** $3a - x$ **3.** $2n - 4$ **5.** $9x - 13y$ **7.** $8 - 5x$
9. $5x - 2a$ **11.** $5b - 10$ **13.** $14x^2y^5z^6$ **15.** $27a^3b^6$
17. $-2a^3x + 2a^2t$ **19.** $2x^2 - x - 10$ **21.** $6a^2 - 11ab - 10b^2$
23. $-2x^3 + 6x^2 + 4x - 16$ **25.** $-4ax^3$ **27.** $-2y^3 + 3x^3$
29. $h - 3j^2 - 6h^3j^3$ **31.** $x + 4$ **33.** $x^2 - x + 1 - 11/(2x + 3)$
35. $x + 2y$ **37.** 5 **39.** $16/3$ **41.** $-2/3$ **43.** $a^2 + 1$
45. $-4x^2 + 8x$ **47.** $S = \dfrac{a - ar^4}{1 - r}$ **49.** $8xd$ **51.** $2a + 7$
53. 1333 mi   **55.** 5 in., 7 in., 8 in.

1. $(2)(5)$ 3. $(2)(2)(7)$ 5. $(2)(2)(2)(2)(2)(3)$

7. $2, x - 1, x + 3$ 9. $3, 5, a, a, c$ 11. $3, 3, c, c, ax - b, cx + d$

13. Yes   15. No   17. No   19. No   21. 3   23. 4

25. $x + 3$ 27. All   29. $a + x^2$

1. $5(x + y)$ 3. $2x(x - 2)$ 5. $a(a + 2)$ 7. $2p(2 - 3q)$

9. $3ab(a + 3)$ 11. $acf(abc - 4)$ 13. $5(x^2 + 3xy - 4y^3)$

15. $4pq(3q - 2 - 7q^2)$ 17. $7a^2b^2(5ab^2c^2 + 2b^3c^3 - 3a)$

19. $3a(2ab - 1 + 3b^2 - 4ab^2)$ 21. $17s(3pqr - 2qrt - rtu - 4tuv)$

23. $3(a - b)(a - b + 2x)$ 25. $2(lw + lh + hw)$

27. $Rv(1 + v + v^2 + v^3 + v^4 + v^5)$ 29. $wx(x^3 - 2Lx^2 + L^3)$

1. $9, 25, 4x^2$ 3. a^2b^4 5. $x^2 - y^2$ 7. $4a^2 - b^2$

9. $49a^2x^4 - p^6$ 11. 399   13. 39,900   15. $(a + b)(a - b)$

17. $(4 + x)(4 - x)$ 19. $(2x^2 + y)(2x^2 - y)$

21. $(ab + 3y)(ab - 3y)$ 23. $(9x^2 + 2y^3)(9x^2 - 2y^3)$

25. $4(x + 5y)(x - 5y)$ 27. $(x^2 + 1)(x + 1)(x - 1)$

29. $4(x^2 + 9y^2)$ 31. $m(v_1 + v_2)(v_1 - v_2)$ 33. $x(x + y)(x - y)$

1. $(x + 1)(x + 2)$ 3. $(x - 3)(x + 4)$ 5. $(y - 5)(y + 1)$

7. $(x + 5)^2$ 9. $(2q + 1)(q + 5)$ 11. Prime

13. $(2s - 3t)(s - 5t)$ 15. $(5x + 2)(x + 3)$ 17. $(2x - 3)(2x - 1)$

19. $(6t - 5u)(t + 2u)$ 21. $(4x - 3)(2x + 3)$ 23. $(6q + 1)(2q + 3)$

25. $2(x - 3)(x - 8)$ 27. $2(2x - 3z)(x + 2z)$

29. $2x(x + 1)(x + 2)$ 31. $a(5x - y)(2x + 5y)$

33. $(x - 10)(x + 4)$ 35. $3(s - 50)(s + 60)$

37. $5(T + 20)(T + 100)$ 39. $(2x - 25)(x - 100)$

1. $5(a - c)$ 3. $3a(a + 2)$ 5. $4ab(3a + 1)$

7. $(2x + y)(2x - y)$ 9. $(4y^2 + x)(4y^2 - x)$ 11. $(x + 1)^2$

13. $(x - 1)(x - 6)$ 15. $a(x^2 + 3ax - a^2)$

17. $2mn(m^2 - 2mn + 3n^2)$ 19. $4t^2(p^3 - 3t^2 - 1 + a)$

21. $(4rs + 3y)(4rs - 3y)$ 23. Prime   25. $(2x + 7)(x + 1)$

27. $(7t + 1)(2t - 3)$ **29.** $(3x + 1)^2$ **31.** $(x + y)(x + 2y)$

33. $(5c - d)(2c + 5d)$ **35.** $(8x + 7)(11x - 12)$

37. $2(x + 3y)(x - 3y)$ **39.** $8x^4y^2(xy + 2)(xy - 2)$

41. $3a(x - 3)(x + 4)$ **43.** $3r(6r - 13s)(3r + 4s)$

45. $16y^3(y - 1)(y - 3)$ **47.** $(4x^2 + 1)(2x + 1)(2x - 1)$

49. $P(N + 2)$ **51.** $k(D + 2r)(D - 2r)$ **53.** $(v_2 - 3v_1)(v_2 - v_1)$

55. $\dfrac{(u - 1)^2}{(u + 1)^2}$ **57.** $(2x + 13)(x - 4)$ **59.** $(T - 10)(T + 530)$

Section 10–1

1. $\dfrac{4}{6}; \dfrac{10}{15}$ **3.** $\dfrac{6a^3x}{2a^2b}; \dfrac{3a^2bx}{ab^2}$ **5.** $\dfrac{x^2 - 2xy + y^2}{x^2 - y^2}; \dfrac{x^2 - y^2}{x^2 + 2xy + y^2}$

7. $\dfrac{4}{7}$ **9.** $\dfrac{2a}{3a^2}$ **11.** $\dfrac{2x - 1}{x + 1}$ **13.** $\dfrac{2}{9}$ **15.** $\dfrac{ab}{4}$ **17.** $\dfrac{2t}{7r^2s}$

19. $\dfrac{(x + 1)(x + 2)}{2(x + 3)}$ **21.** $\dfrac{x + 1}{x - 1}$ **23.** $\dfrac{x}{x + 2}$ **25.** $\dfrac{3x - 2}{4x + 3}$

27. $\dfrac{x + 3y}{3y}$ **29.** $\dfrac{1 - 3x}{3x + 1}$ **31.** $\dfrac{5 - x}{2 + x}$ **33.** $\dfrac{3}{7}$ **35.** -1

Section 10–2

1. $\dfrac{1}{8n}$ **3.** $\dfrac{1}{a^2b}$ **5.** $-\dfrac{3y}{2x^2}$ **7.** $\dfrac{2a}{15}$ **9.** $\dfrac{rt}{12}$ **11.** $\dfrac{81}{256}$

13. $\dfrac{a^{10}}{32x^5}$ **15.** $\dfrac{24mx}{7}$ **17.** $\dfrac{y}{45x}$ **19.** $\dfrac{1}{2a^2b^2}$ **21.** $\dfrac{a + 3b}{a + b}$

23. $\dfrac{5x(x - y)}{6}$ **25.** $\dfrac{(x + 3)(x - 3)}{(x - 2)(x - 4)}$ **27.** $\dfrac{3(a - b)}{(a - 2b)(a + b)}$

29. $\dfrac{(s + 2)(s + 7)}{(s - 12)(s + 11)}$ **31.** $\dfrac{(x - 1)^2}{3x + 2}$ **33.** $\dfrac{2a(a + b)}{(a - b)(2a + b)}$

35. $\dfrac{81a(2x - 3y)(2x + 3y)}{(x - y)(x + y)}$ **37.** $\dfrac{pq}{p + q}$ **39.** 1

Section 10–3

1. $12a$ **3.** $90y$ **5.** $420ax$ **7.** $375ax^2$ **9.** $75a^3$

11. $96a^3b^3$ **13.** $60a^2cx^3$ **15.** $8x(x - 1)$ **17.** $6ax(a - 3)$

19. $6x(x - y)(x + y)$ **21.** $(a - 2b)(a + 2b)(a + b)$

23. $12(x - 3)(x + 3)^2$ **25.** $2(x - 3y)(x + 3y)(3x + 2y)$

Section 10–4

1. $\dfrac{20}{36a} - \dfrac{21}{36a}$ **3.** $\dfrac{5b}{abx} + \dfrac{a}{abx} - \dfrac{4bx}{abx}$ **5.** $\dfrac{8x}{2x^2(x - 1)} - \dfrac{3}{2x^2(x - 1)}$

7. $\dfrac{x(x + 2)^2}{2(x - 2)(x + 2)^2} + \dfrac{10(x + 2)}{2(x - 2)(x + 2)^2} - \dfrac{6x(x - 2)}{2(x - 2)(x + 2)^2}$

9. $\dfrac{26b - 25}{40b}$ **11.** $\dfrac{8y - b}{by^2}$ **13.** $\dfrac{2xy + 5x^2 - 3}{x^2 y}$

15. $\dfrac{42yz - 15xz + 2xy}{12xyz}$ **17.** $\dfrac{2x^2 + 3x + 9}{4(x - 3)(x + 3)}$

19. $\dfrac{y^2 - 6y - 3}{3(y - 3)(y + 3)}$ **21.** $\dfrac{-(x + 6)}{2(2x + 3)}$ **23.** $\dfrac{3x^2 - 17x + 14}{(2 - 3x)(2 + 3x)}$

25. $\dfrac{4 + 15x - 5x^2}{(x - 2)(x + 2)}$ **27.** $\dfrac{7p^2 + 4p + 8q - 175q^2}{8(p - 5q)^2}$ **29.** $\dfrac{326}{75}$ in^2

31. $\dfrac{g_m + 8}{g_m^2}$ **33.** $\dfrac{p^2 - 2gm^2 rM}{2mr^2}$ **35.** $\dfrac{h_1 P_1^2 - h_2 P_2^2}{(h_1 + h_2)(h_1 - h_2)}$

Section 10–5

1. 6   **3.** $\frac{31}{14}$ **5.** $\frac{19}{2}$ **7.** $-\frac{87}{10}$ **9.** 4   **11.** $\frac{21}{19}$

13. -2 **15.** $\frac{9}{2}$ **17.** No solution   **19.** $\frac{23}{8}$

21. $\dfrac{b}{3b - 1}$ **23.** $\dfrac{3}{2n - 4}$ **25.** $\dfrac{a^2 + 3a - 8}{a(a - 1)}$ **27.** $\dfrac{pf}{p - f}$

29. $\dfrac{2D_p}{D_0 - D_p}$ **31.** $\dfrac{2\pi^2 r^2 (P - p)}{m^2}$ **33.** 24 in., 16 in.

35. 4.5 mi/hr

Section 10–6

1. $\dfrac{3rt^4}{s^3}$ **3.** $\dfrac{a}{3bc^2}$ **5.** $\dfrac{4}{x - 2y}$ **7.** $\dfrac{p + q}{3 + 2p^2}$ **9.** $\dfrac{a}{2b}$

11. $\dfrac{3x + y}{2x - y}$ **13.** $\dfrac{10a}{3x^2}$ **15.** $\dfrac{15y}{4x}$ **17.** $\dfrac{6}{a}$ **19.** $\dfrac{2bu}{av}$

21. $\dfrac{10b - 3a}{5a^2 b}$ **23.** $\dfrac{10cd + c - 6}{2c^2 d}$ **25.** $\dfrac{x - 5}{4}$

27. $2y^2 - xy - 6x^2$ **29.** $\dfrac{(x - 1)(x - 3)}{(x - 2)^2}$

31. $\dfrac{-(2x + 3)^2}{(2x + 5)(x - 3)(x + 3)}$ **33.** $\dfrac{2}{5}$ **35.** $\dfrac{(x + 1)(x - 3)}{(x + 2)(x + 3)}$

37. 9   **39.** $\dfrac{a + 6}{4(b - a)}$ **41.** No solution   **43.** $-\dfrac{8}{21}$

45. $\dfrac{nle^2 E}{2mv}$ **47.** $\dfrac{3r - h}{12r^3}$ **49.** $\dfrac{C^2 L^2 \omega^2 - 2LC\omega^2 + 1}{C^2 \omega^2}$

51. $\dfrac{k(h - U)}{hU}$ **53.** $\dfrac{CC_2 + CC_3 - C_2 C_3}{C_2 - C}$ **55.** $\dfrac{\mu R}{r + \mu R + R}$

57. 8 mi/hr

Section 11–1

1. $\dfrac{1}{b^3}$　**3.** a^4　**5.** $\dfrac{2}{b}$　**7.** $\dfrac{b}{2}$　**9.** 1　**11.** 1　**13.** 3^6

15. 6　**17.** $\dfrac{1}{ax}$　**19.** $\dfrac{2}{c^8}$　**21.** $\dfrac{y^2}{x^6}$　**23.** $\dfrac{x^4}{8y^4}$　**25.** $\dfrac{b^7}{9a}$

27. $\dfrac{4}{25a^2b^2}$　**29.** $\dfrac{y^5}{x^4}$　**31.** $\dfrac{a^5c^2}{18}$　**33.** $N = \dfrac{N_0}{e^{kt}}$　**35.** $\dfrac{R}{hR+1}$

37. $g \cdot cm^{-3}$

Section 11–2

1. 4,000,000　**3.** 0.08　**5.** 2.17　**7.** 3×10^3

9. 4.2×10^5　**11.** 7.6×10^{-2}　**13.** 7.04×10^{-1}

15. 9.21×10^0　**17.** 1.03×10　**19.** 1.55×10^8

21. 9.30×10^{-3}　**23.** 1.66×10^2　**25.** 2.21×10^{-3}

27. 1.30×10　**29.** 3.50×10^2 rev/min　**31.** 3.6×10^8 km^2

33. 9.1×10^{-28} g　**35.** 4,000,000,000,000,000,000,000,000,000 lb

37. 0.000001 in.　**39.** 0.0000000000000001 watt/cm^2

41. 6.06×10^7/sec

Section 11–3

1. 6　**3.** -13　**5.** 0.5　**7.** 2　**9.** -2　**11.** -5

13. 0.5　**15.** 2　**17.** 3　**19.** 2　**21.** $2i$　**23.** $0.7i$

25. -25　**27.** -12　**29.** $\sqrt{4}, \sqrt[3]{8}, \sqrt[3]{27}, \sqrt[4]{0.0001}, \sqrt{0.16}$ are rational; $\sqrt{2}, \sqrt[3]{100}$ are irrational　**31.** 3.14 sec　**33.** 8.00 ft

35. 4/3

Section 11–4

1. $2\sqrt{2}$　**3.** $5\sqrt{6}$　**5.** $\dfrac{\sqrt{2}}{2}$　**7.** $\dfrac{\sqrt{2}}{4}$　**9.** $c\sqrt{a}$

11. $ab\sqrt{a}$　**13.** $\dfrac{\sqrt{2a}}{2}$　**15.** $\dfrac{3\sqrt{3ab}}{b}$　**17.** $2ac\sqrt{bc}$

19. $4x^2z^2\sqrt{5yz}$　**21.** $\dfrac{b\sqrt{3a}}{6}$　**23.** $\dfrac{x\sqrt{10y}}{5a^4}$　**25.** 22.36

27. 24.90　**29.** 0.6325　**31.** 0.8165　**33.** $3\sqrt[3]{2}$　**35.** $2a\sqrt[3]{a}$

37. $2a^2\sqrt[4]{a}$　**39.** $2x\sqrt[5]{2x^2}$　**41.** 25.3 in.　**43.** 90 ft by 180 ft

45. 141 ft/sec

Section 11–5

1. $4\sqrt{7} + \sqrt{5}$　**3.** $9\sqrt{2}$　**5.** $\sqrt{7} - 16\sqrt{5}$　**7.** $6\sqrt{3} - \sqrt{2}$

9. $(3 + 4a)\sqrt{2a}$　**11.** $7a\sqrt{2} - 2\sqrt{3a} + 3a\sqrt{3}$

13. $\sqrt{21} - 9\sqrt{2}$ **15.** 26   **17.** $a\sqrt{b} + 3a\sqrt{c}$ **19.** $1 + \sqrt{6}$

21. $-17 - 3\sqrt{15}$ **23.** $2a - 15c - \sqrt{ac}$ **25.** $\sqrt{6} - 2$

27. $\dfrac{17 - 3\sqrt{21}}{25}$ **29.** $\dfrac{a - 2\sqrt{ab}}{a - 4b}$ **31.** $\dfrac{2x + 2y + 5\sqrt{xy}}{4x - y}$

33. $75\sqrt{2}$ ft

35. $(l + \sqrt{l^2 - k^2})^2 - 2l(l + \sqrt{l^2 - k^2}) + k^2$
$$= l^2 + 2l\sqrt{l^2 - k^2} + (l^2 - k^2) - 2l^2 - 2l\sqrt{l^2 - k^2} + k^2 = 0$$

1. $\sqrt{3}$ **3.** $\sqrt[4]{x}$ **5.** $\sqrt[5]{a^2}$ or $(\sqrt[5]{a})^2$ **7.** $\sqrt[3]{x^5}$ or $(\sqrt[3]{x})^5$ Section 11–6

9. 3   **11.** 4   **13.** 2   **15.** -2 **17.** 16   **19.** 27

21. 4   **23.** $\frac{1}{2}$ **25.** $\frac{1}{2}$ **27.** 18   **29.** 2   **31.** $\frac{1}{3375}$

33. $a^{3/2}$ **35.** $a^{3/4}b$ **37.** $x^{29/15}$ **39.** $x^{5/6}$ **41.** $x = A^{1/2}$

43. 24 atm   **45.** $\dfrac{kNia^2}{\sqrt{(a^2 + b^2)^3}}$ **47.** 8.4×10^8 mi

1. $\frac{1}{5}$ **3.** 8   **5.** $\frac{1}{6}$ **7.** 13   **9.** 6   **11.** -16 **13.** $\frac{1}{3}$ Section 11–7

15. $-\frac{3}{11}$ **17.** 10   **19.** 10   **21.** 343   **23.** 1331

25. $\frac{8}{9}$ **27** 324   **29.** $9i$ **31.** $-0.8i$ **33.** 4.9×10^2

35. 6.87×10^0 **37.** 8.08×10^{-5} **39.** 8.695×10 **41.** 83.07

43. 15.49   **45.** 0.6856   **47.** 0.2449   **49.** $\dfrac{3b}{a^2}$ **51.** $\dfrac{2x^5}{3y^3}$

53. $-\dfrac{x^2y^3}{a^2}$ **55.** $a^{7/12}$ **57.** $a^{7/6}$ **59.** $s^{2/3}t^{7/3}$ **61.** $2\sqrt{10}$

63. $8\sqrt{2}$ **65.** $\dfrac{\sqrt{5}}{5}$ **67.** $\dfrac{2\sqrt{7}}{7}$ **69.** $2a$ **71.** $5b\sqrt{5c}$

73. $\dfrac{\sqrt{6a}}{a}$ **75.** $\dfrac{2\sqrt{21a}}{3a}$ **77.** $2a\sqrt[3]{2}$ **79.** $2a\sqrt[5]{2a^3}$

81. $5\sqrt{7} - 2\sqrt{6}$ **83.** $\sqrt{70} - 5\sqrt{10}$ **85.** $(6 - 3a)\sqrt{2}$

87. $-6\sqrt{3}$ **89.** $a\sqrt{b} - 3\sqrt{5ab}$ **91.** $27 - 5\sqrt{30}$

93. $2a - 3b - 5\sqrt{ab}$ **95.** $\dfrac{2 + \sqrt{10}}{3}$ **97.** $5\sqrt{2} - 7$

99. $\dfrac{r^2 + 4R^2}{2\pi R}$ **101.** 2×10^{-7} in.   **103.** 31,000,000,000,000,000 ft

105. 0.0006 g/cm^3 **107.** 3.9 volts   **109.** $v = \dfrac{\sqrt{Ed}}{d}$

111. 0.00208 in.   **113.** 0.182 ft

Section 12–1   **1.** $a = 1$, $b = -7$, $c = -4$ **3.** Not quadratic
5. $a = 1$, $b = 4$, $c = 4$ **7.** $a = 7$, $b = -1$, $c = 0$
9. Not quadratic   **11.** -1 and 2 are solutions
13. $\frac{1}{2}$ and 1 are solutions   **15.** None of listed values is solution
17. 2 is a solution   **19.** -3 and 3 are solutions
21. $x^2 - x - 42 = 0$ **23.** $16t^2 - 96t + 144 = 0$
25. $\dfrac{6000}{v} - 1 = \dfrac{6000}{v + 200}$; $v^2 + 200v - 1{,}200{,}000 = 0$

Section 12–2   **1.** -2, 2 **3.** -2, 1 **5.** -2, $\frac{1}{2}$ **7.** -1, 7 **9.** $-\frac{1}{2}$, $\frac{2}{3}$
11. $\frac{1}{5}$, 4 **13.** -1, $\frac{9}{2}$ **15.** -2, -2 **17.** 0, 5 **19.** 0, 3
21. $-\frac{1}{3}$, 3 **23.** $-2a$, $2a$ **25.** -6, -2 **27.** 4
29. 20 ft by 30 ft   **31.** 8 in.

Section 12–3   **1.** -2, 3 **3.** -1, $\frac{1}{2}$ **5.** $\dfrac{-5 \pm \sqrt{13}}{2}$ **7.** $\frac{1}{2}$, $\frac{3}{2}$

9. $-\frac{3}{2}$, $\frac{3}{2}$ **11.** $-\frac{1}{2}$, $\frac{7}{2}$ **13.** $\dfrac{-1 \pm \sqrt{7}\,i}{2}$ **15.** $\dfrac{-1 \pm \sqrt{33}}{4}$

17. 0, 8 **19.** $\dfrac{3 \pm \sqrt{55}\,i}{4}$ **21.** $-\frac{2}{3}$, 4 **23.** $-\dfrac{1}{3a}$, $-\dfrac{3}{2a}$

25. -3, 1 **27.** 1, 3 **29.** -1, $-\frac{1}{2}$ **31.** 13, 14
33. 0.94 sec and 5.31 sec   **35.** 69.5 yd   **37.** \$9.16

Section 12–4   **1.** -6, -1 **3.** $\frac{5}{2}$, 1 **5.** $-\frac{1}{6}$, 6 **7.** $\frac{3}{4}$, $\frac{3}{4}$ **9.** $-\frac{7}{18}$, 0

11. -11, 10 **13.** 1, 4 **15.** $\frac{5}{6}$, 1 **17.** 1, 1 **19.** $\dfrac{-1 \pm \sqrt{3}\,i}{2}$

21. $\dfrac{5 \pm \sqrt{17}}{4}$ **23.** $3 \pm \sqrt{15}$ **25.** $\dfrac{-2 \pm \sqrt{2}\,i}{2}$

27. $-2i$, $2i$ **29.** -3, 3 **31.** $-1 \pm i$ **33.** 3, $-\frac{1}{2}$

35. $\dfrac{1 \pm \sqrt{7}\,i}{2}$ **37.** 7, 13   **39.** 4 in., 5 in.

41. $-r \pm \sqrt{r^2 - k^2}$ **43.** 200 sec   **45.** 6.14 mm

47. $\dfrac{v \pm \sqrt{v^2 + 2as}}{a}$ **49.** 300 mi/hr

1. $10^{0.2000} = 1.585$ **3.** $10^{0.2857} = 1.931$ **5.** $10^{0.9000} = 7.943$
7. $10^{0.1667} = 1.468$ **9.** $10^{0.4000} = 2.512$ **11.** 6.000
13. 4.000   **15.** $10^{3.3010}$ **17.** $10^{1.5000}$ **19.** 1778
21. 21540   **23.** 50%   **25.** 4 ft

1. 1   **3.** 3   **5.** $9 - 10$ **7.** 1   **9.** $8 - 10$
11. $8 - 10$ **13.** 0.8407   **15.** 0.7007   **17.** 3.7634
19. 2.0212   **21.** 1.4624   **23.** 2.9440   **25.** $8.8075 - 10$
27. $9.4814 - 10$ **29.** $6.9360 - 10$ **31.** $4.9465 - 10$
33. 0.979   **35.** 3.308   **37.** $8.033 - 10$ **39.** $6.788 - 10$
41. 6   **43.** 7.0253   **45.** $8.8129 - 10$

1. 9.52   **3.** 76.5   **5.** 1.91×10^4 **7.** 1.15×10^5
9. 2.65   **11.** 1.36   **13.** 0.0198   **15.** 12.9   **17.** 3.74
19. 73.4   **21.** 4.12   **23.** 0.785   **25.** 155 ft   **27.** 85.4 ft^3
29. 2.13 volts   **31.** 26.7 bu/acre   **33.** $41.9 \text{ ft}^3/\text{hr}$

1. 41.6   **3.** 41.1   **5.** 0.282   **7.** 5.09×10^6 **9.** 5.18
11. 3.85   **13.** 2.38   **15.** 0.770   **17.** 1.99   **19.** 7.20
21. 20.1   **23.** 221   **25.** 17.6 ft   **27.** \$149
29. 3.01×10^6 ft   **31.** 1.29

1. 0.8415   **3.** $9.5007 - 10$ **5.** 1.6912   **7.** 3.4972
9. 4.372   **11.** 87.34   **13.** 287.4   **15.** 2.862×10^{-5}
17. 33.02   **19.** 1.392×10^5 **21.** 4638   **23.** 2.532×10^{-4}
25. 114.4 lb   **27.** 9.632 in.   **29.** $1.97 \times 10^8 \text{ mi}^2$ **31.** 1.797 amp

1. 34.8   **3.** 6.69   **5.** 1.31×10^{-4} **7.** 584.4   **9.** 2.71
11. 16.3   **13.** 7.67×10^{-4} **15.** 9.718   **17.** 1260
19. 3.35×10^7 **21.** 1463   **23.** 4.81   **25.** 1.05   **27.** 36.17
29. 693   **31.** 35.2   **33.** 322.4   **35.** 100 decibels

37. \$5870   **39.** 215 mi   **41.** 39.8%   **43.** 205 ft/sec
45. 7.14×10^{-3} amp   **47.** 364.4 ft-lb   **49.** 4420

Section 14–1   **1.** y is dependent variable, x is independent variable
3. p is dependent variable, V is independent variable
5. Multiply value of independent variable by 3.
7. Subtract square of value of independent variable from 2.
9. $f(x) = 5 - x$ **11.** $f(t) = t^2 - 3t$ **13.** 0, 1   **15.** 7, -5
17. $-2, -\frac{5}{4}$ **19.** $-1, 2.91$ **21.** $-1, 8$ **23.** 2, 2
25. $a^2 - 2a^4, \dfrac{a - 2}{a^2}$ **27.** $\frac{1}{2}$, undefined   **29.** $c = 2\pi r$
31. $A = \dfrac{p^2}{16}$ **33.** $s = 3v$ **35.** $R_1 = R_2 + 1500$ **37.** $i = v/5$

Section 14–2   **1.**

3.

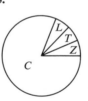

5.

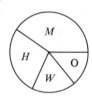

7.

9.

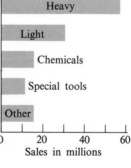

11.

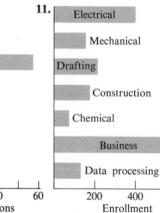

13.

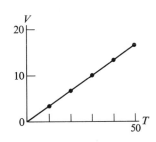

15.

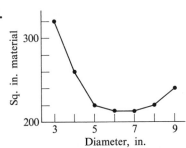

19. No specific solution.

17.

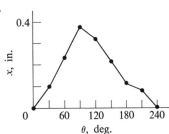

21.

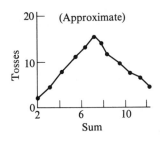

1. $A(2, 1)$, $B(-2, 3)$ **3.** $E(4, 0)$, $F(-\frac{3}{2}, \frac{1}{2})$

Section 14–3

5.

7.

9.

11.

13. 0   **15.** I and III   **17.** IV

19. $(1.25, 1.25)$, $(1.25, -1.25)$, $(-1.25, 1.25)$, $(-1.25, -1.25)$

21. Isosceles   **23.** 3

Section 14–4   Answers show only approximate shape and location of curve.

1.

3.

5.

7.

9.

11.

13.

15.

17.

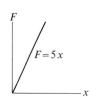

19.

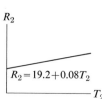

21.

23.

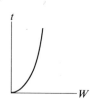

25.

$F = 5x$

27.

$R_2 = 19.2 + 0.08T_2$

29.

$d = 50 + 600t$

31.

33.

1.

3.

5.

Section 14–5

7.

9.

11.

13.

15.

17.

19.

21.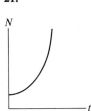

23.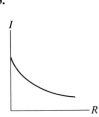

25.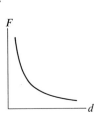

27.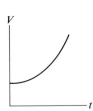

1. 1.4, −1.2   **3.** 9, −8   **5.** 6.5, 11.6   **7.** 9.2, 1.7   Section 14–6
9. 8.9, 2.1   **11.** −2.1, 5.0   **13.** 0.7   **15.** −1.2, 1.7
17. 1.7   **19.** 4.2   **21.** 0.0065 coul, 0.0001 coul   **23.** 35 g, 70 g
25. 340 m/sec, 346 m/sec, 354 m/sec, 360 m/sec
27. 800 ohms, 78 ohms, 15 ohms, 11 ohms   **29.** 28 lb   **31.** 2.1 in.

Section 14–7   **1.** $1, \frac{1}{2}$ **3.** $-20, -11$ **5.** $-9, -16$ **7.** $0, -r^3/8$

9.

11.

13.

15.

17.

19.

21.

23.

25.

27.

29. 1.3
31. $-0.7, 1.0$
33. 0.6

35.

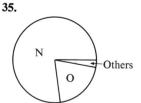

37.

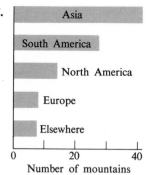

39.

41. $A = 3x$
43. $A = \frac{1}{2}\pi r^2 + 4r$
45. \$700, \$1700, \$2400
47. 101 ft, 103 ft, 112 ft

49.

51.

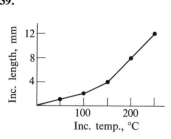

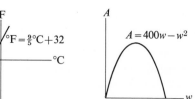

1. $x = 4.0, y = 0.0$ **3.** $x = 1.3, y = 3.3$ **5.** $r = 4.0, x = -3.0$ Section 15–1
7. $x = 2.0, y = 2.0$ **9.** Dependent   **11.** $x = -2.0, y = 1.5$
13. $a = -1.9, b = -0.5$ **15.** Inconsistent   **17.** $p = 2.4, q = 1.1$
19. $x = 5.9, y = -0.2$ **21.** $x = 41$ in., $y = 31$ in.
23. $r_1 = 3.5$ mi/hr, $r_2 = 1.5$ mi/hr   **25.** $R_1 = 2.5$ ohms, $R_2 = 1.0$ ohm

1. $x = 6, y = 11$ **3.** $x = \frac{10}{3}, y = \frac{4}{3}$ **5.** $u = 7, v = 3$ Section 15–2
7. $x = -1, y = 2$ **9.** $x = 2, y = 1$ **11.** $x = 0, y = 0$
13. $k = \frac{20}{17}, u = -\frac{6}{17}$ **15.** $z = \frac{5}{7}, u = \frac{8}{7}$ **17.** $x = \frac{81}{10}, y = \frac{63}{10}$
19. $x = \frac{32}{31}, k = -\frac{69}{31}$ **21.** $p_1 = 12$ hp, $p_2 = 5$ hp
23. $V_1 = 40$ volts, $V_2 = 20$ volts   **25.** $b = 24$ ft, $r = 13$ ft

1. $x = 3, y = 1$ **3.** $x = 6, y = 4$ **5.** $m = 3, n = 6$ Section 15–3
7. $d = -1, t = 4$ **9.** $x = -\frac{21}{11}, n = -\frac{6}{11}$ **11.** $x = 9, y = 2$
13. Inconsistent   **15.** $a = 1, b = 2$ **17.** $p = \frac{3}{2}, q = -\frac{1}{12}$
19. $x = -14, y = -3$ **21.** $x = 1, y = 1$
23. $a = 2000$ cards/min, $b = 3500$ cards/min   **25.** $t_1 = 5$ hr, $t_2 = 4$ hr
27. $I_1 = -\frac{1}{3}$ amp, $I_2 = 1$ amp

1, 3, 5, 7, 9, 11. Verify indicated systems of equations.   Section 15–4
13. 10.5 ft from one end   **15.** 75 hr, 30 hr   **17.** 8 mm, 21 mm
19. $3000 at 3%, $2000 at 4%   **21.** $-40°$ **23.** 40 mi/hr, 45 mi/hr
25. 80 lb, 40 lb   **27.** 15.8 lb

1. $x = \frac{12}{5}, y = \frac{6}{5}$ **3.** $x = 4, y = 4$ **5.** $x = 4, y = 4$ Section 15–5
7. $p = \frac{18}{5}, q = \frac{2}{5}$ **9.** $u = 1, v = -1$ **11.** $a = 12, b = -3$
13. $x = -9, y = 11$ **15.** $y = 1, z = -\frac{1}{2}$ **17.** Dependent
19. $x = -\frac{7}{3}, y = 2$ **21.** $x = \frac{43}{19}, y = -\frac{22}{19}$ **23.** $x = 100, y = -1$
25. $x = 12, y = 24$ **27.** $r = \frac{1}{3}, s = \frac{1}{5}$ **29.** $x = 1.0, y = 0.3$
31. $x = 1.6, y = -1.2$ **33.** $u = 2.0, v = -6.0$ **35.** Inconsistent
37. $i_1 = -\frac{3}{22}$ amp, $i_2 = -\frac{39}{110}$ amp   **39.** $T_2 = 25.0$ lb, $T_3 = 43.3$ lb
41. $4.50 per hr, $3.00 per hr   **43.** $d = 40.0$ ft, $s = 30.0$ ft
45. 8 nickels, 7 dimes   **47.** 45 mi/hr, 55 mi/hr
49. $1500 at 5%, $3500 at 3%

Section 16–1   **1.** 3, 4   **3.** 2, 4; 3, 5   **5.** *AOD, COE*
7. *AOB, BOC, EOF, FOA*   **9.** *AOB, BOC; BOA, AOF; AOF, FOE*
11. 60°   **13.** 60°   **15.** 85°   **17.** 140°   **19.** 25°
21. 25°   **23.** 3   **25.** 3   **27.** 14   **29.** Perpendicular
31. 90°   **33.** 117°   **35.** 5°

Section 16–2   **1.** 5   **3.** 17   **5.** 8   **7.** 4.90   **9.** 10.6   **11.** 28.3
13. 59.9   **15.** 40.9   **17.** 2.67   **19.** 5.66
21. $p = 37.9$ in., $A = 55.4$ in^2 **23.** 56.1 ft   **25.** 601 ft
27. 36.8 ft   **29.** 18.9 ohms   **31.** 902 lb   **33.** 17.5 ft
35. 162 ft

Section 16–3   **1.** Yes, yes   **3.** Yes, no   **5.** No, no   **7.** 8   **9.** 10
11. 8   **13.**   **15.**

    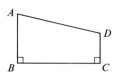

17. 3.3 in., 4.0 in.
19. $\angle XKY = \angle NKF$, $\angle KXY = \angle KNF$, $\angle XYK = \angle NFK$
21. 8.0 in.   **23.** 6.7 ft   **25.** $2\frac{1}{4}$ in.   **27.** 5.3 ft   **29.** 104 ft
31. 30.0 ft   **33.** $AB = 16$ in.

Section 16–4   **1.** 20 ft^3 **3.** 923 in^3 **5.** 153 in^3 **7.** 27.1 ft^3
9. 689 ft^3 **11.** 208 in^2 **13.** 1350 in^2 **15.** 3220 ft^2
17. $A = 3\pi r^2$ **19.** $A = \frac{1}{3}\pi r^2(2r + h)$ **21.** 3,330,000 yd^3
23. 23,500 lb   **25.** 22,000 ft^3 **27.** $400   **29.** 12.9 in^2
31. 990 lb

Section 16–5   **1.** *FEB, EBC; DEB, ABE*   **3.** *ABH, EBC; ABE, HBC*
5. *GED, DEB, ABE, HBC*   **7.** *GED, DEB*   **9.** 55°
11. 125°   **13.** 15   **15.** 48   **17.** 7.5   **19.** 6.3 in.

21. 72 ft^3 **23.** 649 ft^3 **25.** 177 ft^2 **27.** 4

29. 56.1 ft   **31.** 22.5°, 67.5°   **33.** 4.2 in.   **35.** No

37. 23.1 in.   **39.** 32.8 cm   **41.** 5.0 ft   **43.** 865,000 mi

45. 10.0 in.   **47.** 668,000 gal   **49.** 4830 in^3 **51.** 238 in^2

53. 233 gal

1. $\frac{7}{25}, \frac{7}{24}, \frac{7}{25}$ **3.** $\frac{7}{24}, \frac{25}{24}, \frac{24}{7}$ **5.** $\frac{1}{2}, 2, \sqrt{3}$ *Section 17–1*

7. $\dfrac{\sqrt{3}}{3}, \dfrac{1}{2}, \dfrac{2\sqrt{3}}{3}$ **9.** 0.797, 0.754, 1.25   **11.** 0.601, 0.601, 1.33

13. $\frac{3}{5}, \frac{4}{3}$ **15.** $\frac{9}{40}, \frac{40}{41}$ **17.** $1, \dfrac{\sqrt{2}}{2}$ **19.** 1.26, 0.795   **21.** $\dfrac{\sqrt{2}}{2}$

23. 1.40   **25.** 0.49, 1.76

27. $\cot A = \dfrac{\text{side adj. } A}{\text{side opp. } A},\quad \sec A = \dfrac{\text{hypotenuse}}{\text{side adj. } A},\quad \csc A = \dfrac{\text{hypotenuse}}{\text{side opp. } A}$

29. $\cot B, \sec B$

1. 0.6293   **3.** 1.010   **5.** 0.3746   **7.** 0.8290   **9.** 0.8693   *Section 17–2*

11. 0.6293   **13.** 24°   **15.** 30°   **17.** 19°   **19.** 74°

21. 80°   **23.** 87°   **25.** 1.305   **27.** 1.390   **29.** 37°

31. 44°   **33.** 50°   **35.** 84°   **37.** 0.53   **39.** 0.97

41. 1.51

1. 0.438   **3.** 0.970   **5.** 0.0593   **7.** 0.0831   **9.** 1.60   *Section 17–3*

11. 0.317   **13.** 0.0300   **15.** 1.12   **17.** 40.7°   **19.** 26.2°

21. 5.00°   **23.** 88.66°   **25.** 82.7°   **27.** 65.9°   **29.** 5.72°

31. 89.3°   **33.** 23.9 in.

1. $B = 60°$ $b = 20.8$, $c = 24.0$ **3.** $A = 30°$, $a = 11.0$, $b = 19.1$ *Section 17–4*

5. $B = 25°$, $a = 27.2$, $b = 12.7$ **7.** $A = 30°$, $B = 60°$ $b \doteq 1.13$

9. $A = 83°$, $B = 7°$, $a = 44.6$ **11.** $A = 64°$, $B = 26°$, $b = 4.71$

13. 72.8 ft   **15.** 28.6 ft   **17.** 4.3°   **19.** 2.94 in.   **21.** 4.18 in.

23. 1640 ft   **25.** 171 mi   **27.** 6.34 mi   **29.** 6.36 in.

Section 17–5   **1.**    **3.**   **5.**

7. $\theta = 22°$, $R = 5.39$ **9.** $\theta = 59°$, $R = 1460$

11. $\theta = 40°$, $R = 9.92$ **13.** $R_x = 5.74$, $R_y = 3.05$

15. $R_x = 754$, $R_y = 528$ **17.** $R_x = -5.10$, $R_y = 28.9$

19. $\theta = 39°$, $R = 713$ **21.** $\theta = 100°$, $R = 893$

23. $\theta = 20°$, $R = 0.0835$ **25.** 46.0 mi, 34° S of E

27. $v_h = 434$ mi/hr, $v_v = 2460$ mi/hr   **29.** 54 lb, $\theta = 68°$

31. Yes, to the right

Section 17–6   **1.** $\dfrac{\pi}{12}$ **3.** $\dfrac{4\pi}{9}$ **5.** $\dfrac{3\pi}{4}$ **7.** 36°   **9.** 54°   **11.** 105°

13. 0.401   **15.** 1.43   **17.** 0.480   **19.** 115°   **21.** 47°

23. 43°   **25.** 0.866   **27.** 3.73   **29.** 0.454   **31.** 0.644

33. 0.760   **35.** 14.1   **37.** 0.628   **39.** 0.943   **41.** 0.960

Section 17–7   **1.** 10.5 in.   **3.** 27.6 in^2 **5.** 30.0 in.   **7.** 112°   **9.** 3.14 in.

11. 129 mi   **13.** 4970 in.   **15.** 75.4 rad/sec   **17.** 17,600 mi/hr

19. 2.33 ft   **21.** 82.2 rev/min   **23.** 1.35 ft/sec

Section 17–8   **1.** $\frac{5}{13}$, $\frac{5}{12}$ **3.** 3.8, 0.97   **5.** 0.46, 0.42   **7.** 38°   **9.** 13°

11. 28°   **13.** 0.407   **15.** 2.03   **17.** 51.7°   **19.** 81.02°

21. 0.209   **23.** 36.6°   **25.** 1.92   **27.** 0.389   **29.** 0.484

31. $B = 42°$, $b = 16.2$, $c = 24.2$ **33.** $B = 69°$, $a = 2.48$, $b = 6.47$

35. $A = 8°$, $a = 6.46$, $c = 46.4$ **37.** $A = 59°$, $B = 31°$, $c = 10.1$

39. $A = 64°$, $B = 26°$, $b = 47.3$ **41.** $R_x = 6.77$, $R_y = 2.73$

43. $R_x = -1350$, $R_y = 814$ **45.** $\theta = 28°$, $R = 38.7$

47. $\theta = 112°$, $R = 1.14$ **49.** 77 ft   **51.** 420 ft   **53.** 28°

55. 20 sec   **57.** 2680 mi   **59.** 8.78 ft   **61.** 61 mi, 35° N of E

63. 15.3 mi/hr, 11° from direction of ship   **65.** 2160 mi   **67.** 67 ft

69. 21.9 rev/sec   **71.** 21 in.   **73.** No, yes

Tables

No.	Sq.	Sq. Root	Cube	Cube Root	No.	Sq.	Sq. Root	Cube	Cube Root
1	1	1.000	1	1.000	51	2,601	7.141	132,651	3.708
2	4	1.414	8	1.260	52	2,704	7.211	140,608	3.733
3	9	1.732	27	1.442	53	2,809	7.280	148,877	3.756
4	16	2.000	64	1.587	54	2,916	7.348	157,464	3.780
5	25	2.236	125	1.710	55	3,025	7.416	166,375	3.803
6	36	2.449	216	1.817	56	3,136	7.483	175,616	3.826
7	49	2.646	343	1.913	57	3,249	7.550	185,193	3.849
8	64	2.828	512	2.000	58	3,364	7.616	195,112	3.871
9	81	3.000	729	2.080	59	3,481	7.681	205,379	3.893
10	100	3.162	1,000	2.154	60	3,600	7.746	216,000	3.915
11	121	3.317	1,331	2.224	61	3,721	7.810	226,981	3.936
12	144	3.464	1,728	2.289	62	3,844	7.874	238,328	3.958
13	169	3.606	2,197	2.351	63	3,969	7.937	250,047	3.979
14	196	3.742	2,744	2.410	64	4,096	8.000	262,144	4.000
15	225	3.873	3,375	2.466	65	4,225	8.062	274,625	4.021
16	256	4.000	4,096	2.520	66	4,356	8.124	287,496	4.041
17	289	4.123	4,913	2.571	67	4,489	8.185	300,763	4.062
18	324	4.243	5,832	2.621	68	4,624	8.246	314,432	4.082
19	361	4.359	6,859	2.668	69	4,761	8.307	328,509	4.102
20	400	4.472	8,000	2.714	70	4,900	8.367	343,000	4.121
21	441	4.583	9,261	2.759	71	5,041	8.426	357,911	4.141
22	484	4.690	10,648	2.802	72	5,184	8.485	373,248	4.160
23	529	4.796	12,167	2.844	73	5,329	8.544	389,017	4.179
24	576	4.899	13,824	2.884	74	5,476	8.602	405,224	4.198
25	625	5.000	15,625	2.924	75	5,625	8.660	421,875	4.217
26	676	5.099	17,576	2.962	76	5,776	8.718	438,976	4.236
27	729	5.196	19,683	3.000	77	5,929	8.775	456,533	4.254
28	784	5.292	21,952	3.037	78	6,084	8.832	474,552	4.273
29	841	5.385	24,389	3.072	79	6,241	8.888	493,039	4.291
30	900	5.477	27,000	3.107	80	6,400	8.944	512,000	4.309
31	961	5.568	29,791	3.141	81	6,561	9.000	531,441	4.327
32	1,024	5.657	32,768	3.175	82	6,724	9.055	551,368	4.344
33	1,089	5.745	35,937	3.208	83	6,889	9.110	571,787	4.362
34	1,156	5.831	39,304	3.240	84	7,056	9.165	592,704	4.380
35	1,225	5.916	42,875	3.271	85	7,225	9.220	614,125	4.397
36	1,296	6.000	46,656	3.302	86	7,396	9.274	636,056	4.414
37	1,369	6.083	50,653	3.332	87	7,569	9.327	658,503	4.431
38	1,444	6.164	54,872	3.362	88	7,744	9.381	681,472	4.448
39	1,521	6.245	59,319	3.391	89	7,921	9.434	704,969	4.465
40	1,600	6.325	64,000	3.420	90	8,100	9.487	729,000	4.481
41	1,681	6.403	68,921	3.448	91	8,281	9.539	753,571	4.498
42	1,764	6.481	74,088	3.476	92	8,464	9.592	778,688	4.514
43	1,849	6.557	79,507	3.503	93	8,649	9.644	804,357	4.531
44	1,936	6.633	85,184	3.530	94	8,836	9.695	830,584	4.547
45	2,025	6.708	91,125	3.557	95	9,025	9.747	857,375	4.563
46	2,116	6.782	97,336	3.583	96	9,216	9.798	884,736	4.579
47	2,209	6.856	103,823	3.609	97	9,409	9.849	912,673	4.595
48	2,304	6.928	110,592	3.634	98	9,604	9.899	941,192	4.610
49	2,401	7.000	117,649	3.659	99	9,801	9.950	970,299	4.626
50	2,500	7.071	125,000	3.684	100	10,000	10.000	1,000,000	4.642

Table 2   Four-Place Logarithms of Numbers

N	0	1	2	3	4	5	6	7	8	9
10	0000	0043	0086	0128	0170	0212	0253	0294	0334	0374
11	0414	0453	0492	0531	0569	0607	0645	0682	0719	0755
12	0792	0828	0864	0899	0934	0969	1004	1038	1072	1106
13	1139	1173	1206	1239	1271	1303	1335	1367	1399	1430
14	1461	1492	1523	1553	1584	1614	1644	1673	1703	1732
15	1761	1790	1818	1847	1875	1903	1931	1959	1987	2014
16	2041	2068	2095	2122	2148	2175	2201	2227	2253	2279
17	2304	2330	2355	2380	2405	2430	2455	2480	2504	2529
18	2553	2577	2601	2625	2648	2672	2695	2718	2742	2765
19	2788	2810	2833	2856	2878	2900	2923	2945	2967	2989
20	3010	3032	3054	3075	3096	3118	3139	3160	3181	3201
21	3222	3243	3263	3284	3304	3324	3345	3365	3385	3404
22	3424	3444	3464	3483	3502	3522	3541	3560	3579	3598
23	3617	3636	3655	3674	3692	3711	3729	3747	3766	3784
24	3802	3820	3838	3856	3874	3892	3909	3927	3945	3962
25	3979	3997	4014	4031	4048	4065	4082	4099	4116	4133
26	4150	4166	4183	4200	4216	4232	4249	4265	4281	4298
27	4314	4330	4346	4362	4378	4393	4409	4425	4440	4456
28	4472	4487	4502	4518	4533	4548	4564	4579	4594	4609
29	4624	4639	4654	4669	4683	4698	4713	4728	4742	4757
30	4771	4786	4800	4814	4829	4843	4857	4871	4886	4900
31	4914	4928	4942	4955	4969	4983	4997	5011	5024	5038
32	5051	5065	5079	5092	5105	5119	5132	5145	5159	5172
33	5185	5198	5211	5224	5237	5250	5263	5276	5289	5302
34	5315	5328	5340	5353	5366	5378	5391	5403	5416	5428
35	5441	5453	5465	5478	5490	5502	5514	5527	5539	5551
36	5563	5575	5587	5599	5611	5623	5635	5647	5658	5670
37	5682	5694	5705	5717	5729	5740	5752	5763	5775	5786
38	5798	5809	5821	5832	5843	5855	5866	5877	5888	5899
39	5911	5922	5933	5944	5955	5966	5977	5988	5999	6010
40	6021	6031	6042	6053	6064	6075	6085	6096	6107	6117
41	6128	6138	6149	6160	6170	6180	6191	6201	6212	6222
42	6232	6243	6253	6263	6274	6284	6294	6304	6314	6325
43	6335	6345	6355	6365	6375	6385	6395	6405	6415	6425
44	6435	6444	6454	6464	6474	6484	6493	6503	6513	6522
45	6532	6542	6551	6561	6571	6580	6590	6599	6609	6618
46	6628	6637	6646	6656	6665	6675	6684	6693	6702	6712
47	6721	6730	6739	6749	6758	6767	6776	6785	6794	6803
48	6812	6821	6830	6839	6848	6857	6866	6875	6884	6893
49	6902	6911	6920	6928	6937	6946	6955	6964	6972	6981
50	6990	6998	7007	7016	7024	7033	7042	7050	7059	7067
51	7076	7084	7093	7101	7110	7118	7126	7135	7143	7152
52	7160	7168	7177	7185	7193	7202	7210	7218	7226	7235
53	7243	7251	7259	7267	7275	7284	7292	7300	7308	7316
54	7324	7332	7340	7348	7356	7364	7372	7380	7388	7396

Table 2 (*Continued*)

N	0	1	2	3	4	5	6	7	8	9
55	7404	7412	7419	7427	7435	7443	7451	7459	7466	7474
56	7482	7490	7497	7505	7513	7520	7528	7536	7543	7551
57	7559	7566	7574	7582	7589	7597	7604	7612	7619	7627
58	7634	7642	7649	7657	7664	7672	7679	7686	7694	7701
59	7709	7716	7723	7731	7738	7745	7752	7760	7767	7774
60	7782	7789	7796	7803	7810	7818	7825	7832	7839	7846
61	7853	7860	7868	7875	7882	7889	7896	7903	7910	7917
62	7924	7931	7938	7945	7952	7959	7966	7973	7980	7987
63	7993	8000	8007	8014	8021	8028	8035	8041	8048	8055
64	8062	8069	8075	8082	8089	8096	8102	8109	8116	8122
65	8129	8136	8142	8149	8156	8162	8169	8176	8182	8189
66	8195	8202	8209	8215	8222	8228	8235	8241	8248	8254
67	8261	8267	8274	8280	8287	8293	8299	8306	8312	8319
68	8325	8331	8338	8344	8351	8357	8363	8370	8376	8382
69	8388	8395	8401	8407	8414	8420	8426	8432	8439	8445
70	8451	8457	8463	8470	8476	8482	8488	8494	8500	8506
71	8513	8519	8525	8531	8537	8543	8549	8555	8561	8567
72	8573	8579	8585	8591	8597	8603	8609	8615	8621	8627
73	8633	8639	8645	8651	8657	8663	8669	8675	8681	8686
74	8692	8698	8704	8710	8716	8722	8727	8733	8739	8745
75	8751	8756	8762	8768	8774	8779	8785	8791	8797	8802
76	8808	8814	8820	8825	8831	8837	8842	8848	8854	8859
77	8865	8871	8876	8882	8887	8893	8899	8904	8910	8915
78	8921	8927	8932	8938	8943	8949	8954	8960	8965	8971
79	8976	8982	8987	8993	8998	9004	9009	9015	9020	9025
80	9031	9036	9042	9047	9053	9058	9063	9069	9074	9079
81	9085	9090	9096	9101	9106	9112	9117	9122	9128	9133
82	9138	9143	9149	9154	9159	9165	9170	9175	9180	9186
83	9191	9196	9201	9206	9212	9217	9222	9227	9232	9238
84	9243	9248	9253	9258	9263	9269	9274	9279	9284	9289
85	9294	9299	9304	9309	9315	9320	9325	9330	9335	9340
86	9345	9350	9355	9360	9365	9370	9375	9380	9385	9390
87	9395	9400	9405	9410	9415	9420	9425	9430	9435	9440
88	9445	9450	9455	9460	9465	9469	9474	9479	9484	9489
89	9494	9499	9504	9509	9513	9518	9523	9528	9533	9538
90	9542	9547	9552	9557	9562	9566	9571	9576	9581	9586
91	9590	9595	9600	9605	9609	9614	9619	9624	9628	9633
92	9638	9643	9647	9652	9657	9661	9666	9671	9675	9680
93	9685	9689	9694	9699	9703	9708	9713	9717	9722	9727
94	9731	9736	9741	9745	9750	9754	9759	9763	9768	9773
95	9777	9782	9786	9791	9795	9800	9805	9809	9814	9818
96	9823	9827	9832	9836	9841	9845	9850	9854	9859	9863
97	9868	9872	9877	9881	9886	9890	9894	9899	9903	9908
98	9912	9917	9921	9926	9930	9934	9939	9943	9948	9952
99	9956	9961	9965	9969	9974	9978	9983	9987	9991	9996

Table 3   The Trigonometric Ratios

Degrees	Radians	Sin	Cos	Tan	Cot	Sec	Csc		
0°00'	.0000	.0000	1.0000	.0000	--	1.000	--	1.5708	90°00'
1°00'	.0175	.0175	.9998	.0175	57.29	1.000	57.30	1.5533	89°00'
2°00'	.0349	.0349	.9994	.0349	28.64	1.001	28.65	1.5359	88°00'
3°00'	.0524	.0523	.9986	.0524	19.08	1.001	19.11	1.5184	87°00'
4°00'	.0698	.0698	.9976	.0699	14.30	1.002	14.34	1.5010	86°00'
5°00'	.0873	.0872	.9962	.0875	11.43	1.004	11.47	1.4835	85°00'
6°00'	.1047	.1045	.9945	.1051	9.514	1.006	9.567	1.4661	84°00'
7°00'	.1222	.1219	.9925	.1228	8.144	1.008	8.206	1.4486	83°00'
8°00'	.1396	.1392	.9903	.1405	7.115	1.010	7.185	1.4312	82°00'
9°00'	.1571	.1564	.9877	.1584	6.314	1.012	6.392	1.4137	81°00'
10°00'	.1745	.1736	.9848	.1763	5.671	1.015	5.759	1.3963	80°00'
11°00'	.1920	.1908	.9816	.1944	5.145	1.019	5.241	1.3788	79°00'
12°00'	.2094	.2079	.9781	.2126	4.705	1.022	4.810	1.3614	78°00'
13°00'	.2269	.2250	.9744	.2309	4.331	1.026	4.445	1.3439	77°00'
14°00'	.2443	.2419	.9703	.2493	4.011	1.031	4.134	1.3265	76°00'
15°00'	.2618	.2588	.9659	.2679	3.732	1.035	3.864	1.3090	75°00'
16°00'	.2793	.2756	.9613	.2867	3.487	1.040	3.628	1.2915	74°00'
17°00'	.2967	.2924	.9563	.3057	3.271	1.046	3.420	1.2741	73°00'
18°00'	.3142	.3090	.9511	.3249	3.078	1.051	3.236	1.2566	72°00'
19°00'	.3316	.3256	.9455	.3443	2.904	1.058	3.072	1.2392	71°00'
20°00'	.3491	.3420	.9397	.3640	2.747	1.064	2.924	1.2217	70°00'
21°00'	.3665	.3584	.9336	.3839	2.605	1.071	2.790	1.2043	69°00'
22°00'	.3840	.3746	.9272	.4040	2.475	1.079	2.669	1.1868	68°00'
23°00'	.4014	.3907	.9205	.4245	2.356	1.086	2.559	1.1694	67°00'
24°00'	.4189	.4067	.9135	.4452	2.246	1.095	2.459	1.1519	66°00'
25°00'	.4363	.4226	.9063	.4663	2.145	1.103	2.366	1.1345	65°00'
26°00'	.4538	.4384	.8988	.4877	2.050	1.113	2.281	1.1170	64°00'
27°00'	.4712	.4540	.8910	.5095	1.963	1.122	2.203	1.0996	63°00'
28°00'	.4887	.4695	.8829	.5317	1.881	1.133	2.130	1.0821	62°00'
29°00'	.5061	.4848	.8746	.5543	1.804	1.143	2.063	1.0647	61°00'
30°00'	.5236	.5000	.8660	.5774	1.732	1.155	2.000	1.0472	60°00'
31°00'	.5411	.5150	.8572	.6009	1.664	1.167	1.942	1.0297	59°00'
32°00'	.5585	.5299	.8480	.6249	1.600	1.179	1.887	1.0123	58°00'
33°00'	.5760	.5446	.8387	.6494	1.540	1.192	1.836	.9948	57°00'
34°00'	.5934	.5592	.8290	.6745	1.483	1.206	1.788	.9774	56°00'
35°00'	.6109	.5736	.8192	.7002	1.428	1.221	1.743	.9599	55°00'
36°00'	.6283	.5878	.8090	.7265	1.376	1.236	1.701	.9425	54°00'
37°00'	.6458	.6018	.7986	.7536	1.327	1.252	1.662	.9250	53°00'
38°00'	.6632	.6157	.7880	.7813	1.280	1.269	1.624	.9076	52°00'
39°00'	.6807	.6293	.7771	.8098	1.235	1.287	1.589	.8901	51°00'
40°00'	.6981	.6428	.7660	.8391	1.192	1.305	1.556	.8727	50°00'
41°00'	.7156	.6561	.7547	.8693	1.150	1.325	1.524	.8552	49°00'
42°00'	.7330	.6691	.7431	.9004	1.111	1.346	1.494	.8378	48°00'
43°00'	.7505	.6820	.7314	.9325	1.072	1.367	1.466	.8203	47°00'
44°00'	.7679	.6947	.7193	.9657	1.036	1.390	1.440	.8029	46°00'
45°00'	.7854	.7071	.7071	1.0000	1.000	1.414	1.414	.7854	45°00'
		Cos	Sin	Cot	Tan	Csc	Sec	Radians	Degrees

Index